Technology
and Man's Future

DATE DUE			
Sep 26 '72			
Nov 11 '72			
Nov 30 '72			
Jul 25 '73			
Oct 3 '73			
Nov 13 '73			
Mar 26 '74			
Mar 17 '77			
May 22 78			
May 4 '83			

Technology
and Man's Future

ALBERT H. TEICH, EDITOR

Syracuse University Research Corporation

ST. MARTIN'S PRESS   NEW YORK

Contents

3
An Attempt at Synthesis

4
The Movement Toward Control: Technology Assessment

Introduction

I grew up believing in a technological future. The picture of tomorrow's world that I carried around in my head throughout my childhood years corresponded, more or less, to that which one might have acquired from any number of science-fiction movies or from such monuments to technology as the Museum of Science and Industry in Chicago. It was characterized mainly by neatness and order, miles of gleaming chrome, millions of buttons to push, and endless gadgets to do all the work. All of our "old-fashioned" ways of doing things were, I believed, to be replaced by new, modern, better ones. Automated highways would take the place of conventional roads; one nourishment pill in the morning would save us consuming three meals during the day. In retrospect, what I find to be particularly interesting in this childhood image is the fact that the technological future always seemed to be an end in itself. When adults in my life spoke of it, they implied its inevitability—with some interest and some, but not much, enthusiasm. No one seemed to care very much for the prospect, but it was "progress," and only a fool would try to resist its tide.

Similar notions were apparently the main themes of the Century of Progress International Exposition held in Chicago in 1933. In the great world's fair tradition, this extravagant celebration aimed to demonstrate what technology was capable of doing for humanity. In the process, it brought out dramatically what one author has called "technology's triumph over man." Upon entering the Hall of Science, one was confronted by a large sculptural group featuring a life-sized man and woman, their "hands outstretched as if in fear or ignorance." Between this couple stood a giant angular robot almost twice their size, bending down, with a metallic arm "thrown reassuringly around each." The visitor to the fair need not have searched far for the meaning of this image. It could be found in the Exposition motto: SCIENCE FINDS— INDUSTRY APPLIES—MAN CONFORMS.[1]

As I grew older, I naturally began to question my childhood vision, putting aside a fascination with gadgets to ask myself what was lacking in this future. Why, despite all good intentions, did this image of the future always come out looking more like *Brave New World* or *1984* than *Utopia*? What was the meaning of "progress" in these terms, if no one ever asked whether

---

1. I am indebted to Lowell Tozer, "A Century of Progress, 1833-1933: Technology's Triumph Over Man," *American Quarterly* 4 (1952): 78-81, for a fascinating description of this event, which took place a number of years before my birth.

it serves to make people happier? At the same time, I began to seek out ways of developing and shaping alternative futures.

In many ways, I believe, this development of my own mind represents something of a parallel to what has been occurring in American society over the past several years. Within the crisis of confidence that we as a nation are experiencing, we have begun to look critically at the technological future we have been building. This critical examination, which is being felt at many levels, is particularly strong among college-age youth. The mainstream of this generation has matured in an environment characterized by unprecedented material affluence. Able to take for granted the satisfaction of material wants, it has at once the need and the ability to reach beyond them and ask those crucial questions of ultimate purpose: Is material progress an end in itself, or is it, more properly, a means to some higher end? Is the development of technology leading toward a more desirable state of human affairs, or is it actually producing a decline in the quality of life? Is technology a tool that man is capable of using as he chooses, or is it, in a very basic sense, a system gone out of control?

It is a proper function of a college or university to equip its students with the intellectual foundations they need to grapple with these types of mind-expanding questions. These intellectual foundations have many aspects. Some fall within traditional disciplinary bounds; others require a different, transdisciplinary approach. This book is intended to address the latter. It does not, however, aim to *answer* the questions posed by the relationship of technology to society. Rather, it *seeks to expose* the reader to a variety of perspectives— scientific, philosophical, empirical, and policy-oriented—from which others have asked these questions. The readings are not selected to appeal to students of any particular disciplinary bias. Those with backgrounds and interests in music, social science, philosophy, engineering, humanities, business, and science—or virtually any other field—should find them of equal value. Hopefully, the courses and seminars in which these selections will be read and discussed will bring together students with a diversity of outlooks.

A WORD ON CONTEXT

In concentrating on the assembly of divergent perspectives in the *overall* problem of technology's relationship to society, this collection necessarily and knowingly fails to deal with important statements of certain parts of the problem. Thus, one will find here no direct treatment (except as examples) of either the specific benefits that technology has brought to human life or the specific problems for which it is said to be responsible. The absence of material on these matters does not imply any lack of concern for them. It is simply a reflection of the higher level of generality represented here.

By way of setting the stage for the general discussion, it may be useful to review very briefly some of these specific matters. We cannot really even begin to measure the improvements that technology has made in man's capacity to cope with his natural environment. Through technology, man—alone among all known species of life—has developed means by which he may transcend the physical limitations of his body. In agricultural technology, he has devised methods for vastly increasing his food supply; in medical technology, he has learned to maintain his health and extend his lifespan; in construction technology, he has created means for protecting himself against hostile conditions of nature; in communication and transportation technology, he has developed systems for transporting himself and his ideas rapidly across vast distances; and in industrial and information technology, he has learned to perform physical and mental work far beyond his individual abilities.

All of this, however, has not been achieved without some cost. The contention that the continued development of technology will generate corresponding increases in human happiness and societal well-being is being challenged on numerous grounds. (1) It is widely charged that through consumption of nonrenewable resources, indiscriminate discharge of noxious waste products into the environment, and unchecked population growth, we are creating an environmental crisis that could endanger the very existence of life on this planet. (2) Even if one is inclined to discount such charges as exaggerated, it is more generally agreed that man's ability to manipulate his environment has run ahead of his sense of responsibility in doing so. Through such practices as unplanned land development and indiscriminate hunting of wildlife, man has unthinkingly destroyed valuable segments of the environment. (3) At a different level, the technology of modern weaponry and the arms race through which it has been fostered and disseminated have given man the power to destroy all life on the earth—without giving him the wisdom to insure that he will not do so. (4) In the minds of many observers, the manner in which technology is applied to social needs is inextricably interwoven with the perpetuation of a system of domination of one class by another—and consequently with the far-reaching problem of social injustice. Some would go further, in fact, viewing the requirements of technology as being incompatible with the democratic process and as inevitably leading to a totalitarian state. (5) We often hear that the status of the individual has suffered in the technological society. Complex organizations and advanced data processing techniques have, it is claimed, threatened the individual's right to privacy and reduced him to feeling that he is no more than a computer punchcard facing a vast bureaucracy. (6) Finally, projected developments in biology and medicine (including genetic engineering) will soon pose a number of very difficult moral dilemmas for man, as he acquires the potential to create artificial life, duplicate individual human beings, and willfully alter the course of his own evolution.

Each of us may see these several problems as more or less serious, and each of us may have a personal bias about the balance between technology's costs and its benefits. The point is that these are all widespread and important human concerns today and that they represent the types of issues which define the context—if not the substance—of this book.

ON READING THIS BOOK

One of the most difficult conceptual problems in developing an understanding of the technology-society relationship stems from a lack of general agreement about what technology actually is. In conventional usage, technology appears to be associated with, if not defined by, the notion of mechanization. But, it is clear that technology is more than merely machines. How much more depends upon whose definition you are willing to accept. Perhaps the broadest concept is that of Jacques Ellul, who incorporates technology into his idea of "technique." "Technique" he defines as "the totality of methods rationally arrived at and having absolute efficiency in every field of human activity." A narrower and more operationally useful concept, which still extends considerably beyond the simple notion of "hardware" is that employed by the Harvard University Program on Technology and Society: "The organization of knowledge for practical purposes." It is clear that the explicit or implicit definition of technology held by each of the authors represented in this book deeply affects his view of its role in society. In attempting to read and analyze the works presented here, the reader should seek out these differences in concept and constantly bear them in mind.

In this connection, it is worth mentioning a subtle distinction that is often overlooked. In some instances, writers on technology and society appear primarily concerned with the affects of technology *per se*. In others, the apparent emphasis is upon technological *change*. The difference is seldom made explicit. Of course, the notion of change and constant innovation is so very much a part of our system of technology that it may not really be possible to conceive of it as a static system. Nevertheless, some subtle and probably unexplored differences do exist here, and the reader will be well advised to bear this distinction in mind in considering the various articles.

A word is also in order on the relationship between science and technology. While today we are inclined to identify the two quite closely, they have not always been seen in this way. In fact, a number of analyses show that, until recent times, science and technology progressed more or less independently of each other. Today's close identity between the two is a result of the explicit recognition on the part of society that scientific research, which in its purest sense is the pursuit of knowledge for its own sake, provides the basis for technological advance. The scientific community, for its part, has fostered public consciousness of this linkage as at least a partial justification for public financial support of scientific research. As a consequence, science has not only become associated with technology's benefits, but it is also increasingly seen as partially responsible for the problems technology has caused. The links between science and technology thus deserve serious attention in the context of this book.

Many of us have a tendency to view our problems in defining and regulating the role of technology in society as characteristic of our own time. In a sense, the readings in this volume, because they are all of recent vintage, contribute to this impression. We should hasten to point out, therefore, that there is, in fact, a long history of thought in this area. The societal tensions that accompanied the Industrial Revolution were interpreted by thinkers of those times in ways roughly analogous to those we see today. One can trace the view of technology as a Utopian force to such nineteenth-century philosophers as Karl Marx and Auguste Comte. On the other side, one may cite numerous critics of machine technology including Thomas Carlyle, who wrote of an "Age of Machinery, in every inward and outward sense of the word"; the poet, Matthew Arnold; and even Mark Twain, who late in his life authored a little-known essay entitled "Man a Machine?"[2] Among those whose fear of and resistance to technological change impelled them to action were a considerable number of English workers, known as the Luddites, who, in the early nineteenth century, gained wide repute by smashing the machines they hated in a series of riots. We do not presume to review this lengthy history here, but we maintain an awareness of the fact that today's discussions of the role of technology in society are not without their cultural and intellectual forebears.

2. See Victor C. Ferkiss, *Technological Man: The Myth and the Reality* (New York: George Braziller, Inc., 1969), chap. 3, for a discussion of early technological criticism.

STRUCTURE

The book is divided into four sections. The first three consider differing approaches to the understanding of the general problem of technology's role in society. The thrust of Part 1 is the examination of the essentially positive view of technology held by many scientists and engineers. While the extreme and simplistic notion that technology is an unalloyed blessing to mankind is not represented here, the common thread that ties together the three central articles in this section is the unquestioned assumption that further development of science and technology will provide solutions to many of the ills apparent in today's society.

The writings of several contemporary philosophers whose views of technology's role range from apocalyptic to Utopian are assembled in Part 2. The first three articles seem to share the important notion that technology, as a cultural tendency, has somehow transcended man's ability to control it and has thus become a seemingly autonomous force. The last sounds a more hopeful note in forecasting the emergence of a new human type—technological man—who is able to cope with the situation technology has created.

The core of Part 3 is an effort at empirical synthesis. Perhaps the major institutional effort to develop an empirical understanding of the issues with which we are concerned has been undertaken by the Harvard University Program on Technology and Society. In an essay taken from the Program's fourth report, its director sets out some of the principal ideas emerging from and guiding its activities. Juxtaposed with this essay is a highly critical review of the Harvard University Program's basic assumptions, which asserts that they are representative of "a not new but . . . newly aggressive right-wing ideology in this country."

Part 4, the final section of the book, draws upon threads that emerge from the first three sections to deal with one promising (but partial) political response to the problem—the concept of technology assessment. Documents that resulted from the activities of the House Subcommittee on Science, Research, and Development form the core of this section. Responding to them are several independent critiques. Although this part of the collection does not claim to offer definitive solutions to the problems posed, it does seek to add a policy-oriented dimension to discussions of technology and society and thus perhaps render them more satisfying as well as more productive.

ALBERT H. TEICH

1

Scientific Views
of Advancing Technology

Most scientists and engineers, including those with a deep social conscience and significant misgivings about the present course of society, share a basic faith in the ultimate beneficence of science, a faith that appears rooted in their being. The substance of this faith, essentially a form of rationalism, may be simply construed as follows: (1) pure science is the pursuit of knowledge for its own sake; (2) the rules that govern the running of the universe are ultimately knowable to human beings; (3) by understanding these rules, man becomes capable (through technology) of turning the forces of the universe to his advantage and achieving a more satisfying existence.

It is painfully evident today that the development of a better understanding of the physical universe does not in itself guarantee improvement in the human condition. As the introduction to this volume pointed out, and as Part 2 will illustrate, there is a significant body of thought which holds that the application of scientific knowledge is (perhaps inevitably) leading humanity to disaster. Obviously, most scientists do not share this view. In their writings about the future course of technological society, they tend to view the contributions of applied science as leading, one way or another, toward an improved human situation. It would be simplistic to regard this point of view as one of unbridled optimism. The notion of the "endless frontier," in which every refinement of technology brings new wonders to the doorstep of mankind, is hardly current among scientists. In the past, some scientists may have expressed themselves in this manner, particularly when making a case for increased governmental support of research. However, in light of the profound reaction of many scientists to the destructive power unleashed by atomic energy and with a few vocal scientists (such as Paul Ehrlich and Barry Commoner) playing leading roles in the battle to save

1

the environment, it is clear that there are many more subtle elements in the scientists' perspective that we must explore if we are to develop an understanding of it. The five articles that comprise this section differ widely in their substance and intent, yet all contribute to such an understanding.

The stage is set by an exercise in "futurology." In "Forecasts of Some Technological and Scientific Developments and Their Societal Consequences," Theodore Gordon and Robert Ament report on a study carried out by the Institute for the Future—a scientific organization whose main function is developing forecasting tools to aid long-range planning. Gordon and Ament employed the Delphi method to develop a series of forecasts of future events in science and technology. In this technique, a panel of experts is assembled and made to deliberate as a committee without ever coming into face-to-face contact with one another. Thus, the group brings its knowledge and judgment to bear on a problem in a manner independent of personalities and other chance factors that may shape normal committee operations. While there is some dispute over the validity of the Delphi method, and the authors would be the first to caution that their studies are experimental and should be viewed with a rather critical eye, the result is an intriguing excursion into the future as seen by a panel of respected scientists. The projected world bears many characteristics of past and present American science fiction, but it is tempered by informed judgment on what is scientifically and technologically feasible. One should bear in mind here that the future described is not one that the panelists see as necessarily desirable—it is simply one that is probable. Having gained an idea of what may be in store for us, we may turn to the next three articles, in which scientists examine some current problems in the technology-society interface.

In 1969 President Nixon appointed a special task force to conduct a review of the federal government's policies relating to science and technology. The selection, "Science, Technology and National Goals," constitutes the first chapter of this task force's report. It is of special significance since it represents a summary of current thinking on the part of a group of scientists and engineers close to the pulse of governmental power in this country. On the whole, the report is a strong statement in favor of a continuing high level of government investment in science. Continued progress toward achieving our national goals and purposes requires such an effort, according to the task force. Certain deficiencies exist in the application of science and technology, and these should be recognized and corrected. Numerous problems confront us in the realm of science policy. Nevertheless, in the view of these scientists, continued *purposeful* application of science and technology is a sine qua non for the solution of society's problems.

A related viewpoint emerges from Alvin Weinberg's article, "Can Technology Replace Social Engineering?" Weinberg, director of the Atomic Energy Commission's Oak Ridge National Laboratory for many years, and one of the pioneers in large-scale atomic energy research, argues that technology is capable of finding shortcuts to the solution of many pressing social problems. Thus, he proposes the notion of the "technological fix." Since technological problems are intrinsically easier to solve than social problems, Weinberg suggests we transform the latter into the former. Technology defines the limits within which society functions. By developing new technologies we can change the limits of society and thereby remove the conditions creating the problem. Weinberg concludes that technology will not totally replace social engineering, but it may, in his mind, go a long way toward easing some of the pressures that society now faces.

Robert Morison's article, "Science and Social Attitudes," was written several years after Weinberg's, and in it the author finds himself forced to defend the scientific enterprise against what he sees as growing doubts about its societal value. From his vantage point as an eminent scientist and director of the Division of Biological Sciences at Cornell University, Morison identifies several reasons for the slackening in public approval of science over the past decade. Prime among these is the fact that science is central to man's ability to manipulate the world around him, and it is increasingly apparent that this manipulation has not always been for the good of mankind. In Morison's view, science is but one of a whole class of rational systems about which there is growing skepticism in society. Some of Morison's underlying assumptions are clearly revealed in the course of action he prescribes to deal with the situation. The problem is mainly one of education, he says. The public must be made aware of the true nature of scientific activity and must be increasingly informed about the alternative courses of action made available by science. In Morison's view, it is not so much the substance of science that requires change; it is the image.

Throughout these readings, we should bear in mind that the direct links between science and society are relatively few and of rather minor importance. The indirect link—technology—is the important one through which applications of knowledge, both good and bad, are manifested. Technology, however, is not merely the application of knowledge to the solution of *practical* problems. It is a creative art form in itself, a mode of expression independent of society's needs for its products. This point is ingeniously made in the article entitled "Pure Technology," which originates from the satirist's pen of "Daedalus." The pseudonym "Daedalus" protects the anonymity of an imaginative British scientist who writes regularly for the *New Scientist*. In a subtle, tongue-in-cheek manner he carries out an historical analysis of "technology for its own sake." A prime current example of what "Daedalus" regards as pure technology is the SST. Rational analysis, says "Daedalus," clearly shows the pointlessness of the project. The real reason for wanting to carry it through must then be the "sheer entertainment of overcoming all the technical problems and finally flying such a thrilling machine!" It is, in the final analysis, not technology itself that is bringing mankind to the brink of disaster. Rather, it is the passion for practical application. Pure technology must be recognized for its own sake and not limited by the "stifling doctrine of social relevance."

Forecasts of Some Technological and Scientific Developments and Their Societal Consequences

THEODORE J. GORDON AND ROBERT H. AMENT

Scientific and technological developments have profoundly altered man's institutions, his life styles, and his aspirations in the last several generations. What is striking about this transformation is not that it has occurred, but rather that it has occurred without preparation. For the consequences have been pervasive, and many of them, favorable and unfavorable alike, have left today's policy makers and policy advisors seriously behind the course of events, with the result that by the time their efforts have been translated into programs for action they have become infeasible or simply irrelevant. Long-range forecasting of scientific and technological developments can provide some of the information decision makers need to accommodate the long lead-times separating the evaluation of opportunities from the implementation of specific plans. The technological Delphi study reported in this article was undertaken to help provide such information.

The immediate objectives of the study were:

— To generate a list of important prospective events and developments in the physical and biological disciplines;
— To determine, using the judgment of experts, when these events and developments might take place;
— To ascertain what societal changes are likely to accompany these scientific and technological innovations;
— To determine whether the anticipated societal consequences appeared likely to be beneficial or detrimental to society as a whole;
— To determine whether intervention in the processes producing these consequences seemed feasible, and if so, through what means; and
— To test the use of the Delphi method for attaining reasonable consensus among groups of experts in dealing with questions of social change, values, and science policy.

THE DELPHI TECHNIQUE

Most decision makers utilize expert advice in forming their judgment. Where the question being examined is so complex and involves such obscure inter-relationships that no single person could be expected to be expert in the many disciplines required, the traditional approach to the answer is to seek a consensus among experts through open discussion or a conference. How-ever, joint committee activity often introduces certain undesirable psycho-logical factors, "such as specious persuasion, unwillingness to abandon pub-licly expressed opinions, and the bandwagon effect of majority opinion."[1]

The Delphi technique, which was used in this study, makes it possible to avoid some of these difficulties because the experts involved exchange their opinions anonymously and through an intermediary, who controls the feed-back of opinion in subsequent rounds of the inquiry. It has been found in previous studies of this type that the Delphi process—involving anonymity, iteration, and controlled feedback—tends to produce a converging group consensus.

In a typical Delphi investigation, the participants are sent a series of questionnaires through the mail. In the first, they might be asked to provide their judgment as to likely dates of occurrence of a group of events and de-velopments. The collated responses normally reveal a spread of opinions; these data are presented to the respondents in the second questionnaire. In this round, the respondents are given the opportunity to revise their estimates in light of the group response, and those participants whose estimates have fallen earlier or later than those of the majority are asked to provide reasons for their positions. These reasons, along with the new estimates of the group as a whole, are collated and fed back to the respondents on the third ques-tionnaire, and they are again asked to reassess their earlier estimates in view of the new group response and reasons provided for early and late dates.

The Delphi method has proven useful for long-range forecasting of ex-pected technological and societal developments. Several corporations and gov-ernment agencies have conducted future-oriented Delphi studies concerned with such subjects as political alliances,[2] technological potentials,[3] war pre-

1. N. C. Dalkey and O. Helmer, "An Experimental Application of the Delphi Method to the Use of Experts," *Management Science,* vol. 9, no. 3 (April 1963).

2. Joseph Matino, *An Experiment with the Delphi Procedure for Long-Range Fore-casting* (Washington, D.C.: Office of Scientific Research, US Air Force, 1967), AFOSR Document 670175.

3. Harper Q. North and Donald L. Pyke, *A Probe of TRW's Future, The Next 20 Years,* a TRW proprietary document, 1966.

vention techniques,[4] economic indices,[5] and medical developments.[6] Results generally have been satisfactory; that is, in many cases a reasonable consensus seems to have been achieved and the potential developments described provided a basis for subsequent planning, action, and analysis.

Even though this technique has been used with some success, however, it should not be interpreted as a device that produces "truth about the future." The Delphi method is designed to produce consensus judgments in inexact fields; it would be a mistake to consider such judgments as complete or precise descriptions about the future.

The future will contain events that are totally unanticipated today; perhaps this is the only thing that can be said about the future with absolute certainty. Furthermore, all techniques of forecasting that rely on judgment and opinion (rather than on the more rigid laws of causality of the natural sciences) depend on the imagination and technical adequacy of the forecasters. Nevertheless, forecasting the future seems to be a worthwhile enterprise despite the certainty of the unexpected and despite the limitations imposed by relying on human judgment, however well informed. Forecasts, even hazy forecasts, based on careful judgment can provide a seemingly coherent structure for testing alternative contemplated actions, for warning that certain other actions may be needed or should be avoided, and for defining the scope of reasonable expectations in a world where expectations sometimes seem unbounded.

OUTLINE OF THE STUDY

As in all Delphi studies, the value of the results depends largely on the excellence and cooperation of the participants. Since this study dealt with scientific and technological events and their implications for society, the experimenters invited respondents who had, in the aggregate, skills which included the following:

Aerospace technology	Industrialization
Agriculture	Manufacturing
Bacteriology	Mathematics
Biochemistry	Microbiology

4. See, for example, T. J. Gordon and O. Helmer, *Report on a Long-Range Forecasting Study,* The Rand Corporation, Paper P-2982 (September 1964).

5. Robert M. Campbell, "Methodological Study of the Utilization of Experts in Business Forecasting," Ph.D. thesis, University of California, Los Angeles, September, 1966.

6. Alan Sheldon, Laboratory of Community Psychiatry, Boston, 1969.

Brain physiology	Molecular biology
Computer sciences	Natural resources
Cytogenetics	Pediatrics
Electron physics	Philosophy
Engineering	Psychiatry
Finance	Public administration
Genetics	Science journalism
Gerontology	Transportation
History of science	

Four questionnaires were used in this study. The first presented a list of forty technological developments selected by the experimenters and asked that the respondents estimate the dates at which the item had, in their judgment, a 10 percent, a 50 percent, and a 90 percent chance of occurrence. The respondents were also asked to suggest additional scientific and technical developments which they believed might have significant social impact and to indicate how familiar they felt they were with each item. The responses to this questionnaire were collated. In all, forty-three additional items were suggested by the respondents and added to the study.

The new items were presented to the respondents in Questionnaire 2, along with a request that they provide estimates of the dates by which they judged the items to have a 10 percent, a 50 percent, and a 90 percent probability of occurrence. A second part of this questionnaire asked the respondent to list what they considered to be socially important consequences likely to result from all of the technological and scientific events. The questionnaire suggested that the respondents consider a full spectrum of consequences—technological, demographic, political, personal, social.

Questionnaires 3 and 4 further refined the results of the study by informing respondents of items upon which agreement had been reached and asking them to reconsider their responses on other items, as well as (in certain cases) to state the reasons for their opinions. Questionnaire 4 also asked respondents to suggest specific policy strategies that might be used to intervene in the consequences of the events being discussed.

FORECASTS AND CONSEQUENCES

The full range of results obtained from this study tells a fascinating story. Unfortunately, we are unable to present complete tabulations in the limited space afforded by the context of this article.[7] In the next section, these tabulations are used to delineate a series of scenarios, describing possible technological futures. Here, to give the reader a feeling for the type of findings upon which the scenarios were based, we present a number of sample tabulations. Some examples of the forecasts of the time of occurrence of events discussed by the panelists are presented in Figure 1. The polygons are used to depict the final range of opinions generated by the group. The high point on the bar indicates the median date at which the panelists judged there was a 50 percent chance the event would occur. The shorter legs of the polygon define the limits of the upper and lower quartiles, and the bar itself the interquartile range.

For each item in these figures, the asterisk denotes the median date of occurrence forecasted by the subset of respondents who rated themselves "expert" or "generally familiar" with the event in question.

The respondents also developed an extensive list of prospective consequences which they felt might be expected as a result of the forecasted technological and scientific developments. Each of these consequences was judged as to its likelihood of being a result of the event and, assuming it should occur, whether it was favorable or unfavorable.

The list of consequences for those items shown in Figure 1 is given in Figure 2; the polygons again indicate the interquartile range of the responses.

---

7. See the report from which this article was condensed for a full presentation of the results.

Figure 1. Potential Physical and Biological Developments

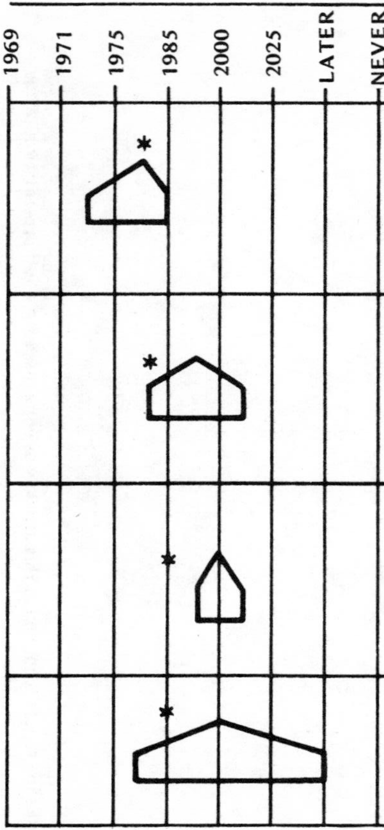

Figure 2. Consequences of Forecasted Events: Their Likelihood and Impact

NEW AUTOMATION AND COMMUNICATION TECHNIQUES		HOW LIKELY IS IT THAT THE RESULT WILL BE A CONSEQUENCE OF THE DEVELOPMENT?				WHAT WILL THE EFFECT OF THE CONSEQUENCE BE?				
IF THESE DEVELOPMENTS WERE TO OCCUR,	THEY MIGHT RESULT IN:	VIRTUALLY CERTAIN	PROBABLE	POSSIBLE	ALMOST IMPOSSIBLE	VERY FAVORABLE	FAVORABLE	LITTLE OR NO IMPORTANCE	DETRIMENTAL	VERY DETRIMENTAL
Establishment of a central data storage facility (or several regional or disciplinary facilities) with wide public access (perhaps in the home) for general or specialized information retrieval primarily in the areas of library, medical and legal data.	Use of home terminals for education; transformation of the home into a part-time school; growing competition between traditional teaching profession and advocates of programmed instruction.									
	Information storage becoming a salable service, resulting in widespread revision to business practices.									
	Improvement in social science research.									
	Individual citizens becoming proficient in law and medicine, through easy availability of the relevant data in the home.									

Figure 2 (continued)

NEW AUTOMATION AND COMMUNICATION TECHNIQUES (con't)		HOW LIKELY IS IT THAT THE RESULT WILL BE A CONSEQUENCE OF THE DEVELOPMENT?				WHAT WILL THE EFFECT OF THE CONSEQUENCE BE?				
IF THESE DEVELOPMENTS WERE TO OCCUR,	THEY MIGHT RESULT IN:	VIRTUALLY CERTAIN	PROBABLE	POSSIBLE	ALMOST IMPOSSIBLE	VERY FAVORABLE	FAVORABLE	LITTLE OR NO IMPORTANCE	DETRIMENTAL	VERY DETRIMENTAL
	The rise of new methods of computer-aided crime.									
	Information overload; the problem will be to select from the available plethora of information that which is important and relevant to the individual.									
	Great revolutions in library sciences, including greatly improved methods of searching for particular subjects.									
	Invasion of privacy (assuming data associated with individual people can be retrieved).									

Figure 2 (continued)

NEW METHODS OF MODIFYING THE ENVIRONMENT

IF THESE DEVELOPMENTS WERE TO OCCUR,	THEY MIGHT RESULT IN:	HOW LIKELY IS IT THAT THE RESULT WILL BE A CONSEQUENCE OF THE DEVELOPMENT?				WHAT WILL THE EFFECT OF THE CONSEQUENCE BE?				
		VIRTUALLY CERTAIN	PROBABLE	POSSIBLE	ALMOST IMPOSSIBLE	VERY FAVORABLE	FAVORABLE	LITTLE OR NO IMPORTANCE	DETRIMENTAL	VERY DETRIMENTAL
Feasibility of limited weather control in the sense of predictably affecting regional weather at acceptable cost.	Great improvements in agricultural efficiency by creating rain on demand, avoidance of floods, and minimizing the number of clouds over farms during sunlight hours.									
	Disruption in ecological balance leading to extinction of some plant and animal species.									
	Weather being used as a military or economic weapon.									
	Great increase in the number of civil suits alleging damage caused by weather manipulation.									
	Emergence of a new power elite: "the weather makers."									

Figure 2 (continued)

NEW REPRODUCTIVE TECHNIQUES		HOW LIKELY IS IT THAT THE RESULT WILL BE A CONSEQUENCE OF THE DEVELOPMENT?				WHAT WILL THE EFFECT OF THE CONSEQUENCE BE?				
IF THESE DEVELOPMENTS WERE TO OCCUR,	THEY MIGHT RESULT IN:	VIRTUALLY CERTAIN	PROBABLE	POSSIBLE	ALMOST IMPOSSIBLE	VERY FAVORABLE	FAVORABLE	LITTLE OR NO IMPORTANCE	DETRIMENTAL	VERY DETRIMENTAL
Human Clone—the nucleus of an ovum is removed and replaced by somatic cells, allowing development in a host mother of an identical twin of the person supplying the somatic cell.	A replication of essential or great men, resulting in a kind of immortality.									
	Creation of a super race, an effective way to preserve and distribute good genotypes.									
	New animal breeding practices.									

Figure 2 (continued)

NEW BEHAVIOR MANIPULATION TECHNIQUES		HOW LIKELY IS IT THAT THE RESULT WILL BE A CONSEQUENCE OF THE DEVELOPMENT?				WHAT WILL THE EFFECT OF THE CONSEQUENCE BE?				
IF THESE DEVELOPMENTS WERE TO OCCUR,	THEY MIGHT RESULT IN:	VIRTUALLY CERTAIN	PROBABLE	POSSIBLE	ALMOST IMPOSSIBLE	VERY FAVORABLE	FAVORABLE	LITTLE OR NO IMPORTANCE	DETRIMENTAL	VERY DETRIMENTAL
Control of the behavior of some people in society by radio stimulation of the brain.	Decisive tool for control of abnormal (including criminal) behavior.									
	A substitution for penal institutions.									
	Development of protective and jamming systems.									
	Stimulation of socially useful responses, such as the wish to work.									
	Use in medicine as a form of sedation.									

SCENARIOS

The forecasts of events and their consequences can be used to form a number of scenarios which may be useful in a variety of long-range planning contexts. The scenarios presented here were written using group median dates as a basis for sorting the events into the various time intervals described; the important consequences of these events were then included.

The Technological World of 1985. Solution of the foreign-body rejection problem will have greatly improved the process of organ transplantation, and to meet the need for natural transplantable organs, "parts" banks will be operating. Competition for organs will have encouraged black markets, although the importance of these markets will have been diminished by legislative regulation of transplantations within the hospital-physician community and by the development of artificial organs, including, for example, implantable artificial hearts with power sources capable of lasting five years. Research will be continuing into the use of tissue-compatible animals to provide yet another source of organs. This activity will have changed the emphasis in medicine from repair to replacement, a development accompanied by the rise of new industries, technologies, and classes of medical personnel.

Several other biological technologies will have significantly affected the world of 1985. Contraceptive drugs will have been developed which will lower fertility rates, being mass-administered as aerosols or as additions to water supplies or staples (as iodine is added to table salt). Societal acceptance of this practice will result from extensive public education about the consequences of overpopulation. But this development will have led to the possibility of a new form of warfare: surreptitious contraception. Research and development projects will have been implemented to create an anticontraceptive pill and detection system. The drug will form only one more addition to the arsenal of biological and chemical weapons.

There will have been an enormous increase in information-handling machines and in the complexities and pervasiveness of their operations. The importance of skilled programmers will have been enhanced. Central data storage facilities with wide public access will have been established and will provide library, medical, and legal data. Privacy will have been challenged by the large data banks, and new methods of computer-aided crime will have come on the scene. New computer and automation uses will include automated language translation capable of coping with idiomatic syntactical complexities and sophisticated teaching machines which will utilize adaptive programs responding not only to the students' answers but also to certain physiological responses, such as extreme tensions.

Perhaps most startling will be new opportunities and innovations in human reproduction. Nonsurgical techniques permitting the choice of the sex of offspring (with 90-percent certainty) will have been demonstrated, and chromosome typing will be used to discover human abnormalities within weeks of conception. There will be concern about the very detrimental effects of fads for sexes, and regulation of the sex ratio may take the form of legislation or financial incentives to those parents who help to maintain a socially desirable sex equilibrium.

Immunizing agents will have been developed to protect against most bacterial and viral diseases. Inexpensive nonnarcotic drugs for producing specific personality changes, such as euphoria, antiaggression, and increased attention, will be available to the public, and these will have led to improvements in mental therapy, education, and criminal control.

A primitive form of artificial life will have been created and protein usable for food will have been produced, spawning new industries and offering the hopeful prospect of specialized diet additives for protein-deficient populations. Conventional agriculture will be augmented by the advent of large-scale desalination plants which may, through their method of distribution, be instruments of international power politics.

Various high-speed transportation systems—such as VTOL-STOL, 200 mph trains, ground-effects machines—will be in wide use, but air traffic control problems and transit congestion in major urban city centers will still exist. Automobile engines, fuels, and accessories will have been produced that will permit operation of vehicles without harmful exhaust. While these devices will have eased the problems of air pollution, traffic congestion will still be with us.

A manned space station of relatively long duration will be orbiting the earth. It will have brought advances in meteorology, cartography, geology, resources mapping, astronomy, geophysics, and military intelligence. Satellite-derived weather forecasting will allow regular and reliable forecasts fourteen days in advance for areas as small as 100 square miles.

The Technological World of 2000. Between 1985 and 2000, biological research and development will have led to many results, including the development of new methods of behavior control, new reproductive techniques, and advances in medical technology. Apparently the threat of starvation will have lent impetus to the development of several new food-producing techniques. There is some fear that these techniques will offer only a short-term reprieve in the onset of world starvation, that the catastrophe of large-scale starvation will yet occur, since these advances will remove some incentives to the limiting of family size. To minimize this threat, some governments will have enacted legislation designed to limit family size; others may have used or encouraged the use of antifertility drugs. World food production will have been expanded through the development of techniques which bring 50 percent more arable acreage under cultivation. Microbial systems converting petroleum to protein will contribute significantly to world food supplies, and ocean fish farming and aquaculture will also be in extensive use. Population pressures will demand all the food the world can produce.

New methods of behavior control which stem from biological research will have included (1) the development and use of LSD-like drugs to heighten perception and learning speed of retardates, (2) knowledge of how to stimulate cognitive growth to a maximum ability in preschool children, (3) brain surgery or psychochemicals for modifying the behavior of criminals, and (4) radio stimulation of the brains of some people in society. These forms of control will have been accompanied by break-throughs concerning our understanding of human behavior and motivation, including knowledge of the significance of dreams and REM (rapid-eye-movement) sleep in human cognitive development.

New reproductive techniques also will have been developed by 2000. For example, human ova will have been fertilized *in vitro* with subsequent implantation into a surrogate mother. The therapeutic uses of this technique will have allowed some mothers to bear children without their former fear of undesirable gene combinations resulting. Human beings will have been successfully cloned, and the technique will be used routinely for the breeding of other animals, especially in cattle farming.

The nations of the world will be using the oceans not only as a major source of food, as mentioned earlier, but also as a source of minerals through mining of the ocean floor. This may have led to extension of national sovereignties farther into the oceans and "claim staking" with concomitant political tensions. International treaties, modeled after the 1959 Antarctica Treaty, will probably have been used to permit more orderly exploitation of the oceans.

An essential feature of man's growing control over his environment will be the relative ease with which he can create ecological catastrophe. His intrusions into the oceans and the advent of weather control, for example, will be subjected not only to political scrutiny but to ecological judgment as well.

This new conscience will lead finally to very strong pressure to control the most threatening of all ecological problems: population expansion in the presence of inadequate food. Legislation, tax incentives, propaganda, and sterilization, as well as abortions in certain cases, will be in intensive use. Many aspects of scientific and technological development will be directed toward coping with problems that stem from the world's increasing population levels. For example, waste disposal will have become even more of a problem by the year 2000, necessitating innovations in the use of self-destroying material. Equally important will be the institution of new types of legislation and incentives which encourage the avoidance of pollution and the creation of a favorable environment.

Several other breakthroughs in physical technologies will have occurred between 1985 and 2000. Complex programmable and self-adaptive robots capable of performing many chores will have found use in the households of advanced countries. With such devices available, discretionary time will also have increased and with it the demand for educational and recreational services. Computers will have been built that will comprehend standard IQ tests and score above 150. On-the-spot communication will be increasingly available to the citizens of most advanced countries; individual, portable two-way communication devices will be in use, much to the consternation of teenagers required to "call in" on dates and to regulatory authorities required to allocate and control frequencies.

A permanent base will have been established on the moon. Its life support systems will be capable of sustaining ten men indefinitely. This base will provide the earth's most important radio and astronomical observatory. A radio observatory designed primarily to search for extraterrestrial life will have been constructed. Planetary exploration, primarily unmanned, will be continuing.

The Technological World of 2025. The biological research begun in the last decades of the twentieth century will have continued into the twenty-first, yielding new techniques of control and understanding of human development and behavior. A range of new human reproductive techniques will exist, including extrauterine development (as a result of the successful simulation of the placenta) and parthenogenesis. Of course, the choice of sex of one's offspring and human cloning, both demonstrated earlier, will have come into wider use. All of these techniques will have raised serious threats to conventional family structuring and many other social institutions that we currently take for granted.

Of particular importance to biomedicine early in the next century will be the capability of modifying genes through molecular engineering to over-come some human hereditary defects. This development will have stemmed from better understanding of the processes of differentiation and develop-ment and will provide the ability to control certain human phenotypes. Fur-thermore, skill in genetic engineering and deeper understanding of the gen-etic processes may have provided the capability to repair the central nervous system through regeneration of individual neurons; perhaps it will have been possible also to stimulate the growth of new organs and limbs in human be-ings.

This development will probably lead to intense discussion about which diseases should or should not be controlled. The arguments may involve the possibility of producing specialized classes, such as menials and supermen, and will probably consider the danger that a division between socioeconomic classes and, perhaps, between developed and less-developed nations will grow, depending on who has the technological capability and required financ-ing to construct molecular engineering centers. Of course, the application of these techniques to food production will have proven beneficial to the world. The spectacular genetic breakthroughs expected earlier will have been matched by our growing control over the aging process; life expectancy at birth may have been extended chemically by fifty years, with a commen-surate increase in vigor. New drugs will also have been used for raising the intelligence of some human beings and for the purpose of producing specific changes in personal characteristics, such as alterations in attitudes and life styles. This new capability of determining the effects of drugs will have re-sulted from the development of a theoretical pharmacological discipline and, thus, the prior analytic prediction of the medical effects of drugs.

The impact of these kinds of changes on social structure will have been immense. Some of the developments might be used to reward special groups, such as high ranking officials. Scientists might organize to prevent these capa-bilities from being used adversely. Less-developed nations might demand be-ing made part of the technological present.

In the first part of the twenty-first century, research into the means of directly stimulating the cortex may have led to demonstration of man-machine symbiosis in which certain men (perhaps with implanted electrodes or other, less repugnant devices) will extend their intelligence by being con-nected to a computer. This development might have the effect of multiplying human intelligence manyfold.

Significant amounts of electrical power will have been transmitted by wireless means; superconductors operating in the range of 20-30°K, or even room temperature, will have been demonstrated. Use of these new materials and processes will have resulted in the development of new families of vehicles and devices; room-temperature superconductors, for example, could be used to make cars that float over magnetic highways. These techniques will permit cheaper electricity to be produced and, with it, the development of new techniques for refrigeration, communication, and transportation, amounting to a new dimension of control by man over his world. It is possible that research into the composition of matter will lead to the ability to produce any element from subatomic particles. If such a capability should be attained, rare earth elements could be produced in whatever quantities needed, and alloys and materials virtually unknown today would come into wide use.

Science, Technology and National Goals

THE PRESIDENT'S TASK FORCE ON SCIENCE POLICY

THE NATIONAL NEED FOR SCIENCE AND TECHNOLOGY

Our national progress will become ever more critically dependent upon the excellence of our science and technology. A vigorous, high-quality program aimed at advancing our scientific and technological capabilities (including the social, economic, and behavioral components) is vital to all national goals and purposes. Such a program is especially vital to our national defense and security and to our international posture generally; to our ability to negotiate properly safeguarded arms limitations; to our continued economic growth and development and to our international trade balance; to the health of business, labor, and the professions; to the quality of our environment; to the personal health and welfare of all; to the scope and quality of our educational processes; and to the culture, spirit, and inspiration of our people generally. The effectiveness of essentially all our social institutions, including particularly government itself, is deeply influenced by the quality of our science and technology.

The nation, therefore, has a fundamental need for excellence in science and technology. Accordingly, it also needs to insure that the effectiveness of our science and technology is not downgraded or destroyed by the unthinking or the uninformed. That is not to say that the limitations of science and technology should not be recognized. We do not suggest complacent acceptance of the unwanted side effects of narrowly motivated or incompletely understood applications of science. Nor do we suggest that technology should dictate social purpose. On the contrary, we wish to emphasize the importance of seeking to optimize utilization of science and technology in the service of social, political, and economic goals.

Anti-Science Attitudes. The rapid rise of attitudes disdainful of science and technology, and the disillusionment of many young people with science and technology is of grave concern. The sources of these attitudes include deficiencies in the application of science and technology which should in fact be criticized and should be corrected. Inanimate technology is not of itself the problem; rather the primary need is "to conceive ways to discover and repair the deficiencies in the processes and institutions by which society puts the tools of science and technology to work."[1] The sources of the shift in attitudes toward science and technology also include widespread lack of perspective and understanding of their nature and role in past and future improvement in the human condition. The public and its elected representatives must have a better grasp of both the limitations and the promise of science and technology. Priority should be given to presenting this complex matter to the public in a balanced and understandable fashion. The responsibility for achieving this understanding starts with the executive and legislative branches of the federal government and spreads to include state and local government, universities, business and professional organizations, and other private institutions in positions of leadership.

Scientific Leadership. The scientific and technological resources of this nation are among its most powerful tools for the achievement of our social, political, and economic purposes. The management, strength, and proper allocation of these vital resources are political responsibilities of the highest significance, with not only short-term but also very long-term implications

---

1. *Technology: Processes of Assessment and Choice,* A Report to the Committee on Science and Astronautics, U.S. House of Representatives, by the National Academy of Sciences, July 1969.

both nationally and internationally. The leadership of today must provide the legacy for tomorrow.

The Task Force believes that one of the important national goals for which this nation should strive is leadership and excellence in science itself— as a long-range investment in achieving the nation's other goals, as a precursor to more directly applicable and controllable technology, and as a contribution to the culture, spirit, and inspiration of our people.

DEFINING LONG-RANGE NATIONAL GOALS AND ISSUES IN QUANTITATIVE TERMS

National policy governing science and technology should in principle be a mirror image of our national goals and purposes. Science policy should in part be a statement about the priorities of the future. While these generalized statements have wide acceptance, many of the mechanisms and concepts implicit in them are difficult to define in detail and complex to administer.

Regional Goals. The machinery of federal, state, and local government is vast. Each major problem, such as environmental pollution, is pervasive and interdependent with others. Hundreds of separate institutions, both private and public, must function as a part of a team if the problems are to be solved. Proper distinctions must be made between the responsibilities and opportunities of federal, state, and local government, as well as between those of universities, business enterprise, and other private institutions. National goals and purposes have distributed (e.g., geographical) as well as central components. The "points of principal action"—and hence the foci of primary responsibility and opportunity for solution—of some of our most urgent national concerns are central (e.g., national defense). Others are regional (e.g., air and water pollution, interurban transportation), while still others can best be managed at the state or city level.

Definition of Goals. The central crisis is one of management, of leadership, of inspiration, with an eye to the future as well as the present. Generalized goals must be broken down into specific subelements and specific realistic milestones established; specific responsibilities must be assigned with clear-cut processes of review, specific attainable criteria and standards with quantitative as well as qualitative substance must be promulgated; and all of these should be projected over suitable periods of time (e.g., ten to twenty years), with specific machinery for review and re-projection.

Such long-range national programs should, of course, have the benefit of searching congressional debate and formal legislative approval as appropriate.

Frequently heard reasons why ten- or fifteen-year national programs cannot be established (e.g., the yearly budget cycle, the short-term nature of legislative and executive terms, the unwillingness to commit future administrations) are not convincing.

The Contribution of Science and Technology. We have been discussing one of the central responsibilities of government. The more restricted question here is: what special contribution can science and technology make to the definition and achievement of long-range national goals? Of course, basic and applied research can contribute to understanding—the vital basis for all other parts of the process—if focused properly on these problems. In addition, "technology has a direct impact on values by virtue of its capacity for creating new opportunities. By making possible what was not possible before, it offers individuals and society new options to choose from."[2] Finally, a great majority of our current urban and environmental problems have important technological or scientific components. That is not to say that science and technology alone can solve these problems or even that the technological component is normally the dominant one—in most cases, it is not.

Because of the technological components inherent in many current problems, however, and because of the nature of the tools of science and technology, they can make a special and vitally needed contribution to the definition of long-range goals, and to the central *management* problems inherent in broad long-range national programs. Detailed quantitative development of qualitative goals—which engineers and scientists are especially equipped to do—can aid in choosing wisely among alternatives. It can also help define the subelements of a particular program with sufficient clarity to permit each of the widely dispersed elements in our society to grasp its part, and to assist in reviewing and re-projecting the program as needed.

It is the view of the Task Force that a special effort is needed to make fuller use of the tools of science and technology in *quantitatively* projecting long-range requirements associated with our many pressing social, urban, and environmental problems: air and water pollution, waste disposal, educational services, health care, mass transportation, housing and urban development, crime prevention, and energy requirements, for example. The magnitude of concern and awareness for such problems, and increasing realization of the urgent need to mobilize our resources to combat them, is clearly reflected in such . . . actions as the establishment by the President of the Council on Urban Affairs and the Council on Environmental Quality.

2. Harvard University Program on Technology and Society, *Fourth Annual Report,* 1967-1968.

We can no longer afford to approach the longer-range future haphazardly. As the pace of change accelerates, the process of change becomes more complex. . . . Our need now is to seize on the future as the key dimension in our decisions, and to chart that future as consciously as we are accustomed to charting the past.

−Richard M. Nixon

THE IMPORTANCE OF SCIENCE AND TECHNOLOGY TO ECONOMIC GROWTH

Economic growth will, over a long period of time, define the total level of resources within which our national goals must be achieved. Because of the central significance of economic growth to all other national goals, it is especially important to point out its dependence on science and technology.

It is generally recognized that the economic growth of highly industrialized countries in the western world has been heavily dependent on the technological developments which have been incorporated into their societies. In the past half century the economic growth of the United States has been as much determined by new technology as it has by the continuous investment of capital. If a major national goal is increasing the quality of life for the mass of our population, it becomes essential that continued technological development also be a high priority national goal. A stagnant technology will mean a stagnant economy. In this regard, it is of interest to note the statement of Mr. Kosygin to the Twenty-third Party Congress in March 1966:

... The course of the economic competition between the two world systems depends on the rate of development of our science, and on the scale on which we use the results of research in production. . . .

The growth and diffusion of technology have expanded the goods and services available to the people by improving the inputs used for production, by improving the outputs flowing from the production line, and by reducing the volume of inputs needed per unit of output. Scientific and technological advances have led to the invention or discovery of new and improved materials, or materials that can substitute for limited or vanishing natural supplies. The quality of machines, plant, and rolling stock has been improved and their ability to deliver output at less cost greatly enhanced. New or better final products have been turned out. Better production processes and better organization of the flow of materials and of production have cut costs. Better control has made for economies in the use of inventories. People have been encouraged to improve their productive capacity and to engage in economically productive work by the attraction of the new products made available for consumption by technological advance.

However, technological change also leads to regional shifts in the distribution of resources, the obsolescence of skills, etc., which require movement, retraining, and other adjustments by people. Such change puts a high premium on those who are current in scientific and technical skills, and on continued education of personnel already in responsible jobs. The costs entailed in all of these adjustments should, of course, be deducted in assessing the contribution of science and technology to the growth of output. Although difficult to measure, some place these costs very high, even to the point of questioning the social value of any significant degree of technological change. Most economists believe, however, that a reasonable allowance for such costs does, on the whole, leave a substantial net gain.

Continued study of the role and potential of science and technology in promoting and enhancing economic growth—both nationally and regionally— is important to the setting of realistic long-range quantitative national goals.

RECOMMENDATIONS

The Task Force recommends that the President explicitly enunciate, as a national policy, the need for vigorous, high-quality science and technology, focusing on our national goals and purposes, and recognizing the cultural and inspirational values in man's scientific progress.

The Task Force also recommends that the President call for—as one national goal—continuing leadership in science and in the technology relevant to our other national goals and purposes.

Finally, it is recommended that the President direct that increasing emphasis be given to using our scientific and technological capabilities quantitatively to develop and project long-range requirements in support of our national goals.

Can Technology Replace
Social Engineering?

ALVIN M. WEINBERG

During the war, and immediately afterward, our federal government mobilized its scientific and technical resources, such as the Oak Ridge National Laboratory, around great technological problems. Nuclear reactors, nuclear weapons, radar, and space are some of the miraculous new technologies that have been created by this mobilization of federal effort. In the past few years there has been a major change in focus of much of our federal research. Instead of being preoccupied with technology, our government is now mobilizing around problems that are largely social. We are beginning to ask what can we do about world population, about the deterioration of our environment, about our educational system, our decaying cities, race relations, poverty. Presidents Johnson [and Nixon have] dedicated the power of a scientifically oriented federal apparatus to finding solutions for these complex social problems.

Social problems are much more complex than are technological problems. It is much harder to identify a social problem than a technological problem: how do we know when our cities need renewing, or when our population is too big, or when our modes of transportation have broken down? The problems are, in a way, harder to identify just because their solutions are never clear-cut: how do we know when our cities are renewed, or our air clean enough, or our transportation convenient enough? By contrast, the availability of a crisp and beautiful technological *solution* often helps focus on the problem to which the new technology is the solution. I doubt that we would have been nearly as concerned with an eventual shortage of energy as we now are if we had not had a neat solution—nuclear energy—available to eliminate the shortage.

There is a more basic sense in which social problems are much more difficult than are technological problems. A social problem exists because many people behave, individually, in a socially unacceptable way. To solve a social problem one must induce social change—one must persuade many people to behave differently than they have behaved in the past. One must persuade many people to have fewer babies, or to drive more carefully, or to refrain from disliking Negroes. By contrast, resolution of a technological problem involves many fewer individual decisions. Once President Roosevelt decided to go after atomic energy, it was by comparison a relatively simple task to mobilize the Manhattan Project.

The resolution of social problems by the traditional methods—by motivating or forcing people to behave more rationally—is a frustrating business. People don't behave rationally; it is a long, hard business to persuade individuals to forego immediate personal gain or pleasure (as seen by the individual) in favor of longer term social gain. And indeed, the aim of social engineering is to invent the social devices—usually legal, but also moral and educational and organizational—that will change each person's motivation and redirect his activities along ways that are more acceptable to the society.

The technologist is appalled by the difficulties faced by the social engineer; to engineer even a small social change by inducing individuals to behave differently is always hard even when the change is rather neutral or even beneficial. For example, some rice eaters in India are reported to prefer starvation to eating wheat which we send to them. How much harder it is to change motivations where the individual is insecure and feels threatened if he acts differently, as illustrated by the poor white's reluctance to accept the Negro as an equal. By contrast, technological engineering is simple: the rocket, the reactor, and the desalination plants are devices that are expensive to develop, to be sure, but their feasibility is relatively easy to assess, and their success relatively easy to achieve once one understands the scientific principles that underlie them. It is, therefore, tempting to raise the following question: In view of the simplicity of technological engineering, and the complexity of social engineering, to what extent can social problems be circumvented by reducing them to technological problems? Can we identify Quick Technological Fixes for profound and almost infinitely complicated social problems, "fixes" that are within the grasp of modern technology, and which would either eliminate the original social problem without requiring a change in the individual's social attitudes, or would so alter the problem as to make its resolution more feasible? To paraphrase Ralph Nader, to what extent can technological *remedies* be found for social problems without first having to remove the *causes* of the problem? It is in this sense that I ask, "Can technology replace social engineering?"

THE MAJOR TECHNOLOGICAL FIXES OF THE PAST

To better explain what I have in mind, I shall describe how two of our profoundest social problems—poverty and war—have in some limited degree been solved by the Technological Fix, rather than by the methods of social engineering. Let me begin with poverty.

The traditional Marxian view of poverty regarded our economic ills as being primarily a question of maldistribution of goods. The Marxist recipe for elimination of poverty, therefore, was to eliminate profit, in the erroneous belief that it was the loss of this relatively small increment from the worker's paycheck that kept him poverty-stricken. The Marxist dogma is typical of the approach of the social engineer: one tries to convince or coerce many people to forego their short-term profits in what is presumed to be the long-term interest of the society as a whole.

The Marxian view seems archaic in this age of mass production and automation not only to us, but apparently to many Eastern bloc economists. For the brilliant advances in the technology of energy, of mass production, and of automation have created the affluent society. Technology has expanded our productive capacity so greatly that even though our distribution is still inefficient, and unfair by Marxian precepts, there is more than enough to go around. Technology has provided a "fix"—greatly expanded production of goods—which enables our capitalistic society to achieve many of the aims of the Marxist social engineer without going through the social revolution Marx viewed as inevitable. Technology has converted the seemingly intractable social problem of *widespread* poverty into a relatively tractable one.

My second example is war. The traditional Christian position views war as primarily a moral issue: if men become good, and model themselves after the Prince of Peace, they will live in peace. This doctrine is so deeply ingrained in the spirit of all civilized men that I suppose it is a blasphemy to point out that it has never worked very well—that men have not been good, and that they are not paragons of virtue or even of reasonableness.

Though I realize it is terribly presumptuous to claim, I believe that Edward Teller may have supplied the nearest thing to a Quick Technological Fix to the problem of war. The hydrogen bomb greatly increases the provocation that would precipitate large-scale war—and not because men's motivations have been changed, not because men have become more tolerant and understanding, but rather because the appeal to the primitive instinct of self-preservation has been intensified far beyond anything we could have imagined before the H-bomb was invented. To point out these things today, with the United States involved in a shooting war, may sound hollow and unconvincing; yet the desperate and partial peace we have now is much better than a full-fledged exchange of thermonuclear weapons. One cannot deny that the Soviet leaders now recognize the force of H-bombs, and that this has surely contributed to the less militant attitude of the USSR. One can only hope that the Chinese leadership, as it acquires familiarity with H-bombs, will also become less militant. If I were to be asked who has given the world a more effective means of achieving peace, our great religious leaders who urge men to love their neighbors and, thus, avoid fights, or our weapons technologists who simply present men with no rational alternative to peace, I would vote for the weapons technologist. That the peace we get is at best terribly fragile, I cannot deny; yet, as I shall explain, I think technology can help stabilize our imperfect and precarious peace.

THE TECHNOLOGICAL FIXES OF THE FUTURE

Are there other Technological Fixes on the horizon, other technologies that can reduce immensely complicated social questions to a matter of "engineering"? Are there new technologies that offer society ways of circumventing social problems and at the same time do *not* require individuals to renounce short-term advantage for long-term gain?

Probably the most important new Technological Fix is the Intra-Uterine Device for birth control. Before the IUD was invented, birth control demanded very strong motivation of countless individuals. Even with the pill, the individual's motivation had to be sustained day in and day out; should it flag even temporarily, the strong motivation of the previous month might go for naught. But the IUD, being a one-shot method, greatly reduces the individual motivation required to induce a social change. To be sure, the mother must be sufficiently motivated to accept the IUD in the first place, but, as experience in India already seems to show, it is much easier to persuade the Indian mother to accept the IUD once, than it is to persuade her to take a pill every day. The IUD does not completely replace social engineering by technology; and indeed, in some Spanish American cultures where the husband's manliness is measured by the number of children he has, the IUD attacks only part of the problem. Yet, in many other situations, as in India, the IUD so reduces the social component of the problem as to make an impossibly difficult social problem much less hopeless.

Let me turn now to problems which from the beginning have had both technical and social components—broadly, those concerned with conservation of our resources: our environment, our water, and our raw materials for production of the means of subsistence. The social issue here arises because many people by their individual acts cause shortages and, thus, create economic, and ultimately social, imbalance. For example, people use water wastefully, or they insist on moving to California because of its climate, and so we have water shortages; or too many people drive cars in Los Angeles with its curious meteorology, and so Los Angeles suffocates from smog.

The water resources problem is a particularly good example of a complicated problem with strong social and technological connotations. Our management of water resources in the past has been based largely on the ancient Roman device, the aqueduct: every water shortage was to be relieved by stealing water from someone else who at the moment didn't need the water or was too poor or too weak to prevent the steal. Southern California would steal from Northern California, New York City from upstate New York, the farmer who could afford a cloud-seeder from the farmer who could not afford a cloud-seeder. The social engineer insists that such shortsighted expedients have got us into serious trouble; we have no water resources policy, we waste water disgracefully, and, perhaps, in denying the ethic of thriftiness in using water, we have generally undermined our moral fiber. The social engineer, therefore, views such technological shenanigans as being shortsighted, if not downright immoral. Instead, he says, we should persuade or force people to use less water, or to stay in the cold Middle West where water is plentiful instead of migrating to California where water is scarce.

The water technologist, on the other hand, views the social engineer's approach as rather impractical. To persuade people to use less water, to get along with expensive water, is difficult, time-consuming, and uncertain in the extreme. Moreover, say the technologists, what right does the water resources expert have to insist that people use water less wastefully? Green lawns and clean cars and swimming pools are part of the good life, American style, . . . and what right do we have to deny this luxury if there is some alternative to cutting down the water we use?

Here we have a sharp confrontation of the two ways of dealing with a complex social issue: the social engineering way which asks people to behave more "reasonably," the technologists' way which tries to avoid changing people's habits or motivation. Even though I am a technologist, I have sympathy for the social engineer. I think we must use our water as efficiently as possible, that we ought to improve people's attitudes toward the use of water, and that everything that can be done to rationalize our water policy will be welcome. Yet as a technologist, I believe I see ways of providing more water more cheaply than the social engineers may concede is possible.

I refer to the possibility of nuclear desalination. The social engineer dismisses the technologist's simpleminded idea of solving a water shortage by transporting more water primarily because, in so doing, the water user steals water from someone else—possibly foreclosing the possibility of ultimately utilizing land now only sparsely settled. But surely water drawn from the sea deprives no one of his share of water. The whole issue is then a technological one; can fresh water be drawn from the sea cheaply enough to have a major impact on our chronically water-short areas like Southern California, Arizona, and the Eastern seaboard?

I believe the answer is yes, though much hard technical work remains to be done. A large program to develop cheap methods of nuclear desalting has been undertaken by the United States, and I have little doubt that within the next ten to twenty years we shall see huge dual-purpose desalting plants springing up on many parched seacoasts of the world. At first these plants will produce water at municipal prices. But I believe, on the basis of research now in progress at ORNL and elsewhere, water from the sea at a cost acceptable for agriculture—less than ten cents per 1,000 gallons—is eventually in the cards. In short, for areas close to the seacoasts, technology can provide water without requiring a great and difficult-to-accomplish change in people's attitudes toward the utilization of water.

The Technological Fix for water is based on the availability of extremely cheap energy from very large nuclear reactors. What other social consequences can one foresee flowing from really cheap energy eventually available to every country regardless of its endowment of conventional resources? Though we now see only vaguely the outlines of the possibilities, it does seem likely that from very cheap nuclear energy we shall get hydrogen by electrolysis of water, and, thence, the all important ammonia fertilizer necessary to help feed the hungry of the world; we shall reduce metals without requiring coking coal; we shall even power automobiles with electricity, via fuel cells or storage batteries, thus reducing our world's dependence on crude oil, as well as eliminating our air pollution insofar as it is caused by automobile exhaust or by the burning of fossil fuels. In short, the widespread availability of very cheap energy everywhere in the world ought to lead to an energy autarky in every country of the world; and eventually to an autarky in the many staples of life that should flow from really cheap energy.

WILL TECHNOLOGY REPLACE SOCIAL ENGINEERING?

I hope these examples suggest how social problems can be circumvented or at least reduced to less formidable proportions by the application of the Technological Fix. The examples I have given do not strike me as being fanciful, nor are they at all exhaustive. I have not touched, for example, upon the extent to which really cheap computers and improved technology of communication can help improve elementary teaching without having first to improve our elementary teachers. Nor have I mentioned Ralph Nader's brilliant observation that a safer car, and even its development and adoption by the auto company, is a quicker and probably surer way to reduce traffic deaths than is a campaign to teach people to drive more carefully. Nor have I invoked some really fanciful Technological Fixes: like providing air conditioners and free electricity to operate them for every Negro family in Watts on the assumption (suggested by Huntington) that race rioting is correlated with hot, humid weather; or the ultimate Technological Fix, Aldous Huxley's soma pills that eliminate human unhappiness without improving human relations in the usual sense.

My examples illustrate both the strength and the weakness of the Technological Fix for social problems. The Technological Fix accepts man's intrinsic shortcomings and circumvents them or capitalizes on them for socially useful ends. The Fix is, therefore, eminently practical and, in the short term, relatively effective. One does not wait around trying to change people's minds: if people want more water, one gets them more water rather than requiring them to reduce their use of water; if people insist on driving autos while they are drunk, one provides safer autos that prevent injuries even after a severe accident.

But the technological solutions to social problems tend to be incomplete and metastable, to replace one social problem with another. Perhaps the best example of this instability is the peace imposed upon us by the H-bomb. Evidently the pax hydrogenica is metastable in two senses: in the short term, because the aggressor still enjoys such an advantage; in the long term, because the discrepancy between have and have-not nations must eventually be resolved if we are to have permanent peace. Yet, for these particular shortcomings, technology has something to offer. To the imbalance between offense and defense, technology says let us devise passive defense which redresses the balance. A world with H-bombs and adequate civil defense is less likely to lapse into thermonuclear war than a world with H-bombs alone, at least if one concedes that the danger of the thermonuclear war mainly lies in the acts of irresponsible leaders. Anything that deters the irresponsible leader is a force for peace: a technologically sound civil defense therefore would help stabilize the balance of terror.

To the discrepancy between haves and have-nots, technology offers the nuclear energy revolution, with its possibility of autarky for haves and have-nots alike. How this might work to stabilize our metastable thermonuclear peace is suggested by the possible political effect of the recently proposed Israeli desalting plant. The Arab states I should think would be much less set upon destroying the Jordan River Project if the Israelis had a desalination plant in reserve that would nullify the effect of such action. In this connection, I think countries like ours can contribute very much. Our country will soon have to decide whether to continue to spend $5.5 x 10^9 per year for space exploration after our lunar landing. Is it too outrageous to suggest that some of this money be devoted to building huge nuclear desalting complexes in the arid ocean rims of the troubled world? If the plants are powered with breeder reactors, the out-of-pocket costs, once the plants are built, should be low enough to make large-scale agriculture feasible in these areas. I estimate that for $4 x 10^9 per year we could build enough desalting capacity to feed more than ten million new mouths per year (provided we use agricultural methods that husband water), and we would, thereby, help stabilize the metastable, bomb-imposed balance of terror.

Yet, I am afraid we technologists shall not satisfy our social engineers, who tell us that our Technological Fixes do not get to the heart of the problem; they are at best temporary expedients; they create new problems as they solve old ones; to put a Technological Fix into effect requires a positive social action. Eventually, social engineering, like the Supreme Court decision on desegregation, must be invoked to solve social problems. And, of course, our social engineers are right. Technology will never *replace* social engineering. But technology has provided and will continue to provide to the social engineer broader options, to make intractable social problems less intractable; perhaps, most of all, technology will buy time—that precious commodity that converts violent social revolution into acceptable social evolution.

Our country now recognizes and is mobilizing around the great social problems that corrupt and disfigure our human existence. It is natural that in this mobilization we should look first to the social engineer. But, unfortunately, the apparatus most readily available to the government, like the great federal laboratories, is technologically oriented, not socially oriented. I believe we have a great opportunity here; for, as I hope I have persuaded

you, many of our seemingly social problems do admit of partial technological solutions. Our already deployed technological apparatus can contribute
to the resolution of social questions. I plead, therefore, first for our government to deploy its laboratories, its hardware contractors, and its engineering
universities around social problems. And I plead, secondly, for understanding and cooperation between technologist and social engineer. Even with all
the help he can get from the technologist, the social engineer's problems are
never really solved. It is only by cooperation between technologist and social
engineer that we can hope to achieve what is the aim of all technologists and
social engineers—a better society, and thereby, a better life, for all of us who
are part of society.

Science and Social Attitudes

ROBERT S. MORISON

Like all people with some scientific training, I suffer from feelings of unease
when attempting to deal with the actions, and especially the attitudes, of
people. For one thing, I do not have at my command the sampling and inter-
view techniques wielded with so much aplomb by my colleagues in the social
sciences. Fortunately for my own peace of mind, my scientific training was
accompanied by enough exposure to the art of medicine so that I retain considerable respect for clinical intuition and judgment. This discussion relies
much more on these elusive instruments than it does on quantitative scientific analysis.

As a matter of fact, it puts no great strain on one's clinical intuition to
observe that large numbers of people in various parts of the world—including, perhaps most significantly, the advanced parts—are less happy about
science and technology than they once were. The evidence is of various
kinds. Perhaps the most quantitative is provided in the United States by the
relative decline in students entering the sciences and the scientifically based
professions. In some instances, such as engineering, the numbers have fallen
absolutely in the face of a steady increase in the total number of potential

students in each age class. Even more quantitative, and certainly more compelling to the individual scientist, is the evidence provided by the slowdown in appropriations for science. Third, one may cite the intuitions and reflections of thoughtful social clinicians like René Dubos,[1] who has so courageously summarized the shortcomings of scientific approaches to human problems. True enough, he finally draws the conclusion that what we need is not less science but more. Nevertheless, the argument depends on a careful demonstration that science raises new problems of increasing complexity as it continues to solve the older and simpler ones.

EARLIER ATTITUDES TOWARD SCIENCE

Before going on to a discussion of the possible reasons for a decline in public regard, we should pause to remind ourselves that the change may not be so large or so profound as we might suppose. It is not very clear that there ever was a time when a substantial part of the population really understood science, cared much about the kind of knowledge it produces, or thought much about its ultimate effects. Improvements in technology were welcomed because of the increased production of what were generally regarded as good things at less cost in human effort. On the other hand, the reduction in human labor was soon recognized to have a negative side. In the first place, as the Luddites saw very early, it tended to throw men out of work, at least temporarily. What was even worse from the psychological point of view, the machine tended to change the status of skills which had been acquired with much effort over long periods of years. Nevertheless, on balance, the industrialization of production both on the farm and in the factory has been regarded by most people as a net good; for, it must be remembered, even at the height of the Medieval and Renaissance periods, skilled craftsmen constituted only a very small portion of society. The great bulk of mankind labored in the most unimaginative and unrewarding way as farmhands with a status little better than that of serfs. Somewhat later than the general recognition of technological improvements in production came an even greater appreciation for the contributions of science to medicine and public health.

Most men probably never did take much interest in what might be called the philosophical aspects of science. Few really read Condorcet or the other Encyclopedists, and it is doubtful that any but a small handful of intellectu-

---

1. R. J. Dubos, *The Dreams of Reason* (Columbia Univ. Press, New York, 1961), p. 167.

als ever thought that science would provide a way of life free of undue aggressions, anxiety, loneliness, and guilt. Perhaps the Communist Party is the only large social organization that has ever seriously believed that man himself may be improved through improving his material circumstances. Among Christians, as among adherents of many other religious faiths, there has always been a substantial body of opinion which holds that the reverse is true and that material prosperity has, in fact, an adverse effect on the human soul.

The progress of science undoubtedly has had some effect in reducing the grosser forms of superstition. One supposes, for example, that most men are in some sense grateful for being less afraid of thunder and lightning than man used to be. But, here again, it is doubtful that the scientific way of looking at the world has ever completely displaced older, more magical approaches to the deep questions. It does not appear that President Nixon, when making up his mind whether or not to deploy the ABM system, consulted an astrologer, but it is not unknown for heads of states in other parts of the world to do so, and most of our metropolitan daily newspapers maintain an astrology column as well as the more sophisticated services of Ann Landers. Indeed, it is estimated that there are 10,000 professional astrologers but only 2,000 astronomers in the United States.[2]

Putting aside the grosser forms of superstition and turning to better-developed and better-thought-out ways of looking at the world, I would hazard a guess that the metaphysical outlook of most people, even in the United States, is more influenced by Plato and Aristotle than by Galileo and Hume. Indeed, it might be interesting for a graduate student in intellectual history to survey this very question. For example, do you suppose the majority of Americans would consider the following statements to be true or false? "Other things being equal, heavy bodies fall faster than light ones." "Metals feel cold to the touch because that is their nature." "Justice and honesty are real things and part of the divine plan of the universe; men try to establish justice through the machinery of the law and the courts, but their efforts will always fall short of the higher ideal of justice as it exists in the divine plan."

Coming down out of the clouds, we might ask ourselves how many people ever really got much fun out of studying mathematics and physics in high school? How many felt pleased to discover that a suction pump doesn't really suck water, but merely creates a potential space into which the water is

2. C. E. Sagen, personal communications.

pushed by atmospheric pressure? If one looks back 40 or 50 years, one seems to remember that rather less than the majority of one's classmates really enjoyed physics and chemistry and the kind of picture they give of the world. Perhaps a somewhat larger number found satisfaction in biology, with its greater emphasis on immediate experience and the pleasure one gets from contemplating nature's wide variety rather than its unifying mechanics.

World War II called a great deal of attention to science and made many people grateful for its role in enabling England and its allies to maintain the integrity of the free world. Along with the extraordinary buildup of military technology came a very great increase in biological knowledge of a kind which could be applied to medicine and public health, and to agriculture.

The press showed increasing interest in reporting scientific events, and the quality of scientific reporting has greatly improved in the quarter century since the war. Most significantly, a grateful and more understanding public provided vastly increased financial support for what the scientist wanted to do.

On the scientist's side there was a burgeoning of interest in making science more accessible to the general public. Most noteworthy in this movement, at least in the United States, was the effort of outstanding university scientists to improve the presentation of science to students in elementary and secondary schools. There is little doubt that this effort has greatly improved preparation for college in all branches of science. The generous men who initiated the program hoped for something more, for they felt that, if the story could only be presented properly, anyone of average intelligence would share the pleasure of the most able scientist in discovering the orderly arrangement of the natural world. Nothing could be more admirable than the dedication and self-sacrifice of men like Zacharias and the late Francis Friedman, and nothing more charming in its humility than their apparent belief that almost everyone is potentially just as bright as they themselves. Unhappily, it has not turned out as they hoped. Elegant though the Physical Science Study Committee Physics Course undoubtedly is, it has not proved much more successful than any other method in making physics attractive to secondary school students.

Nevertheless, on balance, public interest in science became greater after the war than it had been before, and it was further stimulated by the orbiting of Sputnik. It is very difficult to say how much of this interest was due to competition for ever more sophisticated weapons, how much to a pure cultural rivalry which puts the moon race into the same category as an Olympic track meet, and how much to the age-old wish to cast off the shackles which bind us to a single planet. However one apportions the credit among these three factors, it seems reasonably clear that an appreciation for basic science, as the scientists understood science, played a relatively small role.

REASONS FOR THE CHANGE OF MOOD

The decade of the 1960's . . . certainly [saw] a slackening in public approval of science. [Was] this change simply a return to the earlier, more or less normal state of ignorance and indifference, or [were] we witnessing an actively hostile movement? In either case it may do us all good to try to identify some of the more important reasons for the change of mood.

(1) Science is identified in the public mind largely with the manipulation of the material world. It is becoming clearer and clearer that the mere capacity to manipulate the world does not insure that it will be manipulated for the net benefit of mankind. Nowhere is this more obvious, perhaps, than in the matter of national defense. As pointed out above, the generation that knew at least one of the great world wars is grateful to the scientist for having fashioned the means of victory over a grave threat to a free world. The oncoming generation views the situation in quite a different way. To them the obvious alliance between the scientific community and the military is an evil thing: far from making the world more secure, it has produced an uneasy balance of terror, with the weight so great on both sides that any slight shift may lead to unimaginable catastrophe.

It seems undeniable that those of us who have grown up with this situation have also grown somewhat callous to the fact that such a high percentage of support for university science comes from military sources. We tend to remember, for example, the marvelously enlightened policy of the Office of Naval Research, which did so much to foster pure science while the Congress continued to debate the desirability of a National Science Foundation. Those who come upon the situation for the first time, however, see almost nothing but a conspiracy between some of the best brains of the country and the unenlightened military. In any case, it must be admitted that science and technology appear to contribute disproportionately to the more fiendish aspects of an evil business—the defoliation of rice fields, the burning of children with napalm, and the invention of new and more devastating plagues.

(2) Until fairly recently, the contributions of science and technology to increased production both in industry and in agriculture have been generally regarded as on the plus side. Even here, however, doubts are beginning to arise. Much of the increased production comes at the cost of a rapid exhaustion of natural resources and the increasing contamination of what is left of

our natural environment. Nor is it clear that all of the goods and services produced really do a great deal to increase the sum total of human happiness. Indeed, it can be shown that the modern affluent consumer is, in a sense, a victim of synthetic desires which are created rather than satisfied by increased production.[3] On the other hand, a substantial percentage of the population remains without even the bare essentials of life. Rapid increases in agricultural production have pretty well abolished famine in the advanced countries of the world, but the revolution in rural life has benefited only a few of the most successful farmers. The rest are clearly worse off than they were before; and, indeed, the large majority of them are hastening into the cities, where they create problems which have so far proved insoluble. Furthermore, the advanced technologies which make the increased production possible are now found to be doing as much harm to the environment as the more long-standing and better recognized industrial pollutions.

(3) Surely everyone can agree that science has done wonderful things for the improvement of health. But, even here, uncomfortable questions are being asked. Have our best doctors become so preoccupied with the wonders of their technology that they have become indifferent to the plight of large numbers of people who suffer from conditions just as fatal but much less interesting? Even the most earnest advocates of increased research in heart disease, cancer, and stroke must be a little bit embarrassed by the fact that the United States, which used to be a world leader in reducing infant mortality rates, has now fallen to 15th place.

(4) It is not only the maldistribution of resources that concerns the general public; they are becoming increasingly uneasy about the moral and ethical implications of advances in biological science. In many respects these advances seem to threaten the individual's command over his own life.

Actually, of course, the individual never did have as much control over his own life as he felt he had. Science may have simply made his own impotence clear to him by showing how human behavior is molded by genetic and environmental influences. Like everything else, it seems, human behavior is determined quite precisely by a long train of preceding events, and the concept of free will has become more difficult to defend than ever.

Perhaps more immediately threatening is the fact that science puts power to control one's behavior in the hands of other people. Intelligence and personality tests place a label on one's capacity which is used from then on by those who make decisions affecting one's educational and employment op-

---

3. J. K. Galbraith, *The Affluent Society* (Houghton Mifflin, Boston, 1958), chap. 3.

portunities. New methods of conditioning and teaching threaten to shape one's behavior in ways which *someone else* decides are good. Drugs of many kinds are available for changing one's mood or outlook on life, for reducing or increasing aggressive behavior, and so on. So far, these drugs are usually given with the cooperation of the individual himself, except in cases where severely deviant behavior is involved, but the potential for mass control is there. Indeed, there is already serious discussion about the ineffectiveness of family planning as a means of controlling the world's population, and suggestions are made for introduction, into food or water supplies, of drugs that will reduce fertility on a mass basis.

As if these assaults on individuality were not enough, some biologists are proposing to reproduce standard human beings, not by the usual complicated and uncertain methods involving genetic recombination, but by vegetative cloning from stocks of somatic cells. In the face of all this, can we blame the great majority of ordinary men for feeling that science is not greatly interested in human individuality and freedom?

(5) Science is not as much fun as it used to be, even for its most devoted practitioners. The point here is that science encounters more and more difficulty in providing a satisfyingly coherent and unified picture of the world. The flow of pure scientific data is now so prodigious that no one can keep up with more than a small fraction of it. Although most of us still retain some sort of faith that the universe, with all its infinite variety of detail, can in some way be reduced to a relatively simple set of differential equations, most of us recognize that this goal is, in practice, receding from us with something like the speed of light. That simple set of physical and chemical principles on which the older generation grew up is now turning out to be not very simple at all, and the relation between these simple principles and the complex events of biology are not nearly so clear as they were when Starling enunciated his "law of the heart."

Although it is probably too easy to exaggerate the degree to which the progress of science results in the fragmentation of knowledge, the beginning student in the sciences finds a great deal of difficulty in relating his courses in chemistry, physics, and biology to one another. Even within a single discipline, he feels overwhelmed and frustrated by the number of apparently isolated facts that he has to learn.

(6) Closely related to the foregoing thoughts on the growing complexity of science and the decline in the intellectual satisfaction generally derived from it is the question of student attitudes, for most of us make our first serious acquaintance with science as students.

My overall impression, in returning to a university after a lapse of 20 years, is one of disappointment that so few students seem to have very much fun either in their science courses specifically or in university life in general. This lack of pleasure is certainly more striking in the first 2 years, when the student is adjusting to a totally new social environment and devoting his attention to building the groundwork for later, more exciting studies. But I keep asking myself why these first 2 years of foundation-laying have to be so unsatisfying.

In the first place, I have come to believe that we discourage many students by expecting too much of them. We want them all to learn at a rate determined by the best. This can only mean that all *but* the best feel themselves to be dying of a surfeit rather than enjoying a marvelous meal. I am also coming sadly to the conclusion that, no matter how the subject is presented, a substantial number of college-level students have relatively little interest in the facts of science and lack the capacity to find pleasure in its generalizations. Whether the failure is primarily intellectual, in the sense that students simply have difficulty in understanding the nature of the generalization, or whether it is emotional and esthetic, in that they derive little pleasure from the generalization once it is understood, is not easy to determine. In either case, the prospect of unifying the community around a common understanding of science seems relatively remote.

An article by Richard N. Goodwin in the *New Yorker,* entitled "Reflections—sources of the public unhappiness"[4] puts some of the difficulties of science into a larger perspective. It provides a brilliant analysis of the unhappiness not only of our obviously dissident left-wing youth but of the many members of the forgotten middle class who, during the [1968] election, swung rather wildly between George Wallace and Eugene McCarthy. Goodwin discusses this phenomenon in terms of the traditional Jefferson-Hamilton model and comes to the conclusion that a great many Americans feel that they have lost control of certain crucial factors in their life styles. Although I am far from being as convinced as Goodwin is that it will be possible to return a large portion of our decision-making to states and local communities, I agree with much of his analysis of the underlying problem. He is particularly convincing, for example, when he shows how Secretary McNamara, in his apparent efforts to rationalize the Department of Defense and bring the military more closely under civilian control, actually succeeded in constructing a Frankenstein monster which began to control him, as "when

4. R. N. Goodwin, *New Yorker* 1969, 38 (4 Jan. 1969).

he was compelled against his own judgment to go ahead with an antiballistic missile system."

For our purposes, the key word here is "rationalize." Our rationalized systems do, indeed, seem to have developed the capacity to live lives of their own, so that mere men are compelled, against their will, to follow where the logical process leads. As we saw above, the medical profession is following in the footsteps of its dynamic research program and undertakes to perform heart transplants, at great expense, largely because it has found out how to do them. In the same way, we devote several billions of dollars each year in going to the moon, because it is *there* (and, again, because we know how to do it). Everyone who has done much science on his own knows that the next step he takes is determined in large part by the steps that have gone before. It follows that the progress of pure science, at least, is determined by the internal dynamics of the process and by the opening up of new leads rather than by public demand to meet new needs. The practical applications to human welfare, when looked at in this philosophical framework, become accidental bits of fallout, as the nuclear bomb itself "fell out" from the innocent effort of J. J. Thompson, Rutherford, Bohr, Fermi, and others to understand the nature of matter. No doubt all these men felt completely in command of their own research programs, but the public does not look at it this way, and, in a curious sense, the public may be more right than the scientists. This line of thought brings us to point 7 in our bill of indictment.

(7) The continuing momentum of science toward goals of its own choosing appears to be coupled ever less closely to solving problems of clear and pressing consequence to human welfare. As we now see, enlightened congressmen and senators, well aware of the power of the scientific method but skeptical of its capacity to guide itself automatically to the points of greatest human concern, are making explicit legislative attempts to mobilize science to solve the problems of the pollution of our environment and the crime in our cities, if not, indeed, the unsatisfactory nature of our life in general. Realizing that nuclear physics is not very closely coupled to these matters, they are turning to social science in the hope that there is a group of scientists who can do for society what the physicists have done for the natural world.

SKEPTICISM ABOUT RATIONAL SYSTEMS

Skepticism about rational systems is, of course, not confined to science. Indeed, it well may be that the antipathy to science is merely a bit of fallout from the growing antipathy to rational systems in general.[5] The movement has been a long time in the making. Lionel Trilling,[6] for example, traces much of the despair, the irrationality, and the increasing devotion to the absurd of much modern literature to Dostoevski's *Letters from the Underworld,* in which, you will remember, the protagonist, in his violent diatribes against the existing order, concentrates his hatred on those "gentlemen" who believe that 2 and 2 make 4. What is even more frightening for our own time is the way the same anti-hero reassures himself of his own individual freedom by affirming his ability to choose the more evil of two options.[7]

We, who have grown up rejoicing in science, were confident in our acceptance of Sir Francis Bacon's aphorism that we cannot command nature except by obeying her.[8] We really did not mind obeying as long as we knew that we would ultimately command. But now the empirical evidence may be turning to support those who feel that science is in some sense in the grip of natural forces which it does not command. Too often we conjure up genies who produce short-term benefits at the risk of much larger long-term losses. We develop marvelous individual transport systems which poison the air we breathe; learn how to make paper very cheaply at the cost of ruining our rivers; and fabricate weapons that determine our defense strategy and foreign policy rather than being determined by them. Above all, the applications of science have produced an unrestricted increase in the human population which we recognize as fatal to our welfare but have only the vaguest idea how to control. In a short time we will be able to design the genetic structure of a good man. There is some uncertainty about the exact date, but no doubt . . . it will come before we have defined what a good man is.

5. C. E. Schorske, "Professional ethos and public crisis: a historian's reflections," *Mod. Language Ass. Amer. Publ. 83,* 979 (1968).

6. L. Trilling, *Beyond Culture* (Viking, New York, 1965).

7. F. Dostoevsky, *Letters from the Underworld,* C. J. Hogarth, Trans. (Dutton, New York, 1913). All of part 1 is relevant to this discussion, especially page 37: "Moreover, even if man were the keyboard of a piano, and could be convinced that the laws of nature and of mathematics had made him so, he would still decline to change. On the contrary, he would once more, out of sheer ingratitude, attempt the perpetration of something which would enable him to insist upon himself; and if he could not effect this, he would then proceed to introduce chaos and disruption into everything, and to devise enormities of all kinds, for the sole purpose, as before, of asserting his personality . . . . But if you were to tell me that all this could be set down in tables—I mean the chaos, and the confusion, and the curses, and all the rest of it—so that the possibility of computing everything might remain, and reason continue to rule the roost—well, in that case, I believe, man would purposely become a lunatic, in order to become devoid of reason, and therefore able to insist upon himself.

8. F. Bacon, *Novum Organum* (1620), aphorism 129.

In the foregoing analysis, in an effort to obtain intellectual respectability I have painstakingly tried to break our problem down into a series of numbered subheadings. Actually, they all add up to the same thing: Although the general public is grateful to science for some of its more tangible benefits, it is increasingly skeptical and even frightened about its long-term results. The anxiety centers on the concept of science as the prototype—the most magnificent and most frightening example of the rational systems which men make to control their environment and which finally end by controlling *them.* It may be well to recall that the medieval structure of natural law was even more rational than science, in the sense that it depended on the mind alone without submitting its conclusions to empirical checks. It managed for a time to obtain even greater control than science has over both the bodies and (especially) the spirits of the people of the Western world. It, too, developed an interesting life of its own as it followed the paths of reason into ever more subtle areas. It failed, for a number of reasons, but primarily, perhaps, because neither the logic-chopping of the medieval philosophers nor the temporal power of the papacy which it was designed to support appeared to be sufficiently related to the longings of individual human beings. The Reformation, for all the complexity of its theology and, often, the brutality of its methods, was primarily an effort to assert the rights of the individual conscience over the medieval power structure.

A WATERSHED?

I am not really sure that we stand on the kind of watershed Luther stood on when he nailed his theses to the door of the cathedral, but we may make a serious mistake if we do not at least entertain that possibility. If we fail to recognize the average man's need to believe that he has some reasonable command over his own life, he is simply going to give up supporting those systematic elements in society which he sees as depriving him of this ability.

As I noted above, so perceptive a critic as Lionel Trilling traces much of modern literature and art to a long-standing revolt of sensitive and creative men against the systematic constraints of society. The New Left can be regarded as a politization of the same trend. Actually, of course, anarchy had a political as well as a purely intellectual existence when Dostoevski was writing, but the 19th-century political anarchists were effectively liquidated by the Marxists, who felt that they had a better idea. Now that Marxist communism has developed most of the ills of bourgeois industrial society plus its own especially repressive form of bureaucracy, anarchism is again put forward as an attractive alternative to organized, corrupt societies.

There is a difference, however, in the way 19th and 20th-century anarchists regard science. On the whole, the 19th-century ones were atheists and saw religion as the co-conspirator with government and business. Science tended to be favored, partly because of its contributions to man's material welfare, but perhaps even more because of its aid in debunking religion.

Two paragraphs from Mikhail Bakunin are worth quoting, partly because of the flavor of the rhetoric.[9]

[The churches] have never neglected to organize themselves into great corporations . . . the action of the good God . . . has ended at last always and everywhere in founding the prosperous materialism of the few over the fanatical and constantly famishing idealism of the masses.

The liberty of man consists only in this: that he obeys natural laws because he has himself recognized them as such, and not because they have been externally imposed upon him by any extrinsic will whatever, human or divine, collective or individual.

The New Left certainly agrees with Bakunin about the need to destroy the existing order, but it tends to see God in a different light. In the United States, religion has been conscientiously separated from the state for so long that it is no longer regarded as part of the apparatus of repression. Indeed, many draft-card burners and other protestors against the immorality of the existing order are primarily religiously motivated. On the other hand, science as the interpreter of the laws of nature, which Bakunin set against the laws of the state, has lost its revolutionary character and is viewed as a dangerous collaborator of the industrial-military complex. One of the difficulties may be that science has become so complicated that the ordinary man no longer believes that "he himself has recognized them [natural laws] as such" but feels that "they have been externally imposed upon him."

EDUCATING THE PUBLIC

What, then, can we do to improve the image of science as something of human scale, understandable and controllable by ordinary men? In the first place, we will have to continue our efforts toward educating the public, both in school and outside it, through reporting in our newspapers and magazines. Although I have given some reasons for believing that there are limitations to the capacity of much of our population to understand and take pleasure

9. M. Bakunin (Bakounine), *God and the State* (1893).

in the way science understands the natural world, I still believe that much more can be done to improve matters than has been done so far. As for the formal part of education, I propose that we rather deliberately reduce the rate at which students must handle the material set before them, so that they can master it without feeling frustrated and overwhelmed. If we begin the process, as is now fashionable, in the early elementary years, continue it through college, and carefully design things so as to avoid redundancy, students might end up with a much more complete understanding than they do now. This effort is worth even more money and time than have been put into it so far.

As for less formal methods for presenting science to adults, we should devise some analogy that would do for the general public what agricultural extension courses have done for the farmer and his wife. The average successful farmer, although he is far from being a pure scientist, has an appreciation for the way science works. Certainly he understands it well enough to use it in his own business and to support agricultural colleges and the great state universities that grew out of them.

As one who has spent a considerable period of his life worrying about medicine and public health, I am much less happy about our efforts to instruct the average man in a rational or scientific attitude toward the conduct of his own life. It has proved ever so much easier to persuade the average farmer to plant hybrid corn than to persuade the average man to give up smoking cigarettes. We have been almost too successful in persuading farmers to put nitrogen on their fields, while we continue to fail in trying to persuade the average man to put minute amounts of fluorine in his water supply. Few individual doctors seize the opportunity to explain to their patients, in even quasi-scientific terms, what their illnesses are, and I am appalled by the bizarre notions of human physiology which are entertained by some of my best friends.

Granted that doctors do not have enough time to talk to their patients and that many doctors really are not very scientifically oriented themselves, we might think seriously of setting up in every city a kind of paramedical service designed to teach people about their own illnesses. A doctor with a patient who is developing coronary insufficiency, for example, could refer his patient not only for an electrocardiogram, a blood-cholesterol, and clotting-time determinations but for instruction, in a class of cardiacs, on just how the heart and circulation work. Such an enterprise might help individual patients adjust to their illness more suitably, but this is not the real point. The aim would be to take advantage of an unhappy accident in order to increase the individual's motivation to learn something about science. Therefore, such clinics should be paid for not only by the Public Health Service but by the Office of Education.

Second, we must make a major effort to bring the course of science, and especially its technological results, under better and more obvious control by individual human beings and their representatives. We are, it is true, slowly gearing ourselves to do something about pollution of the environment, but the overall guidance and control of this effort is largely in the hands of part-time experts who fly in and out of Washington to attend meetings which issue prophesies of doom or unsupported reassurances, as the composition of the particular panel may dictate. Somehow, thinking about the long-term results of technology, formulating the options in such a way that the public can understand them, and guiding the course of events along the chosen path must become as exciting and rewarding for the best minds as is the present pursuit of basic scientific knowledge. Above all, the options must be made clearly understandable to the people, and the people must feel that they are doing the choosing. The present method of announcing that such-and-such a corporation is about to erect a large atomic power plant on a certain body of water and then engaging in a debate, based on inadequate information, about the effects of the heat on the lake or river, the degree of radioactive contamination, and so on, is totally unsatisfactory.

The process of educating the public should begin much earlier, with discussion of the need for additional power plants and of the probable cost of putting them here or there, in terms of increased power rates on the one hand and increased contamination of the environment on the other. The public must slowly be brought to see that every such occasion involves a real choice between real alternatives, and that the alternatives must be balanced against one another. Similar considerations apply to the use of insecticides. Nobody, as far as I know, has seen fit to make any even approximate estimates of what our food might cost if we were to abandon the use of these agents. Similarly, nobody has told what it would cost to produce high-octane gasoline by means of some method other than the addition of tetra-ethyl lead.

We have been very negligent in devising ways and means of ensuring that the cost of introducing new technologies is borne by the people who immediately benefit from their use. If anything, the trend may be away from emphasis on this relationship. For example, the introduction of the cotton picker and of modern methods of weed and insect control, not to mention the enormous subsidies provided by the American taxpayer, have made the culture of cotton in a few counties in the South and Southwest extremely profitable, so that large landholders have become extremely wealthy. Presumably, the public at large has benefited by a slight reduction in the cost of cotton cloth. On the other hand, the social costs of this industrial revolution in agriculture have been incalculable; they have been borne primarily by the large number of Negro laborers who have been uprooted and transported into the cities, where they found themselves ill-prepared to benefit from the urban amenities enjoyed by their more prosperous fellow citizens. The economic costs of supporting them in an alien environment have been borne, not by the wealthy southern landowners and certainly not by the individuals who paid a bit less for the cotton cloth, but almost entirely by the displaced people themselves and by the people who pay real estate taxes in a handful of our larger cities.

All these problems are, however, subject to some kind of scientific analysis, and the options can be placed scientifically before the public. In preparation for this kind of decision making, we should probably overhaul our teaching of science, and especially of mathematics, so as to give the average man greater ability to evaluate evidence presented in modern scientific form. High school courses in statistics, probability, and systems analysis are clearly more relevant to modern living than Euclidean geometry, and might well replace this and other time-honored introductory courses in mathematics.

ROLE OF SCIENCE IN MILITARY AFFAIRS

Third, an effort should be made to clarify the role of science in military affairs. Although most of us who are acquainted with the facts know that much of the research supported by funds from the military services actually contributes as much to civilian life as to military matters, this fact is not known to the general public or to the student body. Cornell students, for example, are disturbed to learn that the largest single donor to research at their university is the Department of Defense, even though one of the university's two largest research enterprises is the observatory at Arecibo, whose contributions to pure science are of far more consequence than anything it has ever contributed to the Air Force. If the military uses of science occurred as fallout from scientific investigations undertaken for peaceful purposes, this would be far better for morale than continuation of our present course, in which pure science appears as the crumbs that fall from the rich Pentagon's table. The obvious and actually very easy way to accomplish this would be to reduce military appropriations by what, to the military, would be a tiny amount and substantially increase appropriations for the National Science Foundation and the National Institutes of Health. Certain civilian agencies, such as the Department of Commerce and the Department of the Interior, should also be supporting far more basic and applied research than they are now.

Whether the civilian establishment for science should engage in any research of military consequence is a matter for debate, but such debate should be encouraged. Many universities of goodwill long ago decided that secret research has no place on a university campus, but this idea does not prevent them from doing unclassified work which has a clear military bearing, nor does the university ordinarily discourage its faculty from serving as consultants on classified projects carried out elsewhere.

There are obvious theoretical and practical difficulties confronting any other policy. Until now, for example, most scientists have felt that the importance of advancing knowledge overshadowed questions regarding the source of support. The control we now have of malaria is a net gain, regardless of the fact that, from the discovery of the malarial parasite in North Africa to the development of control methods by the American Army during World War II, research on malaria was often carried on by military personnel.

Furthermore, it is clearly important that we have, as consultants to the military, civilian scientists who learn the details of proposed weapons systems so that they can make an appropriate case against, as well as for, deployment of these systems.

Finally, as long as we feel ourselves threatened by the scientific and military establishments of other nations, it is with some difficulty that most of us who have special skills, gained largely through contributions from the American public, can refuse to use those skills for the defense of that same public. This last issue is becoming a rather knotty one, however, since we may have reached a point at which war is so disastrous for both sides that there is simply no point in undertaking the exercise at all.

CONCLUSION

The most important lesson for the scientific community would appear to be one that can be stated as follows: Science can no longer be content to present itself as an activity independent of the rest of society, governed by its own rules and directed by the inner dynamics of its own processes. Too many of these processes have effects which, though beneficial in many respects, often strike the average man as a threat to his individual autonomy. Too often science seems to be thrusting society as a whole in directions which it does not fully understand and which it has certainly not chosen.

The scientific community must redouble its efforts to present science— in the classroom, in the public press, and through education-extension activities of various kinds—as a fully understandable process, "justifiable to man," and controllable by him. Scientists should also take more responsibility for foreseeing and explaining the long-term effects of new applications of scientific knowledge. A promising procedure for planning the control of such effects is presentation of the probable outcomes of various available options so that choices can be made by the public and their representatives. Costs and benefits must be estimated not only in quantitative, dollar terms but, increasingly, in terms of qualitative and esthetic judgments. Thus ends the comfortable isolation of science from the ordinary concerns of men as a "value-free" activity.

Pure Technology

"DAEDALUS OF NEW SCIENTIST"

In a characteristic passage in Plato's *Republic* we find Glaucon and Socrates discussing the nature of the Good. Glaucon suggests that there are three kinds of good: the simple, inconsequential pleasures; then activities pleasurable both in themselves and their consequences; and finally those tasks and duties not inherently pleasant but undertaken for subsequent advantage. He then asks Socrates to locate "honesty" in one of these categories.

Socrates: I should say, in the best of the three, those which a man must like both for their own sake and for their consequences, if he's going to live the kind of life one wants to have.

Glaucon: Well, that's not what most people think; they reckon it belongs to the tedious kind of good, which has to be pursued in order to earn a wage, or, for appearance's sake, to be well thought of.

Glaucon's threefold subdivision remains relevant to this day, and the passage would retain its point if the philosophers had been discussing technology. The usual attitude taken toward technology—certainly by those who put up the money for it—is that its value lies only in its profitable consequences, and research and development in itself is an unavoidable interim expense. Yet to the engineer the chase may be as rewarding as the kill; he may well privately place his activities in the second or even in the first category of good, divorcing it partly or almost wholly from the sordid aftermath of profitable application.

This attitude of mind defines the *Pure Technologist.* Pure technology is the building of machines for their own sake and for the pride or pleasure of accomplishment. It is a creative art form somewhere between art and science. Some examples of pure technology are the record-breaking vehicle, built purely to see if it will behave as intended; the chess-playing computer program, devised for the sheer entertainment of seeing how well it makes out; and that masterpiece in miniature, *Scientific American*'s Great International Paper Airplane Competition.

Most other technical projects have some degree of purity, though the assessment of such a subjective quality will rarely be clear-cut. What is the purity status of a cuckoo in a cuckoo clock, for example? Or on a grander scale, is a particle accelerator pure technology? To the physicist it is as applied as any other of his instruments; to the engineer constructing it, it has only to work as intended, and so is pure; an outsider will judge it as pure or as applied according as he judges nuclear physics itself. Yet despite its confusion with (and indeed, latterly, deliberate disguise as) the applied variety, pure technology is recognizable throughout history as one of the minor muses.

CLASSICAL PIONEERS

The first indubitable instances occur rather late in Classical times. The great Athenian achievements in art and science occurred without any comparable revolution in technology. Nowhere do Glaucon or Socrates express any appreciation of the aesthetically or intellectually stimulating qualities of technology—for them it was firmly in the third, humdrum class of good. Not until Alexandria took over from Athens as the intellectual center of the world did major progress in empirical techniques occur. The "Museum" at Alexandria, founded around 300 B.C. by one of Alexander the Great's generals to be the intellectual showpiece of his regime, was for many centuries a unique library, artistic center, and research institute, and shared so many of the features of modern research establishments that it may fairly be called the MIT of the ancient world.

The Alexandrian pure technologists were the mechanicians, chiefly Ctesibius, Philo, and Hero. That part of their research which directly served the interests of their employers was, as one might expect, military—improving the catapults and ballistas which launched the missiles of the time. But they also carried out much more fundamental and far-reaching research in pure physics.

We know little of Ctesibius except from contemporary references. The Roman engineer Vitruvius tells us that he invented the force-pump, a hydraulic organ, two different forms of catapult, the water-clock, and several types of automata. The stern, practical Roman describes only the pump, the organ, and the clock, and refers us to Ctesibius's own book (now lost) for details of other devices "which serve no useful purpose, but the pleasure of delight."

These delightful inventions are described in one of the surviving treatises of his follower, the famous Hero of Alexandria. Hero probably lived about 100 B.C. and wrote treatises on catapults and missiles, on automata, and on the studies in pneumatics for which he is best known. His books give the first description in recorded history of the works of men who, fascinated by a new science, set out to see what could be done with it for the sheer pleasure of creation. Pure technology was on the march!

Some of the *jeux d'esprit* of the Alexandrian mechanicians is shown in the [treatises'] diagrams. All five "classical machines" (lever, wedge, screw, pulley, and winch) are used in these little contrivances, as well as the float, syphon, water-whistle and other elements discovered or at least first understood at Alexandria. The elasticity of air and the incompressibility of water are recognized and ingeniously exploited; and despite the dry and Euclidean way Hero expounds their working, it is clear what fun he had putting them together.

Some commentators have ridiculed them as "mere scientific toys," but I think this misses the point. Toys they were indeed for the most part, but they were toys embodying new and important principles which the mechanicians used in more practical equipment, and attempted to explain by theory. Hero never quite explicitly expounds the concept of atmospheric pressure, but he is quite sure that air is a material substance, and gives directions for constructing apparatus to prove the existence of a vacuum. For 100 B.C. this is physics of a high order indeed!

The most famous of all Hero's "toys" is his steam reaction-turbine or

Aeolipile, number 50 of the 78 inventions in his *Pneumatics*. This simple machine merely drove itself and illustrated a principle, and there is no reason to suppose that Hero ever envisaged scaling it up. Nowhere in the ancient world was there a more propitious place to make such a revolutionary invention than the Museum at Alexandria; yet nothing came of it. The technical and intellectual and social infrastructure was far too inadequate to handle the application of this piece of pure technology, and the Alexandrian achievement petered out with the general decline of the ancient world in the first few centuries A.D.

The technoscientific reactor did not go critical for over another thousand years, until the European Renaissance. The first really striking piece of pure technology to emerge from the intellectual ferment that followed was the balloon.

THE BALLOON GOES UP

The brothers Montgolfier were papermakers of Annonay in France, and were of an inventive and curious turn of mind. Etienne Montgolfier once tested Leonardo's concept of the parachute by jumping from the top of a building holding a large umbrella! The concept of lighter-than-air flight seems to have matured in their minds from 1767 onwards. They knew of Cavendish's preparation of hydrogen, but a small pilot balloon lost the gas so rapidly by diffusion through the (paper) envelope that they abandoned this notion.

The idea of the fire-balloon is said to have occurred to Etienne on a carriage ride. Immediately on reaching the inn of his destination he called for taffeta and fire, and, to the horror of the proprietor, the world's first lighter-than-air flying machine, made of badly singed taffeta, rose nobly to the ceiling of one of his bedrooms!

The Montgolfiers organized their first demonstration flight from Annonay market square on June 5, 1783. The craft was made of paper (the material they were most familiar with) and reached a height of 6,000 feet. Garbled reports by the mystified local authorities reached Paris, where Professor Cesar Charles (of Charles' Law fame) deduced that the Montgolfiers must have been using hydrogen. Determined to emulate their feat, he set about the frightening task of filling a 1,000-cubic-foot rubberized silk balloon with hydrogen generated from iron and sulphuric acid.

Four days it took, during which time the Professor and his assistants were in constant fear of an explosion: at times the exothermic reaction became so violent that the whole assembly had to have water played over it.

But all went well, and the first hydrogen balloon ascended triumphantly from Paris on August 26, 1783, travelled 15 miles, and was destroyed on landing by horrified peasants. Only when the Montgolfiers exhibited their invention in Paris did Charles realize that he had invented the hydrogen balloon by mistake.

Ballooning soon became a popular activity throughout the Continent. Brave men ascended in both hot-air and hydrogen balloons (Charles reached 10,000 feet on December 1, 1783, and returned safely). The new invention was soon subsidized by the military, who dreamt of balloon transport and aerial observation flights. Indeed, a ballooning corps was formed in the French army after the Revolution; but this near-farcical concept was never a serious threat. The House of Lords dissolved in laughter when Lord St. Vincent, in 1802, speaking of the defense of Britain against Napoleonic invasion, remarked "I do not say they cannot come. I only say they cannot come by sea." Again, a novel extension of human abilities had been developed and exercised for its own sake, and funded by authority on grounds that would not stand up to hostile cost-effectiveness analysis.

MODERN PURE TECHNOLOGY

The massive flowering of invention of the modern era poses for the connoisseur of pure technology the challenge of identifying unambiguous examples of the genre. This is surprisingly difficult. On the face of it, practically every invention made since about 1800 was immediately applied.

But this may not mean that pure technology ceased to exist—only that it was rapidly overtaken by applications. Many of Hero's inventions were never applied at all—the concept of research-based technology scarcely existed in his society. Leonardo da Vinci's beautiful mechanical concepts took centuries to reach fruition (I cannot claim him as a pure technologist because he was essentially a theoretician rather than a practical inventor); Montgolfier's remained pure long enough to recognize as such. But the genius of a technological age lies not in scientific advance or creative imagination, but in seeking applications, in consciously and persistently asking the question, "How can I exploit this?"

Just how automatic and comprehensive this technique of progress has become, with each new piece being fitted into the growing jigsaw puzzle as soon as the development of neighboring fields permits, may be judged by trying to think of inventions in the mainstream of technology which might have been made much before they actually were. (After some cogitation, I can list only seven: gas-phase chromatography, the hovercraft, the standardized goods-container, prestressed concrete, the disc brake, casein glue, and DDT-based insecticides. Perhaps readers can add to—or subtract from—the list?) The great majority of inventions appear just as soon as they become feasible.

The clue to discovering pure technology—things made for the sake of making them—in this relentless advance, is to identify developments which, although they occupy obvious and clearly fillable gaps in the jigsaw, are simply unnecessary: gaps which are not worth filling on any rational basis. This test works best on fairly new inventions, before the patina of age and seeming inevitability has settled on them.

A prime example is the SST, an indubitable masterpiece of thinly disguised pure technology. I need not detail here the ample demonstrations which have been given of the pointlessness and social drawbacks of this project. But given a journey of, say, seven hours at an average of 10 mi./h and another six at 600 mi./h (a fair profile of a typical translantic air excursion), the expenditure of millions of dollars to clip a few hours off the *high-speed* section seems misguided to say the least, even assuming it is worth shortening the time at all in view of the increased disruption of circadian rhythms. Balancing this insignificant gain and the tiny minority who gain it against the solid debit in expense and noise pollution inflicted on the majority, we can see how unexpectedly powerful is the drive to pure technology in our supposedly cost-conscious society—for the only really compelling reason for building the SST (and of course its rival the Concorde) is the sheer entertainment of overcoming all the technical problems and finally flying such a thrilling machine!

MORE EXAMPLES

The same motivation applies in a practically overt manner to the space rocket. The big rocket is the twentieth-century pure-technological achievement par excellence, but all its pioneers—Oberth, Goddard, von Braun—saw it not as an end in itself but as a means toward the larger pure-technological goal of space flight. Even when the first successful V-2 ballistic rocket was fired in 1942, officially part of German war research, von Braun exclaimed jubilantly that the only trouble was that it landed on the wrong planet! Again, no scientific or technical considerations can justify on economic grounds the billions of dollars invested in the space program. Even the solid military interest in rocketry and radar and long-distance communication would have been far better served at a fraction of the cost by normal research and development. Yet the splendor of setting foot on our satellite, the sheer poetry of sending our creations out to scan other worlds and report back what they see—these represent pure technology at its best. It seems almost carping and small-souled to query whether the money might not have been better spent on more urgent terrestrial matters.

A quite different instance of modern pure technology, this time not quite rapidly enough overtaken by events to obscure its real appeal, is the laser. The appearance of the first practical prototype in 1960 created such interest that, in the words of the *New York Times,* "almost every corporation and every self-respecting university in the nation obtained a laser of some sort." The appeal of the new device was so widespread, and yet actual commercial applications so elusive, that the laser rapidly acquired the reputation of a solution in search of a problem. In particular, the millions of dollars disbursed by the military to explore its potential as a destructive weapon had so little result that one cynic exclaimed in disgust that the most offensive use you could make of a laser was to hit someone over the head with it.

The laser is still (judging by the number used in research compared to that in solid commercial applications) a machine with few uses—yet there is no doubt of its powerful hold on the imagination of the technical community. The charm of being able to drill a hole in a razorblade with a beam of light, or bounce photons off the moon, is so great that the actual value of being able to do so is irrelevant.

THE MILITARY TRADITION

These instances of pure technology past and present give an insight into the nature of the discipline. Its central characteristic, like those of art and science, is acceptance of self-imposed challenge and the aggrandizement of the human spirit. It occurs alongside and within applied technology in dynamic and intellectually active societies. It is one of the dramatic arts, and since by and large the human sense of the dramatic is rather direct and unsophisticated, pure technology tends to address itself to naive and, in the fashionable term, charismatic challenges—making large objects go fast, discharging high concentrations of energy, "conquering" space. It is funded on misleading grounds. And behind it, more often than not, lurks the military, like a dim but suspicious creditor, paying up uneasily in the hope of ultimate advantage.

I believe the closeness of the association between militarism and pure technology to be significant. In the convoluted, multidimensional psycho-space of all human mental constructs which it is the ultimate goal of psychology to map, the two are very close together. Both are manifestations of aggression, of dynamic material response to a felt challenge, posed in one case by a like-minded group of people and in the other by Nature herself. In both of them the emotive appeal loosely summed up by the word "glory" is as important as the overt goals. This thesis is implicit in the common claim that the space race with Russia is a valuable "sublimation" of political rivalries, but it also explains many other features of military history.

Historians have long debated the motives behind the replacement of the longbow by the musket in European armies around 1600, despite the former's clear superiority in cheapness, accuracy, range, reliability, and rate of fire—advantages it held until the invention of the rifle in the nineteenth century! It has been suggested that expertise in archery declined for some reason after the twelfth century, and that less trainable conscripts had to be used. But the overwhelming melodramatic appeal of the thunderous discharge of gunpowder weapons was probably the key factor.

The same lure of the grandiose is evident in the archmilitarist Prussian tradition. Big Bertha, the enormous gun that shelled Paris from 76 miles away during World War I, was hardly a cost-effective weapon. And the development of the German V-weapons during World War II is an even clearer instance. V-1, a pilotless aircraft, cost about $600 (then) to produce, whereas V-2, the ballistic rocket, cost $25,500; both delivered about the same warhead (around a ton of high explosive) with comparable range and accuracy. Clearly V-1 was by far the better weapon, comparing favorably in cost-effectiveness with manned bombers. Yet V-2, which replaced it, was far more flamboyant.

D. Irving[1] supports the conclusion of Dr. R. V. Jones, a British intelligence officer concerned with countermeasures to the V-weapons, that V-2 was supported for "romantic" reasons. He describes the overwhelming, Wagnerian impact repeatedly produced on Nazi officials by the ". . . intoxicating sight of the 13-ton rocket blasting aloft atop a lengthening pillar of fire and condensation, and the roar of its motor echoing back over the sea"—and concludes that such military romanticism probably cost Germany the war. Certainly in the later stages of the struggle von Braun's expensive piece of pure technology, by its wholesale consumption of vital raw materials and labor, inflicted far more damage on Germany than it ever did on Britain. As an in-

1. See Suggested Reading at the end of this article.

habitant of old London town at the time, it is clear that my attitude should be one of gratitude.

All approved weapons of war seem to have evolved to meet some minimum level of flashing, banging, shrieking romantic appeal. Subsequent developments have given us the doubly dramatic nuclear ICBM, and promise to deliver a still more expensive, problematically effective, but pure-technologically challenging toy, the ABM. In *Scientific American* (Vol. 221, No. 2, p. 17) H. F. York outlined the grave drawbacks of this strictly technological approach to security. But what fun to make a missile like Sprint, which goes so fast that its outside gets hotter than its inside! Indeed, one must suspect that the universal opprobrium directed at chemical and biological weapons stems not from any deviation from accepted standards of beastliness or efficacy, but simply from their deplorable lack of theatrical impact.

STATIC PURE TECHNOLOGY

But not all fields of pure technology are complicated by military appeal. Architectural pure technology, for example, is concerned with the grandeur of impressive monuments, rather than of wonderful machines. The most outstanding example may also be the very first—the Egyptian pyramids. Kurt Mendelssohn (*Science Journal*, Vol. 4, No. 3, p. 48) has argued persuasively from structural and historical evidence that these were not primarily built as tombs to ensure personal immortality for the Pharaohs (though presumably this suggestion was as attractive to the Pharaohs as any hinted prestigious or military implications in a modern grant application), but as gigantic exercises in pure technology, "built because man had reached the stage at which he was able to build them." Similarly one must acknowledge the considerable pure-technological component in the magnificent cathedrals created in Europe during the ages of faith. But the finest recent example is undoubtedly the Eiffel Tower in Paris. This completely purposeless structure, simply a fine piece of megastatuary, has become a proud symbol and a focal point of the city. One can hardly imagine Paris without it.

Yet, increasingly, modern architectural practice disdains such overt frivolity, and degrades pure-technological aspirations into commercially respectable but inhuman office blocks. The architect W. W. Frischmann believes that it is now technically possible to build a tower two miles high, so naturally he wants to do it (*Science Journal*, Vol. 1, No. 8, p. 62). But in justification he feels impelled to suggest it as a "vertical city" holding half a million people—thus creating about the most obscene human environment of all time.

WHAT TO DO ABOUT IT

It is clear that the malevolent aspect which pure technology is increasingly assuming stems not from its own proud nature but from our obsession with applications. It would take a brave man openly to deny the grey dogma of our time that all human activity must be economically justified, that nothing should ever be done unless it will return 8 percent on capital.

The worst consequences of accepting it can, however, be evaded. And it is here, I believe, that the more flexible and devious European mind has much to teach the innocent technologists of the USA. Consider the noble record of the British aerospace industry. A long series of pure-technological triumphs—among them the Princess Flying Boat, the Brabazon super-airliner, the Blue Streak ICBM and the TSR2 supersonic fighter-bomber—were developed just to the point where the prototype had successfully flown, and were then cancelled (though Blue Streak was kept on in a pure-technological capacity as a space-launcher).

All the satisfaction of dramatic pure technology was gained without inflicting the products on a helpless public or on an already unstable situation. (I like to think that in the case of Blue Streak and TSR2, the engaging British habit of "leaking" information on such machines to the Russians was designed to encourage them to invest heavily in countermeasures tailored to the weak points of weapons that were in fact purely hypothetical. But even the devious European mind rarely attains such an Oriental level of duplicity.)

There is every reason to hope that the pattern will be repeated with Concorde. Once the prototype has been exhaustively tested, the program will be cancelled to save money, and peace-loving citizens will be able to breathe freely again. But this civilized technique has only imperfectly crossed the Atlantic. The American counterpart of TSR2, the F-111, was, after prototype testing, procured for the armed forces, to everybody's sorrow. And if the American SST is once successfully flown, what considerations can hope to arrest it?

We are mishandling the forces of pure technology. We dare not suppress it: for the subjective motivation of every dedicated inventor is basically pure-technological—to rise to envisaged challenge and create objects of pride. The nineteenth-century inventors and engineers understood this: that is why their creations had a style and confidence almost unknown today. The economic prudery which forces the once proud art form to don the respectable mantle of application is now actively harmful, and does much to justify the growing and well-founded dislike of juggernautical technomania.

So pure technology must be recognized and fostered. Even in Britain, one of the world's leaders in pure technology, the stifling doctrine of social relevance and immediate profitability is beginning to clip the wings of the more imaginative and high-flying research projects. I would like to see official bodies set up to protect pure technological endeavor, equivalent in function to Britain's Arts Council. In the United States, this might take the form of a National Pure Technology Foundation. Given such a source of funds, it would be possible to devote one's efforts to seeing in the dark, or making machines that play with building-blocks, or constructing mechanical elephants, without having to waste time on the shaky sophistry of practical application at present required.

Allowing pure technology an honest existence will not only leave certain pure-technologically hag-ridden industries free to return to humane and reasonable techniques (I am particularly thinking of the adoption by the airlines of silent, safe, luxurious, city-center to city-center helium-filled airships) but may also restore confidence in technology among a suspicious populace, and introduce a welcome component of aesthetics into the technical scene at large. But most importantly, pure technology promises to be that "moral equivalent of war" advocated by the great American philosopher William James. Its close psychological affinity to military display may fit it to replace actual combat, just as in the animal kingdom the professional carnivores such as wolves have perfected aggression-rituals which resolve their disputes without bloodshed. Technology has given us the power to exterminate ourselves, and it is fitting that technology should also provide the safe outlet for our overamplified aggression. Let us hope that the space race, that triumph of pure technology, may be an archetype of triumphs yet to come!

Suggested Reading

Plato, *Republic,* Book 2, pp. 357a ff. K. J. Dover trans.

J. Mander, G. Dippel, and H. Gossage, *The Great International Paper Airplane Book,* Simon and Schuster, New York, 1967.

Hero of Alexandria, *A Treatise on Pneumatics,* section 15 ff. Bennett Woodcroft, ed., Lord, 1851.

K. Lorenz, *On Aggression,* Methuen, 1967.

D. Irving, *The Mare's Nest,* William Kimber, 1964.

Suggested Listening

T. Lehrer, "A Song of Wernher von Braun," *That Was the Year That Was,* Reprise LP Album No. 6179.

2

Philosophers
of the
Technological Age

The variety of scientific views explored in Part 1 conceptualize the relationship between science, technology, and society as more or less linear in form. Man develops technology; its effects, positive and negative, anticipated and unanticipated, are manifested on the fabric of society; and man observes them. Several of the contemporary philosophers whose works are sampled in this second part find meaning in the exploration of an additional dimension. In their view, technology affects not only social and political structures, it affects the human psyche—the very way man sees, thinks about, and relates to his world. In developing technology and incorporating it into his social institutions, man is therefore not only changing these institutions, but he is changing *himself* in ways he may neither foresee nor desire. This level of analysis is rather deep and not always easy to understand. The selections in this portion of the book are extracts from complex and often difficult works. They merit close attention and special effort on the part of the reader to reflect upon what is being presented.

Now that the McLuhan fad has died down somewhat, it is possible to examine, in a more or less dispassionate manner, some of the ideas with which Marshall McLuhan created an intellectual furor in the mid 1960s. Indeed, *Understanding Media*, from which the selections presented here are taken, is a remarkable work. Rejecting the form of a carefully argued dissertation, McLuhan presents a cafeteria of ideas that immerses the reader in his thought process, in much the same way he says technology immerses the human psyche. In the now-classic phrase "the medium is the message" lies the central theme of McLuhan's vision. The content of a technology is really irrelevant, as is any argument over its moral neutrality. It is the changes produced in ourselves that are important. "The effects of technology do not occur at the level of opinions or concepts, but alter sense ratios or patterns of perception steadily and without any resistance." McLuhan sees technology as the prime mover behind all social change; yet in his view it operates not through the social structure, but through the individual. Despite all this, the essence of *Understanding Media* is not a cry of alarm about where technology is leading us. It is rather a paean to the wonders of the new technology, especially the technology of communications, and an attempt to deal with technology on its own terms.

The writings of Herbert Marcuse, although similar to those of McLuhan in certain ways, are strikingly different in their pessimistic evaluation of technology's role in social change. *One-Dimensional Man,* from which the selection in our reader is taken, is a major work of contemporary philosophy. A full understanding of the ideas Marcuse presents here requires that the reader have a substantial philosophical background, particularly in Hegel and Marx. Nevertheless, Marcuse's influence as a philosopher of the technological society has been at least as great among those who lack such a background as among those who possess it, and it is in this light that we treat it here. Like McLuhan, Marcuse sees the most profound effects of technology as being manifested through changes in human character. The technological system creates "false needs" in individuals which serve to sustain the system while repressing true human needs. The technological state is basically totalitarian. From the inside, it appears completely rational, but from the outside, one can see that it is totally irrational, since it excludes qualitative social change. Marcuse is pessimistic, although not without hope, about the prospects for humanity in the face of the technological system. Nevertheless, in the final analysis, he does not seek to do away with technology. Rather, he sees technology as potentially capable of ending man's constant "struggle for existence." Thus, if man can find the means to reassert his control over the system, technology offers him his one real chance to attain true freedom and fulfillment.

Even this slim ray of hope appears beyond the reach of man in the view of the contemporary French philosopher and social critic, Jacques Ellul. In his long, complex, often obscure, and enormously influential work, *The Technological Society,* from which we have included several excerpts here, Ellul analyzes technology as the central factor in modern society. Like Marcuse, Ellul sees technology as a self-enclosed, totalitarian system. In this totalitarian system, true human values are lost and technology becomes an autonomous force guided by internal values which bear no necessary relation to the needs of humanity. Means become ends, and every aspect of society—the individual, the family, the state—becomes subservient to the system. If Ellul sees a way out of this dilemma, he does not share it with us. In his view, the domination of technology is complete and inevitable.

A much more sanguine assessment of man's prospects is contained in the final selection, "Toward the Creation of Technological Man," whose author, Victor Ferkiss, is not a philosopher but a political scientist. In his book, *Technological Man: The Myth and the Reality*, Ferkiss examines the major strains of philosophical thought and social science research relevant to an analysis of the future of technological society. As a result of this examination, he develops the conviction that man's ability to cope with the problems of the future depends upon the evolution of "a new cultural type," whose philosophy will derive from science and technology and whose ethos will be composed of three central elements: the "new holism," the "new immanentism," and the "new naturalism." "Technological man," according to Ferkiss, "will be man in control of his own development within the context of a meaningful philosophy of the role of technology in human evolution." Sounding a bit like Charles Reich in *The Greening of America*, Ferkiss proclaims that technological man must arise spontaneously in civilization. In his ascendancy, humanity will find salvation from the technological abyss—and, as Ferkiss sees it, there are signs that he is already beginning to emerge.

from Understanding Media

MARSHALL MCLUHAN

In a culture like ours, long accustomed to splitting and dividing all things as a means of control, it is sometimes a bit of a shock to be reminded that, in operational and practical fact, the medium is the message. This is merely to say that the personal and social consequences of any medium—that is, of any extension of ourselves—result from the new scale that is introduced into our affairs by each extension of ourselves, or by any new technology. Thus, with automation, for example, the new patterns of human association tend to eliminate jobs, it is true. That is the negative result. Positively, automation creates roles for people, which is to say depth of involvement in their work and human association that our preceding mechanical technology had destroyed. Many people would be disposed to say that it was not the machine, but what one did with the machine, that was its meaning or message. In terms of the ways in which the machine altered our relations to one another and to ourselves, it mattered not in the least whether it turned out cornflakes or Cadillacs. The restructuring of human work and association was shaped by the technique of fragmentation that is the essence of machine technology. The essence of automation technology is the opposite. It is integral and decentralist in depth, just as the machine was fragmentary, centralist, and superficial in its patterning of human relationships.

The instance of the electric light may prove illuminating in this connection. The electric light is pure information. It is a medium without a message, as it were, unless it is used to spell out some verbal ad or name. This fact, characteristic of all media, means that the "content" of any medium is always another medium. The content of writing is speech, just as the written word is the content of print, and print is the content of the telegraph. If it is asked, "What is the content of speech?," it is necessary to say, "It is an actual process of thought, which is in itself nonverbal." An abstract painting represents direct manifestation of creative thought processes as they might appear in computer designs. What we are considering here, however, are the psychic and social consequences of the designs or patterns as they amplify or accelerate existing processes. For the "message" of any medium or technology is the change of scale or pace or pattern that it introduces into human affairs. The railway did not introduce movement or transportation or wheel or road into human society, but it accelerated and enlarged the scale of previous human functions, creating totally new kinds of cities and new kinds of work and leisure. This happened whether the railway functioned in a tropical or a northern environment, and is quite independent of the freight or content of the railway medium. The airplane, on the other hand, by accelerating the rate of transportation, tends to dissolve the railway form of city, politics, and association, quite independently of what the airplane is used for.

Let us return to the electric light. Whether the light is being used for brain surgery or night baseball is a matter of indifference. It could be argued that these activities are in some way the "content" of the electric light, since they could not exist without the electric light. This fact merely underlines the point that "the medium is the message" because it is the medium that shapes and controls the scale and form of human association and action. The content or uses of such media are as diverse as they are ineffectual in shaping the form of human association. Indeed, it is only too typical that the "content" of any medium blinds us to the character of the medium. It is only today that industries have become aware of the various kinds of business in which they are engaged. When IBM discovered that it was not in the business of making office equipment or business machines, but that it was in the business of processing information, then it began to navigate with clear vision. The General Electric Company makes a considerable portion of its profits from electric light bulbs and lighting systems. It has not yet discovered that, quite as much as A.T.&T., it is in the business of moving information.

The electric light escapes attention as a communication medium just because it has no "content." And this makes it an invaluable instance of how people fail to study media at all. For it is not till the electric light is used to spell out some brand name that it is noticed as a medium. Then it is not the light but the "content" (or what is really another medium) that is noticed. The message of the electric light is like the message of electric power in industry, totally radical, pervasive, and decentralized. For electric light and power are separate from their uses, yet they eliminate time and space factors in human association exactly as do radio, telegraph, telephone, and TV, creating involvement in depth.

*   *   *   *   *

In accepting an honorary degree from the University of Notre Dame a few years ago, General David Sarnoff made this statement: "We are too prone to make technological instruments the scapegoats for the sins of those who wield them. The products of modern science are not in themselves good or bad; it is the way they are used that determines their value." That is the voice of the current somnambulism. Suppose we were to say, "Apple pie is in itself neither good nor bad; it is the way it is used that determines its value." Or, "The smallpox virus is in itself neither good nor bad; it is the way it is used that determines its value." Again, "Firearms are in themselves neither good nor bad; it is the way they are used that determines their value." That is, if the slugs reach the right people firearms are good. If the TV tube fires the right ammunition at the right people it is good. I am not being perverse. There is simply nothing in the Sarnoff statement that will bear scrutiny, for it ignores the nature of the medium, of any and all media, in the true Narcissus style of one hypnotized by the amputation and extension of his own being in a new technical form. General Sarnoff went on to explain his attitude to the technology of print, saying that it was true that print caused much trash to circulate, but it had also disseminated the Bible and the thoughts of seers and philosophers. It has never occurred to General Sarnoff that any technology could do anything but *add* itself on to what we already are.

*   *   *   *   *

Our conventional response to all media, namely, that it is how they are used that counts, is the numb stance of the technological idiot. For the "content" of a medium is like the juicy piece of meat carried by the burglar to distract the watchdog of the mind. The effect of the medium is made strong and intense just because it is given another medium as "content." The content of a movie is a novel or a play or an opera. The effect of the movie form is not related to its program content. The "content" of writing or print is speech, but the reader is almost entirely unaware either of print or of speech.

Arnold Toynbee is innocent of any understanding of media as they have shaped history, but he is full of examples that the student of media can use. At one moment he can seriously suggest that adult education, such as the Workers Educational Association in Britain, is a useful counterforce to the popular press. Toynbee considers that although all of the oriental societies have in our time accepted the industrial technology and its political consequences: "On the cultural plane, however, there is no uniform corresponding tendency." (Somervell, 1:267) This is like the voice of the literate man, floundering in a milieu of ads, who boasts, "Personally, I pay no attention to ads." The spiritual and cultural reservations that the oriental peoples may have toward our technology will avail them not at all. The effects of technology do not occur at the level of opinions or concepts, but alter sense ratios or patterns of perception steadily and without any resistance. The serious artist is the only person able to encounter technology with impunity, just because he is an expert aware of the changes in sense perception.

The operation of the money medium in seventeenth-century Japan had effects not unlike the operation of typography in the West. The penetration of the money economy, wrote G. B. Sansom (in *Japan,* Cresset Press, London, 1931) "caused a slow but irresistible revolution, culminating in the breakdown of feudal government and the resumption of intercourse with foreign countries after more than two hundred years of seclusion." Money has reorganized the sense life of peoples just because it is an *extension* of our sense lives. This change does not depend upon approval or disapproval of those living in the society.

Arnold Toynbee made one approach to the transforming power of media in his concept of "etherialization," which he holds to be the principle of progressive simplification and efficiency in any organization or technology. Typically, he is ignoring the *effect* of the challenge of these forms upon the response of our senses. He imagines that it is the response of our opinions that is relevant to the effect of media and technology in society, a "point of view" that is plainly the result of the typographic spell. For the man in a literate and homogenized society ceases to be sensitive to the diverse and discontinuous life of forms. He acquires the illusion of the third dimension and the "private point of view" as part of his Narcissus fixation, and is quite shut off from Blake's awareness or that of the Psalmist, that we become what we behold.

Today when we want to get our bearings in our own culture, and have need to stand aside from the bias and pressure exerted by any technical form of human expression, we have only to visit a society where that particular form has not been felt, or a historical period in which it was unknown. Professor Wilbur Schramm made such a tactical move in studying *Television in the Lives of Our Children.* He found areas where TV had not penetrated at all and ran some tests. Since he had made no study of the peculiar nature of the TV image, his tests were of "content" preferences, viewing time, and vocabulary counts. In a word, his approach to the problem was a literary one, albeit unconsciously so. Consequently, he had nothing to report. Had his methods been employed in 1500 A.D. to discover the effects of the printed book in the lives of children or adults, he could have found out nothing of the changes in human and social psychology resulting from typography. Print created individualism and nationalism in the sixteenth century. Program and "content" analysis offer no clues to the magic of these media or to their subliminal charge.

Leonard Doob, in his report *Communication in Africa,* tells of one African who took great pains to listen each evening to the BBC news, even though he could understand nothing of it. Just to be in the presence of those sounds at 7 P.M. each day was important for him. His attitude to speech was like ours to melody—the resonant intonation was meaning enough. In the seventeenth century our ancestors still shared this native's attitude to the forms of media, as is plain in the following sentiment of the Frenchman Bernard Lam expressed in *The Art of Speaking* (London, 1696):

'Tis an effect of the Wisdom of God, who created Man to be happy, that whatever is useful to his conversation (way of life) is agreeable to him . . . because all victual that conduces to nourishment is relishable, whereas other things that cannot be assimilated and be turned into our substance are insipid. A Discourse cannot be pleasant to the Hearer that is not easie to the Speaker; nor can it be easily pronounced unless it be heard with delight.

Here is an equilibrium theory of human diet and expression such as even now we are only striving to work out again for media after centuries of fragmentation and specialism.

Pope Pius XII was deeply concerned that there be serious study of the media today. On February 17, 1950, he said:

It is not an exaggeration to say that the future of modern society and the stability of its inner life depend in large part on the maintenance of an equilibrium between the strength of the techniques of communication and the capacity of the individual's own reaction.

Failure in this respect has for centuries been typical and total for mankind. Subliminal and docile acceptance of media impact has made them prisons without walls for their human users. As A. J. Liebling remarked in his book *The Press,* a man is not free if he cannot see where he is going, even if he has a gun to help him get there. For each of the media is also a powerful weapon with which to clobber other media and other groups. The result is that the present age has been one of multiple civil wars that are not limited to the world of art and entertainment. In *War and Human Progress,* Professor J. U. Nef declared: "The total wars of our time have been the result of a series of intellectual mistakes . . ."

If the formative powers in the media are the media themselves, that raises a host of large matters that can only be mentioned here, although they deserve volumes. Namely, that technological media are staples or natural resources, exactly as are coal and cotton and oil. Anybody will concede that society whose economy is dependent upon one or two major staples like cotton, or grain, or lumber, or fish, or cattle is going to have some obvious social patterns of organization as a result. Stress on a few major staples creates extreme instability in the economy but great endurance in the population. The pathos and humor of the American South are embedded in such an economy of limited staples. For a society configured by reliance on a few commodities accepts them as a social bond quite as much as the metropolis does the press. Cotton and oil, like radio and TV, become "fixed charges" on the entire psychic life of the community. And this pervasive fact creates the unique cultural flavor of any society. It pays through the nose and all its other senses for each staple that shapes its life.

That our human senses, of which all media are extensions, are also fixed charges on our personal energies, and that they also configure the awareness and experience of each one of us, may be perceived in another connection mentioned by the psychologist C. G. Jung:

Every Roman was surrounded by slaves. The slave and his psychology flooded ancient Italy, and every Roman became inwardly, and of course unwittingly, a slave. Because living constantly in the atmosphere of slaves, he became infected through the unconscious with their psychology. No one can shield himself from such an influence (*Contributions to Analytical Psychology,* London, 1928).

*　　*　　*　　*　　*

Any invention or technology is an extension or self-amputation of our physical bodies, and such extension also demands new ratios or new equilibriums among the other organs and extensions of the body. There is, for example, no way of refusing to comply with the new sense ratios or sense "closure" evoked by the TV image. But the effect of the entry of the TV image will vary from culture to culture in accordance with the existing sense ratios in each culture. In audile-tactile Europe TV has intensified the visual sense, spurring them toward American styles of packaging and dressing. In America, the intensely visual culture, TV has opened the doors of audile-tactile perception to the nonvisual world of spoken languages and food and the plastic arts. As an extension and expediter of the sense life, any medium at once affects the entire field of the senses, as the Psalmist explained long ago in the 113th Psalm:

Their idols are silver and gold,
The work of men's hands.
They have mouths, but they speak not;

Eyes they have, but they see not;
They have ears, but they hear not;
Noses they have, but they smell not;
They have hands, but they handle not;
Feet have they, but they walk not;
Neither speak they through their throat.
They that make them shall be like unto them;
Yea, every one that trusteth in them.

The concept of "idol" for the Hebrew Psalmist is much like that of Narcissus for the Greek mythmaker. And the Psalmist insists that the *beholding* of idols, or the use of technology, conforms men to them. "They that make them shall be like unto them." This is a simple fact of sense "closure." The poet Blake developed the Psalmist's ideas into an entire theory of communication and social change. It is in his long poem of *Jerusalem* that he explains why men have become what they have beheld. What they have, says Blake, is "the spectre of the Reasoning Power in Man" that has become fragmented and "separated from Imagination and enclosing itself as in steel." Blake, in a word, sees man as fragmented by his technologies. But he insists that these technologies are self-amputations of our own organs. When so amputated, each organ becomes a closed system of great new intensity that hurls man into "martyrdoms and wars." Moreover, Blake announces as his theme in *Jerusalem* the organs of perception:

If Perceptive Organs vary, Objects of Perception seem to vary:
If Perceptive Organs close, their Objects seem to close also.

To behold, use or perceive any extension of ourselves in technological form is necessarily to embrace it. To listen to radio or to read the printed page is to accept these extensions of ourselves into our personal system and to undergo the "closure" or displacement of perception that follows automatically. It is this continuous embrace of our own technology in daily use that puts us in the Narcissus role of subliminal awareness and numbness in relation to these images of ourselves. By continuously embracing technologies, we relate ourselves to them as servomechanisms. That is why we must, to use them at all, serve these objects, these extensions of ourselves, as gods or minor religions. An Indian is the servo-mechanism of his canoe, as the cowboy of his horse or the executive of his clock.

Physiologically, man in the normal use of technology (or his variously extended body) is perpetually modified by it and in turn finds ever new ways of modifying his technology. Man becomes, as it were, the sex organs of the machine world, as the bee of the plant world, enabling it to fecundate and to evolve ever new forms. The machine world reciprocates man's love by expediting his wishes and desires, namely, in providing him with wealth. One of the merits of motivation research has been the revelation of man's sex relation to the motorcar.

Socially, it is the accumulation of group pressures and irritations that prompt invention and innovation as counterirritants. War and the fear of war have always been considered the main incentives to technological extension of our bodies. Indeed, Lewis Mumford, in his *The City in History,* considers the walled city itself an extension of our skins, as much as housing and clothing. More even than the preparation for war, the aftermath of invasion is a rich technological period; because the subject culture has to adjust all its sense ratios to accommodate the impact of the invading culture. It is from such intensive hybrid exchange and strife of ideas and forms that the greatest social energies are released, and from which arise the greatest technologies. Buckminster Fuller estimates that since 1910 the governments of the world have spent 3½ trillion dollars on airplanes. That is 62 times the existing gold supply of the world.

The principle of numbness comes into play with electric technology, as with any other. We have to numb our central nervous system when it is extended and exposed, or we will die. Thus the age of anxiety and of electric media is also the age of the unconscious and of apathy. But it is strikingly the age of consciousness of the unconscious, in addition. With our central nervous system strategically numbed, the tasks of conscious awareness and order are transferred to the physical life of man, so that for the first time he has become aware of technology as an extension of his physical body. Apparently this could not have happened before the electric age gave us the means of instant, total field-awareness. With such awareness, the subliminal life, private and social, has been hoisted up into full view, with the result that we have "social consciousness" presented to us as a cause of guilt-feelings. Existentialism offers a philosophy of structures, rather than categories, and of total social involvement instead of the bourgeois spirit of individual separateness or points of view. In the electric age we wear all mankind as our skin.

The New Forms of Control

HERBERT MARCUSE

A comfortable, smooth, reasonable, democratic unfreedom prevails in advanced industrial civilization, a token of technical progress. Indeed, what could be more rational than the suppression of individuality in the mechanization of socially necessary but painful performances; the concentration of individual enterprises in more effective, more productive corporations; the regulation of free competition among unequally equipped economic subjects; the curtailment of prerogatives and national sovereignties which impede the international organization of resources. That this technological order also involves a political and intellectual coordination may be a regrettable and yet promising development.

The rights and liberties which were such vital factors in the origins and earlier stages of industrial society yield to a higher stage of this society: they are losing their traditional rationale and content. Freedom of thought, speech, and conscience were—just as free enterprise, which they served to promote and protect—essentially *critical* ideas, designed to replace an obsolescent material and intellectual culture by a more productive and rational one. Once institutionalized, these rights and liberties shared the fate of the society of which they had become an integral part. The achievement cancels the premises.

To the degree to which freedom from want, the concrete substance of all freedom, is becoming a real possibility, the liberties which pertain to a state of lower productivity are losing their former content. Independence of thought, autonomy, and the right to political opposition are being deprived of their basic critical function in a society which seems increasingly capable of satisfying the needs of the individuals through the way in which it is organized. Such a society may justly demand acceptance of its principles and institutions, and reduce the opposition to the discussion and promotion of alternative policies *within* the status quo. In this respect, it seems to make little difference whether the increasing satisfaction of needs is accomplished by an authoritarian or a nonauthoritarian system. Under the conditions of a rising standard of living, nonconformity with the system itself appears to be socially useless, and the more so when it entails tangible economic and political disadvantages and threatens the smooth operation of the whole. Indeed, at least in so far as the necessities of life are involved, there seems to be no reason why the production and distribution of goods and services should proceed through the competitive concurrence of individual liberties.

Freedom of enterprise was from the beginning not altogether a blessing. As the liberty to work or to starve, it spelled toil, insecurity, and fear for the vast majority of the population. If the individual were no longer compelled to prove himself on the market, as a free economic subject, the disappearance of this kind of freedom would be one of the greatest achievements of civilization. The technological processes of mechanization and standardization might release individual energy into a yet uncharted realm of freedom beyond necessity. The very structure of human existence would be altered; the individual would be liberated from the work world's imposing upon him alien needs and alien possibilities. The individual would be free to exert autonomy over a life that would be his own. If the productive apparatus could be organized and directed toward the satisfaction of the vital needs, its control might well be centralized; such control would not prevent individual autonomy, but render it possible.

This is a goal within the capabilities of advanced industrial civilization, the "end" of technological rationality. In actual fact, however, the contrary trend operates: the apparatus imposes its economic and political requirements for defense and expansion on labor time and free time, on the material and intellectual culture. By virtue of the way it has organized its technological base, contemporary industrial society tends to be totalitarian. For "totalitarian" is not only a terroristic political coordination of society, but also a nonterroristic economic-technical coordination which operates through the manipulation of needs by vested interests. It thus precludes the emergence of an effective opposition against the whole. Not only a specific form of government or party rule makes for totalitarianism, but also a specific system of production and distribution which may well be compatible with a "pluralism" of parties, newspapers, "countervailing powers," etc.

Today political power asserts itself through its power over the machine process and over the technical organization of the apparatus. The government of advanced and advancing industrial societies can maintain and secure itself only when it succeeds in mobilizing, organizing, and exploiting the technical, scientific, and mechanical productivity available to industrial civilization. And this productivity mobilizes society as a whole, above and beyond any particular individual or group interests. The brute fact that the machine's physical (only physical?) power surpasses that of the individual, and of any particular group of individuals, makes the machine the most effective political instrument in any society whose basic organization is that of the machine process. But the political trend may be reversed; essentially the power of the machine is only the stored-up and projected power of man. To the extent to which the work world is conceived of as a machine and mechanized accordingly, it becomes the *potential* basis of a new freedom for man.

Contemporary industrial civilization demonstrates that it has reached the stage at which "the free society" can no longer be adequately defined in the traditional terms of economic, political, and intellectual liberties, not because these liberties have become insignificant, but because they are too significant to be confined within the traditional forms. New modes of realization are needed, corresponding to the new capabilities of society.

Such new modes can be indicated only in negative terms because they would amount to the negation of the prevailing modes. Thus economic freedom would mean freedom *from* the economy—from being controlled by economic forces and relationships; freedom from the daily struggle for existence, from earning a living. Political freedom would mean liberation of the individuals *from* politics over which they have no effective control. Similarly, intellectual freedom would mean the restoration of individual thought now absorbed by mass communication and indoctrination, abolition of "public opinion" together with its makers. The unrealistic sound of these propositions is indicative, not of their utopian character, but of the strength of the forces which prevent their realization. The most effective and enduring form of warfare against liberation is the implanting of material and intellectual needs that perpetuate obsolete forms of the struggle for existence.

The intensity, the satisfaction and even the character of human needs, beyond the biological level, have always been preconditioned. Whether or not the possibility of doing or leaving, enjoying or destroying, possessing or rejecting something is seized as a *need* depends on whether or not it can be seen as desirable and necessary for the prevailing societal institutions and interests. In this sense, human needs are historical needs and, to the extent to which the society demands the repressive development of the individual, his needs themselves and their claim for satisfaction are subject to overriding critical standards.

We may distinguish both true and false needs. "False" are those which are superimposed upon the individual by particular social interests in his repression: the needs which perpetuate toil, aggressiveness, misery, and injustice. Their satisfaction might be most gratifying to the individual, but this happiness is not a condition which has to be maintained and protected if it serves to arrest the development of the ability (his own and others) to recognize the disease of the whole and grasp the chances of curing the disease. The result then is euphoria in unhappiness. Most of the prevailing needs to relax, to have fun, to behave and consume in accordance with the advertisements, to love and hate what others love and hate, belong to this category of false needs.

Such needs have a societal content and function which are determined by external powers over which the individual has no control; the development and satisfaction of these needs is heteronomous. No matter how much such needs may have become the individual's own, reproduced and fortified by the conditions of his existence; no matter how much he identifies himself with them and finds himself in their satisfaction, they continue to be what they were from the beginning—products of a society whose dominant interest demands repression.

The prevalence of repressive needs is an accomplished fact, accepted in ignorance and defeat, but a fact that must be undone in the interest of the happy individual as well as all those whose misery is the price of his satisfaction. The only needs that have an unqualified claim for satisfaction are the vital ones—nourishment, clothing, lodging at the attainable level of culture. The satisfaction of these needs is the prerequisite for the realization of *all* needs, of the unsublimated as well as the sublimated ones.

For any consciousness and conscience, for any experience which does not accept the prevailing societal interest as the supreme law of thought and behavior, the established universe of needs and satisfactions is a fact to be questioned—questioned in terms of truth and falsehood. These terms are historical throughout, and their objectivity is historical. The judgment of needs and their satisfaction, under the given conditions, involves standards of *priority*— standards which refer to the optimal development of the individual, of all individuals, under the optimal utilization of the material and intellectual resources available to man. The resources are calculable. "Truth" and "falsehood" of needs designate objective conditions to the extent to which the universal satisfaction of vital needs and, beyond it, the progressive alleviation of toil and poverty, are universally valid standards. But as historical standards, they do not only vary according to area and stage of development, they also can be defined only in (greater or lesser) *contradiction* to the prevailing ones. What tribunal can possibly claim the authority of decision?

In the last analysis, the question of what are true and false needs must be answered by the individuals themselves, but only in the last analysis; that is, if and when they are free to give their own answer. As long as they are kept incapable of being autonomous, as long as they are indoctrinated and manipulated (down to their very instincts), their answer to this question cannot be taken as their own. By the same token, however, no tribunal can justly arrogate to itself the right to decide which needs should be developed and satisfied. Any such tribunal is reprehensible, although our revulsion does not do away with the question: how can the people who have been the object of effective and productive domination by themselves create the conditions of freedom?

The more rational, productive, technical, and total the repressive administration of society becomes, the more unimaginable the means and ways by which the administered individuals might break their servitude and seize their own liberation. To be sure, to impose Reason upon an entire society is a paradoxical and scandalous idea—although one might dispute the righteousness of a society which ridicules this idea while making its own population into objects of total administration. All liberation depends on the consciousness of servitude, and the emergence of this consciousness is always hampered by the predominance of needs and satisfactions which, to a great extent, have become the individual's own. The process always replaces one system of preconditioning by another; the optimal goal is the replacement of false needs by true ones, the abandonment of repressive satisfaction.

The distinguishing feature of advanced industrial society is its effective suffocation of those needs which demand liberation—liberation also from that which is tolerable and rewarding and comfortable—while it sustains and absolves the destructive power and repressive function of the affluent society. Here, the social controls exact the overwhelming need for the production and consumption of waste; the need for stupefying work where it is no longer a real necessity; the need for modes of relaxation which soothe and prolong this stupefication; the need for maintaining such deceptive liberties as free competition at administered prices, a free press which censors itself, free choice between brands and gadgets.

Under the rule of a repressive whole, liberty can be made into a powerful instrument of domination. The range of choice open to the individual is not the decisive factor in determining the degree of human freedom, but *what* can be chosen and what *is* chosen by the individual. The criterion for free choice can never be an absolute one, but neither is it entirely relative. Free election of masters does not abolish the masters or the slaves. Free choice among a wide variety of goods and services does not signify freedom if these goods and services sustain social controls over a life of toil and fear—that is, if they sustain alienation. And the spontaneous reproduction of superimposed needs by the individual does not establish autonomy; it only testifies to the efficacy of the controls.

Our insistence on the depth and efficacy of these controls is open to the objection that we overrate greatly the indoctrinating power of the "media," and that by themselves the people would feel and satisfy the needs which are now imposed upon them. The objection misses the point. The preconditioning does not start with the mass production of radio and television and with the centralization of their control. The people enter this stage as preconditioned receptacles of long standing; the decisive difference is in the flattening out of the contrast (or conflict) between the given and the possible, between the satisfied and the unsatisfied needs. Here, the so-called equalization of class distinctions reveals its ideological function. If the worker and his boss enjoy the same television program and visit the same resort places, if the typist is as attractively made up as the daughter of her employer, if the Negro owns a Cadillac, if they all read the same newspaper, then this assimilation indicates not the disappearance of classes, but the extent to which the needs and satisfactions that serve the preservation of the Establishment are shared by the underlying population.

Indeed, in the most highly developed areas of contemporary society, the transplantation of social into individual needs is so effective that the difference between them seems to be purely theoretical. Can one really distinguish between the mass media as instruments of information and entertainment, and as agents of manipulation and indoctrination? Between the automobile as nuisance and as convenience? Between the horrors and the comforts of functional architecture? Between the work for national defense and the work for corporate gain? Between the private pleasure and the commercial and political utility involved in increasing the birth rate?

We are again confronted with one of the most vexing aspects of advanced industrial civilization: the rational character of its irrationality. Its productivity and efficiency, its capacity to increase and spread comforts, to turn waste into need, and destruction into construction, the extent to which this civilization transforms the object world into an extension of man's mind and body makes the very notion of alienation questionable. The people recognize themselves in their commodities; they find their soul in their automobile, hi-fi set, split-level home, kitchen equipment. The very mechanism which ties the individual to his society has changed, and social control is anchored in the new needs which it has produced.

The prevailing forms of social control are technological in a new sense. To be sure, the technical structure and efficacy of the productive and destructive apparatus has been a major instrumentality for subjecting the population to the established social division of labor throughout the modern period. Moreover, such integration has always been accompanied by more obvious forms of compulsion: loss of livelihood, the administration of justice, the police, the armed forces. It still is. But in the contemporary period, the technological controls appear to be the very embodiment of Reason for the benefit of all social groups and interests—to such an extent that all contradiction seems irrational and all counteraction impossible.

No wonder then that, in the most advanced areas of this civilization, the social controls have been introjected to the point where even individual protest is affected at its roots. The intellectual and emotional refusal "to go along" appears neurotic and impotent. This is the sociopsychological aspect of the political event that marks the contemporary period: the passing of the historical forces which, at the preceding stage of industrial society, seemed to represent the possibility of new forms of existence.

But the term "introjection" perhaps no longer describes the way in which the individual by himself reproduces and perpetuates the external controls exercised by his society. Introjection suggests a variety of relatively spontaneous processes by which a Self (Ego) transposes the "outer" into the "inner." Thus introjection implies the existence of an inner dimension distinguished from and even antagonistic to the external exigencies—an individual consciousness and an individual unconscious *apart from* public opinion and behavior.[1] The idea of "inner freedom" here has its reality: it designates the private space in which man may become and remain "himself."

Today this private space has been invaded and whittled down by technological reality. Mass production and mass distribution claim the *entire* individual, and industrial psychology has long since ceased to be confined to the factory. The manifold processes of introjection seem to be ossified in almost mechanical reactions. The result is, not adjustment but *mimesis:* an immediate identification of the individual with *his* society and, through it, with the society as a whole.

This immediate, automatic identification (which may have been characteristic of primitive forms of association) reappears in high industrial civilization; its new "immediacy," however, is the product of a sophisticated, scien-

---

1. The change in the function of the family here plays a decisive role: its "socializing" functions are increasingly taken over by outside groups and media. See my *Eros and Civilization* (Boston: Beacon Press, 1955), p. 96 ff.

tific management and organization. In this process, the "inner" dimension of the mind in which opposition to the status quo can take root is whittled down. The loss of this dimension, in which the power of negative thinking— the critical power of Reason—is at home, is the ideological counterpart to the very material process in which advanced industrial society silences and reconciles the opposition. The impact of progress turns Reason into submission to the facts of life, and to the dynamic capability of producing more and bigger facts of the same sort of life. The efficiency of the system blunts the individuals' recognition that it contains no facts which do not communicate the repressive power of the whole. If the individuals find themselves in the things which shape their life, they do so, not by giving, but by accepting the law of things—not the law of physics but the law of their society.

I have just suggested that the concept of alienation seems to become questionable when the individuals identify themselves with the existence which is imposed upon them and have in it their own development and satisfaction. This identification is not illusion but reality. However, the reality constitutes a more progressive stage of alienation. The latter has become entirely objective; the subject which is alienated is swallowed up by its alienated existence. There is only one dimension, and it is everywhere and in all forms. The achievements of progress defy ideological indictment as well as justification; before their tribunal, the "false consciousness" of their rationality becomes the true consciousness.

This absorption of ideology into reality does not, however, signify the "end of ideology." On the contrary, in a specific sense advanced industrial culture is *more* ideological than its predecessor, inasmuch as today the ideology is in the process of production itself. In a provocative form, this proposition reveals the political aspects of the prevailing technological rationality. The productive apparatus and the goods and services which it produces "sell" or impose the social system as a whole. The means of mass transportation and communication, the commodities of lodging, food, and clothing, the irresistible output of the entertainment and information industry carry with them prescribed attitudes and habits, certain intellectual and emotional reactions which bind the consumers more or less pleasantly to the producers and, through the latter, to the whole. The products indoctrinate and manipulate; they promote a false consciousness which is immune against its falsehood. And as these beneficial products become available to more individuals in more social classes, the indoctrination they carry ceases to be publicity; it becomes a way of life. It is a good way of life—much better than before—and as a good way of life, it militates against qualitative change. Thus emerges a pattern of *one-*

dimensional thought and behavior in which ideas, aspirations and objectives that, by their content, transcend the established universe of discourse and action are either repelled or reduced to terms of this universe. They are redefined by the rationality of the given system and of its quantitative extension.

The trend may be related to a development in scientific method: operationalism in the physical, behaviorism in the social sciences. The common feature is a total empiricism in the treatment of concepts; their meaning is restricted to the representation of particular operations and behavior. The operational point of view is well illustrated by P. W. Bridgman's analysis of the concept of length:[2]

> We evidently know what we mean by length if we can tell what the length of any and every object is, and for the physicist nothing more is required. To find the length of an object, we have to perform certain physical operations. The concept of length is therefore fixed when the operations by which length is measured are fixed: that is, the concept of length involves as much and nothing more than the set of operations by which length is determined. In general, we mean by any concept nothing more than a set of operations; *the concept is synonymous with the corresponding set of operations.*

Bridgman has seen the wide implications of this mode of thought for the society at large:

> To adopt the operational point of view involves much more than a mere restriction of the sense in which we understand "concept," but means a far-reaching change in all our habits of thought, in that we shall no longer permit ourselves to use as tools in our thinking concepts of which we cannot give an adequate account in terms of operations.

Bridgman's prediction has come true. The new mode of thought is today the predominant tendency in philosophy, psychology, sociology, and other fields. Many of the most seriously troublesome concepts are being "eliminated" by showing that no adequate account of them in terms of operations or behavior can be given. The radical empiricist onslaught . . . thus provides the methodological justification for the debunking of the mind by the intellectuals—a positivism which, in its denial of the transcending elements of Reason, forms the academic counterpart of the socially required behavior.

---

2. P. W. Bridgman, *The Logic of Modern Physics* (New York: Macmillan, 1928), p. 5 ff. The operational doctrine has since been refined and qualified. Bridgman himself has extended the concept of "operation" to include the "paper-and-pencil" operations of the theorist (in Philipp J. Frank, *The Validation of Scientific Theories* [Boston: Beacon Press, 1954], Chap. 2). The main impetus remains the same: it is "desirable" that the paper-and-pencil operations "be capable of eventual contact, although perhaps indirectly, with instrumental operations."

Outside the academic establishment, the "far-reaching change in all our habits of thought" is more serious. It serves to coordinate ideas and goals with those exacted by the prevailing system, to enclose them in the system, and to repel those which are irreconcilable with the system. The reign of such a one-dimensional reality does not mean that materialism rules, and that the spiritual, metaphysical, and bohemian occupations are petering out. On the contrary, there is a great deal of "Worship together this week," "Why not try God," Zen, existentialism, and beat ways of life, etc. But such modes of protest and transcendence are no longer contradictory to the status quo and no longer negative. They are rather the ceremonial part of practical behaviorism, its harmless negation, and are quickly digested by the status quo as part of its healthy diet.

One-dimensional thought is systematically promoted by the makers of politics and their purveyors of mass information. Their universe of discourse is populated by self-validating hypotheses which, incessantly and monopolistically repeated, become hypnotic definitions or dictations. For example, "free" are the institutions which operate (and are operated on) in the countries of the Free World; other transcending modes of freedom are by definition either anarchism, communism, or propaganda. "Socialistic" are all encroachments on private enterprises not undertaken by private enterprise itself (or by government contracts), such as universal and comprehensive health insurance, or the protection of nature from all too sweeping commercialization, or the establishment of public services which may hurt private profit. This totalitarian logic of accomplished facts has its Eastern counterpart. There, freedom is the way of life instituted by a communist regime, and all other transcending modes of freedom are either capitalistic, or revisionist, or leftist sectarianism. In both camps, nonoperational ideas are nonbehavioral and subversive. The movement of thought is stopped at barriers which appear as the limits of Reason itself.

Such limitation of thought is certainly not new. Ascending modern rationalism, in its speculative as well as empirical form, shows a striking contrast between extreme critical radicalism in scientific and philosophic method on the one hand, and an uncritical quietism in the attitude toward established and functioning social institutions. Thus Descartes' *ego cogitans* was to leave the "great public bodies" untouched, and Hobbes held that "the present ought always to be preferred, maintained, and accounted best." Kant agreed with Locke in justifying revolution *if and when* it has succeeded in organizing the whole and in preventing subversion.

However, these accommodating concepts of Reason were always contradicted by the evident misery and injustice of the "great public bodies" and the effective, more or less conscious rebellion against them. Societal conditions existed which provoked and permitted real dissociation from the established state of affairs; a private as well as political dimension was present in which dissociation could develop into effective opposition, testing its strength and the validity of its objectives.

With the gradual closing of this dimension by the society, the self-limitation of thought assumes a larger significance. The interrelation between scientific-philosophical and societal processes, between theoretical and practical Reason, asserts itself "behind the back" of the scientists and philosophers. The society bars a whole type of oppositional operations and behavior; consequently, the concepts pertaining to them are rendered illusory or meaningless. Historical transcendence appears as metaphysical transcendence, not acceptable to science and scientific thought. The operational and behavioral point of view, practiced as a "habit of thought" at large, becomes the view of the established universe of discourse and action, needs and aspirations. The "cunning of Reason" works, as it so often did, in the interest of the powers that be. The insistence on operational and behavioral concepts turns against the efforts to free thought and behavior *from* the given reality and *for* the suppressed alternatives. Theoretical and practical Reason, academic and social behaviorism meet on common ground: that of an advanced society which makes scientific and technical progress into an instrument of domination.

"Progress" is not a neutral term; it moves toward specific ends, and these ends are defined by the possibilities of ameliorating the human condition. Advanced industrial society is approaching the stage where continued progress would demand the radical subversion of the prevailing direction and organization of progress. This stage would be reached when material production (including the necessary services) becomes automated to the extent that all vital needs can be satisfied while necessary labor time is reduced to marginal time. From this point on, technical progress would transcend the realm of necessity, where it served as the instrument of domination and exploitation which thereby limited its rationality; technology would become subject to the free play of faculties in the struggle for the pacification of nature and of society.

Such a state is envisioned in Marx's notion of the "abolition of labor." The term "pacification of existence" seems better suited to designate the historical alternative of a world which—through the contradictions within the established societies—advances on the brink of a global war. "Pacification of existence" means the development of man's struggle with man and with nature, under conditions where the competing needs, desires, and aspirations are no longer organized by vested interests in domination and scarcity—an organization which perpetuates the destructive forms of this struggle.

Today's fight against this historical alternative finds a firm mass basis in the underlying population, and finds its ideology in the rigid orientation of thought and behavior to the given universe of facts. Validated by the accomplishments of science and technology, justified by its growing productivity, the status quo defies all transcendence. Faced with the possibility of pacification on the grounds of its technical and intellectual achievements, the mature industrial society closes itself against this alternative. Operationalism, in theory and practice, becomes the theory and practice of *containment.* Underneath its obvious dynamics, this society is a thoroughly static system of life: self-propelling in its oppressive productivity and in its beneficial coordination. Containment of technical progress goes hand-in-hand with its growth in the established direction. In spite of the political fetters imposed by the status quo, the more technology appears capable of creating the conditions for pacification, the more are the minds and bodies of man organized against this alternative.

The most advanced areas of industrial society exhibit throughout these two features: a trend toward consummation of technological rationality, and intensive efforts to contain this trend within the established institutions. Here is the internal contradiction of this civilization: the irrational element in its rationality. It is the token of its achievements. The industrial society which makes technology and science its own is organized for the ever-more-effective domination of man and nature, for the ever-more-effective utilization of its resources. It becomes irrational when the success of these efforts opens new dimensions of human realization. Organization for peace is different from organization for war; the institutions which served the struggle for existence cannot serve the pacification of existence. Life as an end is qualitatively different from life as a means.

Such a qualitatively new mode of existence can never be envisaged as the mere by-product of economic and political changes, as the more or less spontaneous effect of the new institutions which constitute the necessary prerequisite. Qualitative change also involves a change in the *technical* basis on which this society rests—one which sustains the economic and political institutions through which the "second nature" of man as an aggressive object of administration is stabilized. The techniques of industrialization are political techniques; as such, they prejudge the possibilities of Reason and Freedom.

To be sure, labor must precede the reduction of labor, and industrialization must precede the development of human needs and satisfactions. But as all freedom depends on the conquest of alien necessity, the realization of freedom depends on the *techniques* of this conquest. The highest productivity of labor can be used for the perpetuation of labor, and the most efficient industrialization can serve the restriction and manipulation of needs.

When this point is reached, domination—in the guise of affluence and liberty—extends to all spheres of private and public existence, integrates all authentic opposition, absorbs all alternatives. Technological rationality reveals its political character as it becomes the great vehicle of better domination, creating a truly totalitarian universe in which society and nature, mind and body are kept in a state of permanent mobilization for the defense of this universe.

from The Technological Society

JACQUES ELLUL

No social, human, or spiritual fact is so important as the fact of technique in the modern world. And yet no subject is so little understood. Let us try to set up some guideposts to situate the technical phenomenon.

SITUATING THE TECHNICAL PHENOMENON

Machines and Technique. Whenever we see the word *technology* or *technique,* we automatically think of machines. Indeed, we commonly think of our world as a world of machines. This notion—which is in fact an error—is found, for example, in the works of Oldham and Pierre Ducassé. It arises from the fact that the machine is the most obvious, massive, and impressive example of technique, and historically the first. What is called the history of technique usually amounts to no more than a history of the machine; this very formulation is an example of the habit of intellectuals of regarding forms of the present as identical with those of the past.

Technique certainly began with the machine. It is quite true that all the rest developed out of mechanics; it is quite true also that without the machine the world of technique would not exist. But to explain the situation in this way does not at all legitimatize it. It is a mistake to continue with this confusion of terms, the more so because it leads to the idea that, because the machine is at the origin and center of the technical problem, one is dealing with the whole problem when one deals with the machine. And that is a greater mistake still. Technique has now become almost completely independent of the machine, which has lagged far behind its offspring.

It must be emphasized that, at present, technique is applied outside industrial life. The growth of its power today has no relation to the growing use of the machine. The balance seems rather to have shifted to the other side. It is the machine which is now entirely dependent upon technique, and the machine represents only a small part of technique. If we were to characterize the relations between technique and the machine today, we could say not only that the machine is the result of a certain technique, but also that its social and economic applications are made possible by other technical advances. The machine is now not even the most important aspect of technique (though it is perhaps the most spectacular); technique has taken over all of man's activities, not just his productive activity.

From another point of view, however, the machine is deeply symptomatic: it represents the ideal toward which technique strives. The machine is solely, exclusively, technique; it is pure technique, one might say. For, wherever a technical factor exists, it results, almost inevitably, in mechanization: technique transforms everything it touches into a machine.

Another relationship exists between technique and the machine, and this relationship penetrates to the very core of the problem of our civilization. It is said (and everyone agrees) that the machine has created an inhuman atmosphere. The machine, so characteristic of the nineteenth century, made an abrupt entrance into a society which, from the political, institutional, and human points of view, was not made to receive it; and man has had to put up with it as best he can. Men now live in conditions that are less than human. Consider the concentration of our great cities, the slums, the lack of space, of air, of time, the gloomy streets and the sallow lights that confuse night and day. Think of our dehumanized factories, our unsatisfied senses, our working women, our estrangement from nature. Life in such an environment has no meaning. Consider our public transportation, in which man is less important than a parcel; our hospitals, in which he is only a number. Yet we call this progress. . . . And the noise, that monster boring into us at every hour of the night without respite.

It is useless to rail against capitalism. Capitalism did not create our world; the machine did. Painstaking studies designed to prove the contrary have buried the obvious beneath tons of print. And, if we do not wish to play the demagogue, we must point out the guilty party. "The machine is antisocial," says Lewis Mumford. "It tends, by reason of its progressive character, to the most acute forms of human exploitation." The machine took its place in a social milieu that was not made for it, and for that reason created the inhuman society in which we live. Capitalism was therefore only one aspect of the deep disorder of the nineteenth century. To restore order, it was necessary to question all the bases of that society—its social and political structures, its art and its way of life, its commercial system.

But let the machine have its head, and it topples everything that cannot support its enormous weight. Thus everything had to be reconsidered in terms of the machine. And that is precisely the role technique plays. In all fields it made an inventory of what it could use, of everything that could be brought into line with the machine. The machine could not integrate itself into nineteenth-century society; technique integrated it. Old houses that were not suited to the workers were torn down; and the new world technique required was built in their place. Technique has enough of the mechanical in its nature to enable it to cope with the machine, but it surpasses and transcends the machine because it remains in close touch with the human order. The metal monster could not go on forever torturing mankind. It found in technique a rule as hard and inflexible as itself.

Technique integrates the machine into society. It constructs the kind of world the machine needs and introduces order where the incoherent banging of machinery heaped up ruins. It clarifies, arranges, and rationalizes; it does in the domain of the abstract what the machine did in the domain of labor. It is efficient and brings efficiency to everything. Moreover, technique is sparing in the use of the machine, which has traditionally been exploited to conceal defects of organization. "Machines sanctioned social inefficiency," says Mumford. Technique, on the other hand, leads to a more rational and less indiscriminate use of machines. It places machines exactly where they ought to be and requires of them just what they ought to do.

This brings us to two contrasting forms of social growth. Henri Guitton says: "Social growth was formerly reflexive or instinctive, that is to say, unconscious. But new circumstances (the machine) now compel us to recognize a kind of social development that is rational, intelligent, and conscious. We may ask ourselves whether this is the beginning not only of the era of a spatially finite world but also the era of a conscious world." All embracing technique is in fact the consciousness of the mechanized world.

Technique integrates everything. It avoids shock and sensational events. Man is not adapted to a world of steel; technique adapts him to it. It changes the arrangement of this blind world so that man can be a part of it without colliding with its rough edges, without the anguish of being delivered up to the inhuman. Technique thus provides a model; it specifies attitudes that are valid once and for all. The anxiety aroused in man by the turbulence of the machine is soothed by the consoling hum of a unified society.

As long as technique was represented exclusively by the machine, it was possible to speak of "man *and* the machine." The machine remained an external object, and man (though significantly influenced by it in his professional, private, and psychic life) remained none the less independent. He was in a position to assert himself apart from the machine; he was able to adopt a position with respect to it.

But when technique enters into every area of life, including the human, it ceases to be external to man and becomes his very substance. It is no longer face to face with man but is integrated with him, and it progressively absorbs him. In this respect, technique is radically different from the machine. This transformation, so obvious in modern society, is the result of the fact that technique has become autonomous.

When I state that technique leads to mechanization, I am not referring to the simple fact of human adaptation to the machine. Of course, such a process of adaptation exists, but it is caused by the action of the machine. What we are concerned with here, however, is a kind of mechanization in itself. If we may ascribe to the machine a superior form of "know-how," the mechanization which results from technique is the application of this higher form to *all* domains hitherto foreign to the machine; we can even say that technique is characteristic of precisely that realm in which the machine itself can play no role. It is a radical error to think of technique and machine as interchangeable; from the very beginning we must be on guard against this misconception.

*   *   *   *   *

The enormous effort required to put this technical civilization into motion supposes that all individual effort is directed toward this goal alone and that all social forces are mobilized to attain the mathematically perfect structure of the edifice. ("Mathematically" does not mean "rigidly." The perfect technique is the most adaptable and, consequently, the most plastic one. True technique will know how to maintain the illusion of liberty, choice, and individuality; but these will have been carefully calculated so that they will be integrated into the mathematical reality merely as appearances!) Henceforth, it will be wrong for a man to escape this universal effort. It will be inadmissible for any part of the individual not to be integrated in the drive toward technicization; it will be inadmissible that any man even aspire to escape this necessity of the whole society. The individual will no longer be able, materially or spiritually, to disengage himself from society. Materially, he will not be able to release himself because the technical means are so numerous that they invade his whole life and make it impossible for him to escape the collective phenomena. There is no longer an uninhabited place, or any other geographical locale, for the would-be solitary. It is no longer possible to refuse entrance into a community to a highway, a high-tension line, or a dam. It is vain to aspire to live alone when one is obliged to participate in all collective phenomena and to use all the collective's tools, without which it is impossible to earn a bare subsistence. Nothing is gratis any longer in our society; and to live on charity is less and less possible. "Social advantages" are for the workers alone, not for "useless mouths." The solitary is a useless mouth and will have no ration card—up to the day he is transported to a penal colony. (An attempt was made to institute this procedure during the French Revolution, with deportations to Cayenne.)

Spiritually, it will be impossible for the individual to disassociate himself from society. This is due not to the existence of spiritual techniques which have increasing force in our society, but rather to our situation. We are constrained to be "engaged," as the existentialists say, with technique. Positively or negatively, our spiritual attitude is constantly urged, if not determined, by this situation. Only bestiality, because it is unconscious, would seem to escape this situation, and it is itself only a product of the machine.

Every conscious being today is walking the narrow ridge of a decision with regard to technique. He who maintains that he can escape it is either a hypocrite or unconscious. The autonomy of technique forbids the man of today to choose his destiny. Doubtless, someone will ask if it has not always been the case that social conditions, environment, manorial oppression, and the family conditioned man's fate. The answer is, of course, yes. But there is no common denominator between the suppression of ration cards in an authoritarian state and the family pressure of two centuries ago. In the past, when an individual entered into conflict with society, he led a harsh and miserable life that required a vigor which either hardened or broke him. Today the concentration camp and death await him; technique cannot tolerate aberrant activities.

Because of the autonomy of technique, modern man cannot choose his means any more than his ends. In spite of variability and flexibility according to place and circumstance (which are characteristic of technique) there is still only a single employable technique in the given place and time in which an individual is situated. We have already examined the reasons for this.

At this point, we must consider the major consequences of the autonomy of technique. This will bring us to the climax of this analysis.

Technical autonomy explains the "specific weight" with which technique is endowed. It is not a kind of neutral matter, with no direction, quality, or structure. It is a power endowed with its own peculiar force. It refracts in its own specific sense the wills which make use of it and the ends proposed for it. Indeed, independently of the objectives that man pretends to assign to any given technical means, that means always conceals in itself a finality which cannot be evaded. And if there is a competition between this intrinsic finality and an extrinsic end proposed by man, it is always the intrinsic finality which carries the day. If the technique in question is not exactly adapted to a proposed human end, and if an individual pretends that he is adapting the technique to this end, it is generally quickly evident that it is the end which is being modified, not the technique. Of course, this statement must be qualified by what has already been said concerning the endless refinement of techniques and their adaptation. But this adaptation is effected with reference to the techniques concerned and to the conditions of their applicability. It does not depend on external ends. Perrot has demonstrated this in the case of judicial techniques, and Giedion in the case of mechanical techniques. Concerning the over-all problem of the relation between the ends and the means, I take the liberty of referring to my own work, *Présence au monde moderne.*

Once again we are faced with a choice of "all or nothing." If we make use of technique, we must accept the specificity and autonomy of its ends, and the totality of its rules. Our own desires and aspirations can change nothing.

The second consequence of technical autonomy is that it renders technique at once sacrilegious and sacred. (*Sacrilegious* is not used here in the theological but in the sociological sense.) Sociologists have recognized that the world in which man lives is for him not only a material but also a spiritual world; that forces act in it which are unknown and perhaps unknowable; that there are phenomena in it which man interprets as magical; that there are relations and correspondences between things and beings in which material connections are of little consequence. This whole area is mysterious. Mystery (but not in the Catholic sense) is an element of man's life. Jung has shown that it is catastrophic to make superficially clear what is hidden in man's innermost depths. Man must make allowance for a background, a great deep above which lie his reason and his clear consciousness. The mystery of man perhaps creates the mystery of the world he inhabits. Or perhaps this mystery is a reality in itself. There is no way to decide between these two alternatives. But, one way or the other, mystery is a necessity of human life.

Man cannot live without a sense of the secret. The psychoanalysts agree on this point. But the invasion of technique desacralizes the world in which man is called upon to live. For technique nothing is sacred, there is no mystery, no taboo. Autonomy makes this so. Technique does not accept the existence of rules outside itself, or of any norm. Still less will it accept any judgment upon it. As a consequence, no matter where it penetrates, what it does is permitted, lawful, justified.

To a great extent, mystery is desired by man. It is not that he cannot understand, or enter into, or grasp mystery, but that he does not desire to do so. The sacred is what man decides unconsciously to respect. The taboo becomes compelling from a social standpoint, but there is always a factor of adoration and respect which does not derive from compulsion and fear.

Technique worships nothing, respects nothing. It has a single role: to strip off externals, to bring everything to light, and by rational use to transform everything into means. More than science, which limits itself to explaining the "how," technique desacralizes because it demonstrates (by evidence and not by reason, through use and not through books) that mystery does not exist. Science brings to the light of day everything man had believed sacred. Technique takes possession of it and enslaves it. The sacred cannot resist. Science penetrates to the great depths of the sea to photograph the unknown fish of the deep. Technique captures them, hauls them up to see if they are edible— but before they arrive on deck they burst. And why should technique not act thus? It is autonomous and recognizes as barriers only the temporary limits of its action. In its eyes, this terrain, which is for the moment unknown but not mysterious, must be attacked. Far from being restrained by any scruples before the sacred, technique constantly assails it. Everything which is not yet technique becomes so. It is driven onward by itself, by its character of self-augmentation. Technique denies mystery a priori. The mysterious is merely that which has not been technicized.

*   *   *   *   *

Technique Unchecked. At present there is no counterbalance to technique. In a society in equilibrium, every new cultural tendency, every new impulse, encounters a certain number of obstacles which act as the society's first line of defense. This is not due to the interplay of conservative and revolutionary forces in general, nor in particular to the play between the means of production and the organs of consumption. It is rather due to the simple fact that every new factor must be integrated into the cultural framework, and this process requires a certain period of time because it entails modifications of the two interacting elements. It is never initially clear that the new factor will be acceptable to the cultural complex. On one hand is a kind of process of selection and, on the other, a resistance that gradually abates. A number of different forces play this restraining role. I shall discuss four of them.

The first is morality. Every civilization has rules of precise conduct, which are covered by the term *morality* in either its French or its Anglo-Saxon meaning. They may be conscious and thought out, or unconscious and spontaneous. They determine what is good and what is bad and, consequently, admit or reject a given innovation.

Very close to morality, public opinion comprises a set of much more irrational reactions which are not necessarily related to good and evil. For reasons still poorly understood, public opinion may be impelled in a certain direction under the influence of a given impulse, or it may remain refractory. Obviously, public opinion is decisive in the interaction between morality and a new factor. It can render morality obsolete or lead it to triumph.

A third restraining force is social structure, which includes both social morphology and economic or legal structure. The social structure reacts strongly whenever new factors threaten to modify it. (This, incidentally, is the only one of the four factors retained by Marxism.) Systems or ideas are no longer the sole operative factors; economic relations or sociological factors can disturb the equilibrium even of a situation the stability of which was previously thought assured.

Finally, there is the state, the special organ of defense of a society, which reacts with every means at its disposal against all disturbing forces.

We may now ask what position we are in today with respect to these factors insofar as technique is concerned. Let us put aside the problem of morality and concern ourselves with public opinion. It is completely oriented in favor of technique; only technical phenomena interest modern men. The machine has made itself master of the heart and brain both of the average man and of the mob. What excites the crowd? Performance—whether performance in sports (the result of a certain sporting technique) or economic performance (as in the Soviet Union), in reality these are the same thing. Technique is the instrument of performance. What is important is to go higher and faster; the object of the performance means little. The act is sufficient unto itself. Modern man can think only in terms of figures, and the higher the figures, the greater his satisfaction. He looks for nothing beyond the marvelous escape mechanism that technique has allowed him, to offset the very repressions caused by the life technique forces him to lead. He is reduced, in the process, to a near nullity. Even if he is not a worker on the assembly line, his share of autonomy and individual initiative becomes smaller and smaller. He is constrained and repressed in thought and action by an omnivorous reality which is external to him and imposed upon him. He is no longer permitted to display any personal power. Then, suddenly, he learns that the airplane his factory manufactures has flown at 700 miles an hour! All his repressed power soars into flight in that figure. Into that record speed he sublimates everything that was repressed in himself. He has gone one step further toward fusion with the mob, for it is the mob as a whole that is moved by a performance that incarnates its will to power. Every modern man expresses his will to power in records he has not established himself.

Public opinion is all the more important in that it is a two-pronged element. In the first place, there is modern man's collective worship of the power of fact, which is displayed in every technique and which is manifested in his total devotion to its overwhelming progress. This adoration is not passive but truly mystical. Men sacrifice themselves to it and lose themselves in the search for it. In this sense Mussolini was right in speaking of men realizing themselves in and through the state, the collective instrument of power. The martyrs of science or of the air force or of the atomic pile give us the most profound sense of this worship when we see the deference the crowd pays them. "I have faith in technique," declared Henry Wallace, the former Secretary of Commerce of the United States. His faith indeed dwells in men's hearts. Man is scandalized when he is told that technique causes evil; the scourges engendered by one technique will be made good by still other techniques. This is society's normal attitude.

In the second place, there is the deep conviction that technical problems are the only serious ones. The amused glance people give the philosopher; the lack of interest displayed in metaphysical and theological questions ("Byzantine" quarrels); the rejection of the humanities which comes from the conviction that we are living in a technical age and education must correspond to it; the search for the immediately practical, carrying the implication that history is useless and can serve no practical ends—all these are symptomatic of that "reasonable" conviction which pervades the social hierarchy and is identical for all social classes. "Only technique is not mere gab." It is positive and brings about real achievements.

In these two ways, the mystic and the rational, public opinion is completely oriented toward technique. And at present another precise technique molds public opinion with reference to any given question. This technique has never been fully exploited because public opinion is favorable enough to technique without it. But if a sudden change should occur and public opinion should turn against technique, we would see the propaganda machinery set into motion to recreate a favorable atmosphere, for the whole social edifice would be at stake.

As to the third traditional restraining force—the social structure—the question is whether the social structure of our world acts as a brake on technical evolution. By way of answer, I have shown that progress has been rapid only because social morphology has favored it. This phenomenon has not fluctuated very much; and at present we are witnessing the penetration of social structure by techniques. The life of the modern world is to an ever greater degree dominated by economics, and economics in turn is more and more dominated by technique. The whole of the material world in which we live rests on this technical base. (It is a commonplace of science-fiction writers to imagine what would happen if the use of technical instruments were to be suddenly stopped.) Likewise, our analysis has led us to recognize that as technique progresses in a given society, it tends to reproduce in that society the social structures that gave birth to it.

The individualist and atomized society of the nineteenth century was, from the sociological point of view, favorable to technical development. Today we are witnessing a kind of technical reconstitution of the scattered fragments of society; communities and associations flourish everywhere. Men seem overjoyed at this creation of new social frameworks independent of the state. The social solidification of today contrasts sharply with the fluidity of the nineteenth century. Does this phenomenon then present an effective opposition to techniques? The answer must be in the negative. If we examine these new sociological forms in detail, we find them all organized as functions of techniques. We hardly need to examine industrial associations, but the same applies to all other twentieth-century associations. They may be associations for sport or for culture, the goal of which is clearly recognizable. They may be labor unions, which have their characteristic relation to life through the economy, this last being conditioned by technique. They may be communities like the *Kibbutzim,* whose object is to exploit techniques while allowing man a normal life. In every kind of modern society there is a predominance of techniques. The social morphology of these societies indeed differs radically from that of traditional societies. Traditional societies were centered upon human needs and instincts (for example, in family, clan, seignory). Modern societies, on the other hand, are centered on technical necessity and derivatively, of course, on human adherence. Man, in modern societies, is not situated in relation to other men, but in relation to technique; for this reason the sociological structure of these societies is completely altered. There is no longer any question of autonomous collectivities or groups with specific values and orientations. Modern collectivities and groups have no existence beyond technique—they are representative of the major tendency of our time.

In the transition from the individualist to the collectivist society, there are then two stages of evolution, both of which are favorable to technique, not two different attitudes of society toward technique. Comparably, it is clear that collectivist society cannot be established, or even conceived of, except as growing out of an extreme technical development. This might not be true in a communal society (although the communities that exist today are markedly dependent on technique); but we do not seem to be moving in the direction of such societies.

Hence, we must conclude that our social structures, viewed in any light whatsoever, are unanimously favorable to technique and could hardly act as a check upon it.

Only the state remains, then, as a possible brake upon technique. But we have already seen that the state has abdicated this function, renouncing its directive role in favor of technique. Indeed, since the nineteenth century every social element which traditionally acted as a restraint on innovating forces has been overthrown as far as technique is concerned. *Inverted* might be a better term; the factors which formerly acted as hindrances have today become powerful auxiliaries to technique. (We have only to reflect on public opinion and the expansion of the economy to realize this.) Technique, therefore, encounters no possible obstacles or checks to its progress. It can advance as it will, since it encounters no limiting factors other than its own powers (which seem unlimited and inexhaustible).

A technique without limits is not in itself disquieting. If we look at our technical society without our idealist spectacles, what seems most disquieting is that the character of technique renders it *independent of man himself.* We do not mean by this that the machine tends to replace the human being; that fact is already well known. The important thing is that man, practically speaking, no longer possesses any means of bringing action to bear upon technique. He is unable to limit it or even to orient it. I am well acquainted with the claims of those who think that society has technique under firm control because man is always inventing it anew. I know too of the hopes of those who are always prescribing remedies for this sorcerer's apprentice whom they feel free to invoke without discernment. But these claims and hopes are mere words. The reality is that man no longer has any means with which to subjugate technique, which is not an intellectual, or even, as some would have it, a spiritual phenomenon. It is above all a sociological phenomenon; and in order to cure or change it, one would have to oppose to it checks and barriers of a sociological character. By such means alone man might possibly bring action to bear upon it. But everything of a sociological character has had its character changed by technique. There is, therefore, nothing of a sociological character available to restrain technique, because everything in society is its servant. Technique is essentially independent of the human being, who finds himself naked and disarmed before it. Modern man divines that there is only one reasonable way out: to submit and take what profit he can from what technique otherwise so richly bestows upon him. If he is of a mind to oppose it, he finds himself really alone.

It has been said that modern man surrounded by techniques is in the same situation as prehistoric man in the midst of nature. This is only a metaphor; it cannot be carried very far, even though it is as exact as a metaphor can be. Both environments give life but both place him in utter peril. Both represent terrifying powers, worlds in which man is a participant but which are closed against him. In the joy of conquest, he has not perceived that what he has created takes from him the possibility of being himself. He is like a rich man of many possessions who finds himself a nonentity in his own household. The state, man's last protector, has made common cause with alien powers.

The Role of the State in the Development of Modern Techniques. The state plays a role of prime importance with respect to techniques. We have noted that until recently different techniques were unrelated to one another. This unrelatedness was true of state techniques because they were localized and their domains were not contiguous; it held for private techniques because they were the result of highly uncoordinated activity which, while fruitful, was also anarchical and was dominated, moreover, by specialization.

The basic effect of state action on techniques is to coordinate the whole complex. The state possesses the power of unification, since it is the planning power par excellence in society. In this it plays its true role, that of coordinating, adjusting, and equilibrating social forces. It has played this role with respect to techniques for half a century by bringing hitherto unrelated techniques into contact with one another, for example, economic and propaganda techniques. It relates them by establishing organisms responsible for this function, as, for example, the simple organs of liaison between ministries. It integrates the whole complex of techniques into a plan. Planning itself is the result of well-applied techniques, and only the state is in a position to establish plans which are valid on the national level. We are, at present, beginning to see plans on a continental scale, not only the so-called five-year plans, but the Marshall Plan and plans for assisting underdeveloped countries.

It is only in the framework of planning that such operations are arranged and find their exact place. The state appears less as the brain which orders them organically and more as the relational apparatus which enables the separate techniques to confront one another and to coordinate their movements. We find concrete evidence of this again and again; in the coordination of rail and automobile traffic, the coordination of the production of steel and motor vehicles and aircraft, in the coordination of the medical profession and social security, the coordination of foreign and colonial commerce, and of all commerce with finance, and so forth.

The more closely related the different sectors, the more does a discovery in one involve repercussions in the others, and the more it becomes necessary to create organisms of transmission, cogs and gears, so to speak, connecting the different techniques. This is an impossible task for private enterprise, not only because the phenomenon in question is a global one but because the technicians themselves are specialists. The state alone can undertake the indispensable task of bridging these specializations. The state knows approximately the available resources in men and techniques and can undertake the still embryonic function of coordinator. Since discoveries in one technical sector are so useful in others, the role of coordinator is bound to become more and more important.

Consider, for example, the diversity of techniques necessary for the production of a motion picture. There are financial, literary, and cinematographic techniques; there are lesser techniques, such as make-up techniques and the techniques of light and sound. There are completely new techniques, such as script techniques, and so on. These cinematic techniques, though complicated, can be grasped by the brain of a single man, and hence there are still some cases of one-man management. But consider the magnitude of the task of coordinating, on a national scale, even more complicated clusters of techniques which offer active resistance to being coordinated. In such cases the role of organizer, manager, coordinator—whatever it is called—becomes more necessary in proportion as the state takes over that function. Moreover, the state alone can fulfill it. This state of affairs is already a reality; the state is already engaged in bridging the isolated technical specialties. Individual specialized disciplines—for example, those of the biologist, the engineer, the sociologist, the psychologist—are combined to yield new techniques such as psychotechniques and industrial relations. But these individual disciplines are also joined together in a more organic way, as, for example, when the so-called human techniques, physics and politics, are combined in propaganda.

In addition to coordinating the different techniques, the state furnishes material means far beyond the power of any individuals to supply. An expedition to the North Pole, which only a half century ago was within the resources of one or at most a few private persons, is no longer possible on a private basis. Formerly all that was needed was Eskimo equipment, such as a boat, sledges, dogs—and, above all, courage. Today complicated mechanical equipment is necessary: airplanes (especially equipped for the cold and for ice landings), caterpillar trucks, radio and radio telephones, prefabricated housing, and so on. Every possible means to lessen danger is available to him who dreams of exploring unknown territory. It would doubtless be possible to revive old traditions—by risking one's life. But why reject the new means? Why endanger one's life when one can do a better job without that? Obviously, bravado is unreasonable. One must employ the maximum means to assure optimal results with the least danger. But no private person has the means to set into motion the enormous apparatus that is needed. The means must be requisitioned by the state, which alone is in a position to find indefinite supplies of cash and to exploit financial techniques forbidden to individuals. The same applies in submarine exploration. When one leaves the domain of the merely amateurish and desires to give one's work status, legal or otherwise, it is necessary to solicit the support of the state to cover expenses and to resolve administrative problems.

But the state demands something in return for subventions. The state does not think it important for an individual to go to the North Pole, either for sport's sake or for honors. The state desires tangible *technical* results. It agrees to furnish assistance for purposes of scientific research and for the acquisition of certain rights it hopes to exploit; for example, mineral resources and aviation. The result must be the technical aggrandizement of the state; that is the only condition under which a contract between state and individual is possible.

That the state acts to promote scientific research is not new; in the eighteenth century the state offered recompenses to inventors, and these recompenses had much to do with the discovery of certain navigational methods (compensating chronometer, mathematical tables, and so on). The state thereafter seemed to lose interest, but for the last thirty years it has resumed the policy of recompensating technologists and inventors.

*   *   *   *   *

A Look at the Year 2000. In 1960 the weekly *l'Express* of Paris published a series of extracts from texts by American and Russian scientists concerning society in the year 2000. As long as such visions were purely a literary concern of science-fiction writers and sensational journalists, it was possible to smile at them. Now we have like works from Nobel Prize winners, members of the Academy of Sciences of Moscow, and other scientific notables whose qualifications are beyond dispute. The visions of these gentlemen put science fiction in the shade. By the year 2000, voyages to the moon will be commonplace; so will inhabited artificial satellites. All food will be completely synthetic. The world's population will have increased fourfold but will have been stabilized. Sea water and ordinary rocks will yield all the necessary metals. Disease, as well as famine, will have been eliminated; and there will be universal hygienic inspection and control. The problems of energy production will have been completely resolved. Serious scientists, it must be repeated, are the source of these predictions, which hitherto were found only in philosophic utopias.

The most remarkable predictions concern the transformation of educational methods and the problem of human reproduction. Knowledge will be accumulated in "electronic banks" and transmitted directly to the human nervous system by means of coded electronic messages. There will no longer be any need of reading or learning mountains of useless information; everything will be received and registered according to the needs of the moment. There will be no need of attention or effort. What is needed will pass directly from the machine to the brain without going through consciousness.

In the domain of genetics, natural reproduction will be forbidden. A stable population will be necessary, and it will consist of the highest human types. Artificial insemination will be employed. This, according to Muller, will "permit the introduction into a carrier uterus of an ovum fertilized *in vitro,* ovum and sperm . . . having been taken from persons representing the masculine ideal and the feminine ideal, respectively. The reproductive cells in question will preferably be those of persons dead long enough that a true perspective of their lives and works, free of all personal prejudice, can be seen. Such cells will be taken from cell banks and will represent the most precious genetic heritage of humanity. . . . The method will have to be applied universally. If the people of a single country were to apply it intelligently and intensively . . . they would quickly attain a practically invincible level of superiority. . . ." Here is a future Huxley never dreamed of.

Perhaps, instead of marveling or being shocked, we ought to reflect a little. A question no one ever asks when confronted with the scientific wonders of the future concerns the interim period. Consider, for example, the problems of automation, which will become acute in a very short time. How, socially, politically, morally, and humanly, shall we contrive to get there? How are the prodigious economic problems, for example, of unemployment, to be solved? And, in Muller's more distant utopia, how shall we force humanity to refrain from begetting children naturally? How shall we force them to submit to constant and rigorous hygienic controls? How shall man be persuaded to accept a radical transformation of his traditional modes of nutrition? How and where shall we relocate a billion and a half persons who today make their livings from agriculture and who, in the promised ultrarapid conversion of the next forty years, will become completely useless as cultivators of the soil? How shall we distribute such numbers of people equably over the surface of the earth, particularly if the promised fourfold increase in population materializes? How will we handle the control and occupation of outer space in order to provide a stable modus vivendi? How shall national boundaries be made to disappear? (One of the last two would be a necessity.) There are many other "hows," but they are conveniently left unformulated. When we reflect on the serious although relatively minor problems that were provoked by the industrial exploitation of coal and electricity, when we reflect that after a hundred and fifty years these problems are still not satisfactorily resolved, we are entitled to ask whether there are any solutions to the infinitely more complex "hows" of the next forty years. In fact, there is one and only one means to their solution, a world-wide totalitarian dictatorship which will allow technique its full scope and at the same time resolve the concomitant difficulties. It is not difficult to understand why the scientists and worshippers of technology prefer not to dwell on this solution, but rather to leap nimbly across the dull and uninteresting intermediary period and land squarely in the golden age. We might indeed ask ourselves if we will succeed in getting through the transition period at all, or if the blood and the suffering required are not perhaps too high a price to pay for this golden age.

If we take a hard, unromantic look at the golden age itself, we are struck with the incredible naiveté of these scientists. They say, for example, that they will be able to shape and reshape at will human emotions, desires, and thoughts and arrive scientifically at certain efficient, pre-established collective decisions. They claim they will be in a position to develop certain collective desires, to constitute certain homogeneous social units out of aggregates of individuals, to forbid men to raise their children, and even to persuade them to renounce having any. At the same time, they speak of assuring the triumph of freedom and of the necessity of avoiding dictatorship at any price. They seem incapable of grasping the contradiction involved, or of understanding that what they are proposing, even after the intermediary period, is in fact the harshest of dictatorships. In comparison, Hitler's was a trifling affair. That it is to be a dictatorship of test tubes rather than of hobnailed boots will not make it any less a dictatorship.

When our savants characterize their golden age in any but scientific terms, they emit a quantity of down-at-the-heel platitudes that would gladden the heart of the pettiest politician. Let's take a few samples. "To render human nature nobler, more beautiful, and more harmonious." What on earth can this mean? What criteria, what content, do they propose? Not many, I fear, would be able to reply. "To assure the triumph of peace, liberty, and reason." Fine words with no substance behind them. "To eliminate cultural lag." What culture? And would the culture they have in mind be able to subsist in this harsh social organization? "To conquer outer space." For what purpose? The conquest of space seems to be an end in itself, which dispenses with any need for reflection.

We are forced to conclude that our scientists are incapable of any but the emptiest platitudes when they stray from their specialties. It makes one think back on the collection of mediocrities accumulated by Einstein when he spoke of God, the state, peace, and the meaning of life. It is clear that Einstein, extraordinary mathematical genius that he was, was no Pascal; he knew nothing of political or human reality, or, in fact, anything at all outside his mathematical reach. The banality of Einstein's remarks in matters outside his specialty is as astonishing as his genius within it. It seems as though the specialized application of all one's faculties in a particular area inhibits the consideration of things in general. Even J. Robert Oppenheimer, who seems receptive to a general culture, is not outside this judgment. His political and social declarations, for example, scarcely go beyond the level of those of the man in the street. And the opinions of the scientists quoted by *l'Express* are not even on the level of Einstein or Oppenheimer. Their pomposities, in fact, do not rise to the level of the average. They are vague generalities inherited from the nineteenth century, and the fact that they represent the furthest limits of thought of our scientific worthies must be symptomatic of arrested development or of a mental block. Particularly disquieting is the gap between the enormous power they wield and their critical ability, which must be estimated as null. To wield power well entails a certain faculty of criticism, discrimination, judgment, and option. It is impossible to have confidence in men who apparently lack these faculties. Yet it is apparently our fate to be facing a "golden age" in the power of sorcerers who are totally blind to the meaning of the human adventure. When they speak of preserving the seed of outstanding men, whom, pray, do they mean to be the judges. It is clear, alas, that they propose to sit in judgment themselves. It is hardly likely that they will deem a Rimbaud or a Nietszche worthy of posterity. When they announce that they will conserve the genetic mutations which appear to them most favorable, and that they propose to modify the very germ cells in order to produce such and such traits; and when we consider the mediocrity of the scientists themselves outside the confines of their specialties, we can only shudder at the thought of what they will esteem most "favorable."

None of our wise men ever pose the question of the end of all their marvels. The "wherefore" is resolutely passed by. The response which would occur to our contemporaries is: for the sake of happiness. Unfortunately, there is no longer any question of that. One of our best-known specialists in diseases of the nervous system writes: "We will be able to modify man's emotions, desires and thoughts, as we have already done in a rudimentary way with tranquilizers." It will be possible, says our specialist to produce a conviction or an impression of happiness without any real basis for it. Our man of the golden age, therefore, will be capable of "happiness" amid the worst privations. Why, then, promise us extraordinary comforts, hygiene, knowledge, and nourishment if, by simply manipulating our nervous systems, we can be happy without them? The last meager motive we could possibly ascribe to the technical adventure thus vanishes into thin air through the very existence of technique itself.

But what good is it to pose questions of motives? of Why? All that must be the work of some miserable intellectual who balks at technical progress. The attitude of the scientists, at any rate, is clear. Technique exists because it is technique. The golden age will be because it will be. Any other answer is superfluous.

Toward the Creation
of Technological Man

VICTOR C. FERKISS

Technological man is more myth than reality. This is the lesson that even as cursory a survey of modern society as ours clearly points to. Bourgeois man is still in the saddle. Or, to put it more accurately, things are in the saddle, since bourgeois man is increasingly unable to cope with his problems. At the same time, an existential revolution is under way that may destroy the identity of the human race, make society unmanageable and render the planet literally uninhabitable. Bourgeois man is incapable of coping with this revolution. The race's only salvation is in the creation of technological man.

But what does this mean? What can it mean? Will technological man be a new ruling class, performing a new role based on new sources of power? For the most part, no. Science confers power, but ruling classes perform political roles, not scientific roles as such. Technological man will not be a new ruling class in the usual sense of the term. Will technological man then be a new personality type—hyperrational, objective, manipulative? Not noticeably so. The link between certain types of society and certain kinds of dominant personality types is easily oversimplified, and in any event we have had rationalistic, instrumental, hard-nosed human beings dominating Western society since the beginnings of the modern era; the economic man of the classical economists was such a type. Nor will technological man be a new biological type, created either by manipulation of man's genetic structure or by carrying man-machine symbiosis to the point of altering human integrity. Such a development would mean that technological man had failed to come into existence, and bourgeois civilization had fallen prey to the monsters of its own creation.

Technological man will be man in control of his own development within the context of a meaningful philosophy of the role of technology in human evolution. He will be a new cultural type that will leaven all the leadership echelons of society. Technological man will be man at home with science and technology, for he will dominate them rather than be dominated by them; indeed he will be so at home that the question of who is in charge will never even arise. To state that man should rule technology rather than vice versa is almost a truism, of course. It serves no intellectual function save implicitly to deny the contention of those who argue that man cannot control technology and of those who argue that he should not. But otherwise it is an empty exhortation to virtue, fit more for the political stump than as a basis for serious discussion of human problems. Control technology yes, but in whose interest, in accordance with what norms?

Any useful definition of technological man must therefore include within it some definition of what his outlook on life will be. For to control technology, to control the direction of human evolution, we must have some idea of where we are going and how far, else we will be mere passengers rather than drivers of the chariot of evolution. We are thus forced to try to do two difficult things, simultaneously to predict the future and to develop a new philosophy of society based on the future's needs. But though technological man will create himself and cannot be programmed in advance, the needs that call him forth go far toward defining both his task and the world view he must bring to it.

How can one possibly lay down a future philosophy for general acceptance? Even if such dominant world views as traditional Christianity, orthodox Marxism and classical liberalism have clearly failed to provide a rationale for dealing with the existential revolution, may they not simply be replaced not by a new philosophy but by a variety of conflicting value systems determined by individual histories, whims and tastes? Have we not defined lack of a common value system in the declining period of bourgeois civilization as part of our problem? Will not any new philosophy be intellectually arbitrary, capable of being spread, if at all, only through coercion or an irrational persuasion, which would be self-defeating since a unifying world philosophy for technological man must, above all, be based on shared perceptions and values?

Technological man, by definition, will be possessed of the world view of science and technology, which will themselves provide a standard of value for future civilization. At this point many readers may be tempted to throw up their hands. Those enamored of certain versions of Greek and medieval philosophy and of traditional religious systems will snort that values are either transcendent in nature or are derived from an analysis of the natural world which is essentially deductive and nonempirical in nature. Others will simply object that part of the whole mission of philosophy from Kant to Wittgenstein has been to show that values cannot be derived from natural philosophy: the belief that the "ought" cannot be derived from the "is" is now an elementary commonplace in every primer in ethics or the social sciences.[1]

But the matter is not so simply resolved. Many leading modern philosophers, such as John Dewey, have argued from what man is to what he should do and be, and many who formally deny that the data of existence provide ethical imperatives sneak their values in through the back door by appeals to common sense as a standard when all is said and done. Various subterfuges are used to get around the problem. Psychologists decide what is proper conduct through application of the concepts of "deviance" and "mental health," which are clearly based on the "is" of common experience. Skinner has been faulted by critics such as Joseph Wood Krutch for assuming in his utopia, *Walden Two*, that the problem of social values could be easily solved, since survival and health are universally acknowledged as values. But what is the alternative to Skinner's position (in essence, that of Aristotle) save to locate values in a transcendent source communicating through mysterious forms of revelation that all men may not accept, in the irrational desires of the individual or in some innate knowledge implanted in the individual brain and available through individual introspection?

Fortunately, we do not have to answer all the fundamental questions about ethics that this discussion raises. The problem is not finding a sanction for values but simply defining them, which though a difficult problem is at least one capable of rational discussion. That is, we can assume we ought to do what is good for us if we can decide the latter. If our doctor tells us smoking will cause cancer this does not prove we should stop smoking. We have the option of preferring an earlier and possibly more painful death. If someone tells us the arms race is suicidal, he does not thereby prove that collectively we should eschew suicide.

In this sense, the "ought" can never be derived from empirically grounded predictions about the consequences of actions. Any preference for pleasure over pain, knowledge over ignorance, health over disease, and survival over destruction is incapable of justification unless we first agree that there is some inherent reason for respecting the order of nature that impels all creatures

---

1. For example, Eugene J. Meehan, *The Theory and Method of Political Analysis* (Homewood: Dorsey, 1965), p. 47. For some recent critiques of the effects of this attitude see Kenneth Boulding, "Philosophy, Behavioral Science, and the Nature of Man," *World Politics,* 12 (1960), 272–279, and Christian Bay, "Politics and Pseudopolitics," *American Political Science Review,* 59 (1965), 39–51. See also T. H. Weldon, *The Vocabulary of Politics* (Hammondsworth: Penguin Books, 1953).

toward survival, activity and growth. Stated thus, the proposition that science cannot be the source of values is irrefutable.[2]

But what practical consequences does this have for most of mankind? Whether we choose to restrain the suicidal or masochistic is a problem in civil liberties, but few would deny that we should restrain the murderer or torturer. Problems arise from the fact that even if we admit that survival or happiness is desirable these may require different conditions for different people, since what makes me prosperous may make you poor. Not the nature of "goods," but their scarcity, allocation and occasional incompatibility present difficulties. So, too, at a general social level the problem arises of priorities among goods: granted that health and survival are both desirable, what happens if society must risk the health of all, or even just of some, in order to ensure its survival?

But these problems, however complex, may be more amenable to analysis and solution than we assume. Jeremy Bentham's hedonistic calculus may have to be rejected as simplistic, but Bentham did not have the resources of modern science (including the social sciences) to provide data as to what the effects of alternative policies might be, and he lacked computers to manipulate this data. Whether science can help us to reconcile conflicting values is a question that must be decided on the basis of experience and experiment, and the idea that it can help us cannot be dismissed out of hand through essentially irrelevant assumptions about the differences between the descriptive and normative orders. Dewey is certainly right in saying that a culture that permits science to destroy its values without permitting science to create new ones is a culture that destroys itself.

The increasing knowledge of the order of nature provided by contemporary scientific discovery, the increasing power over that nature given to man by his technology and the fact that increases in population have raised the amount and intensity of human interaction to a new plane that bespeaks an evolutionary breakthrough, all combine to present technological man with the outlines of a new philosophy of human existence, a philosophy that can provide general guidelines that he can and must take advantage of if he is to retain control of his civilization.

---

2. A more subtle problem arises in defining health, happiness or even survival, which we cannot go into here save to note that it is a problem for all men, not for technical philosophers alone.

BASIC ELEMENTS OF A NEW PHILOSOPHY

A basic element in this new philosophy is what might be called the *new naturalism,* which asserts that man is in fact part of nature rather than something apart from it, but that nature is not the rigid, mindless deterministic machine that earlier eras conceived it to be. The totality of the universe is a dynamic process, a constant movement and becoming. Some scientists have gone so far as to contend that some form of mind exists in even nonliving matter, but such an assumption is not necessary to the belief that the universe is, in a sense, a moving equilibrium of which man is a part.

However, man is not merely a part of nature, but the highest part, an element in a semidetermined system of nature with himself, for all practical purposes, private and undetermined, his mind the most complex thing in the universe. "If this property of complexity could somehow be transformed into visible brightness," writes a leading molecular biologist, "the biological world would become a walking field of light compared to the physical world . . . an earthworm would be a beacon . . . human beings would stand out like blazing suns of complexity, flashing bursts of meaning to each other through the dull night of the physical world between."[3] Man gains in dignity as he is seen as part of physical nature, while his most complex mechanical creations pale into insignificance.

Closely related to the new naturalism is the *new holism,* that is, the realization of how interconnected everything is. From the evolutionary philosophies of the nineteenth century has come the idea of becoming, which destroys the traditional distinctions between being and nonbeing, thus paving the way for the rejection of the Newtonian view of the world as matter in motion, a complex of forces exerted on objects, and of analogies based on leverage and weight and anything else associated with the primitive machinery of the early industrial era. The image of the mechanical universe must give way to the idea of process.

The basic concepts of process and system imply a recognition that no part is meaningful outside the whole, that no part can be defined or understood save in relation to the whole. There are few closed or isolated systems in nature and none in society, save for the desert islands of legend. Gestalt psychologists have always regarded the mind-body relationship as that of an inte-

---

3. John Rader Platt, *The Step to Man* (New York: Wiley, 1966), p. 151.

grated whole, but it is really mind-body-society-nature that is the totality.[4]
All men are linked with each other and with their social and physical environments in a fantastically complex moving equilibrium, so that in thinking about social questions we must, in the words of M.I.T. president Julius Stratton, "advance from the anatomy of components to the physiology of the organic whole—which indeed is now the society itself."[5]

But this whole, the universal as well as the social, is a new kind of whole, determined not from outside but from within. For another element in the new world outlook is the *new immanentism.* Eastern philosophies have always stressed the immanent, leading to a pantheism not unlinked to the panpsychism of some modern biologists. But for the Western world, especially the Judaic-Christian tradition, God, the principle of order and change, was primarily outside. Though in theory He was everywhere, He was envisioned as "up there" or "out there." A civilization whose world view was dominated by the physicist and the mechanic could think of the Deity as a cosmic watchmaker, of the universe as in some sense having been created and set down. But the modern world view increasingly rejects this viewpoint as the biological sciences come to the fore. However physicists may look upon the development of the physical universe as a whole, the world of living things is somehow different. Nature here works another way, life is antientropic. "The factory that makes the parts of a flower is inside, and is not a factory but a development. . . . The creative principle of the universe," John Rader Platt

4. See Theodore Roszak, "The Counter Culture," *The Nation,* 206 (1968), Part 4. For some approaches to the total problem of man in nature see Marston Bates, *The Forest and the Sea* (New York: Random House, 1960); Nigel Calder, *Eden Was No Garden* (New York: Holt, Rinehart and Winston, 1967); Lynton C. Caldwell, *Planned Control of the Biophysical Environment* (Bloomington: Comparative Administration Group, American Society for Public Administration, 1964); William R. Ewald, Jr., ed., *Environment for Man* (Bloomington: Indiana University Press, 1967); Aldous Huxley, *The Politics of Ecology* (Santa Barbara: Center for the Study of Democratic Institutions, 1964); S. Dillon Ripley and Helmut K. Buechner, "Ecosystem Science as a Point of Synthesis," *Daedalus,* 96 (1967), 1192–1199; Paul B. Sears, "Utopia and the Living Landscape," *Daedalus,* 94 (1965), 474–486; Paul Shepard, *Man in the Landscape* (New York: Knopf, 1967); and Philip L. Wagner, *The Human Use of the Earth* (Glencoe: The Free Press, 1960). On man himself see Jacob Bronowski, *The Identity of Man* (New York: Messner, 1956); Alexis Carrell, *Man, the Unknown* (New York: Harper, 1939); and P. B. Medewar, *The Future of Man* (London: Methuen, 1959).

5. M.I.T. commencement address, 1964, in John G. Burke, ed., *The New Technology and Human Values* (Belmont: Wadsworth, 1967), p. 94.

writes, "is not an external but an internal one."[6] Nothing is isolated. Life exists within systems. And systems create themselves.

These three principles—the new naturalism, the new holism and the new immanentism—provide the necessary basis for the outlook that must come to dominate human society if man is to survive the existential revolution already under way. Technological man must so internalize these ideas and make them so much a part of his instinctive world view that they inform his personal, political and cultural life. They in turn lead to certain further principles. If man and nature are one, then society and the environment are one. Therefore, meaningful social policies must be ecological in character, that is, they must be based on a recognition that the interrelationship of men to each other and to the total environment means that any decision, any change, affects everything in the total system.

Thus, in a sense, nature has rights as well as man, since its activity and that of man are inextricably intermingled. The new holism, with its emphasis on process, means that not only must every decision be seen in ecological perspective, but it must be recognized that there are no individual decisions any more than there are actually geometric points in the empirical world. Decision-making is part of a seamless process. Man cannot become free by being outside or apart from the process. He is affected by what others do—that is, he is the subject of power—and he exercises power because his actions affect others. For in this holistic process every action of the whole passes through and is modified by the state of every cell or particle. Freedom consists in responding autonomously and authentically to the currents of life and action passing through one; the loss of freedom is not the loss of an impossible complete self-determination—which would necessitate standing outside the universe—but is a synonym for being bypassed and not being allowed to play one's part in shaping the whole.

For the whole shapes itself. This is the meaning of the new immanentism. Order is not imposed from outside in accordance with a predetermined plan of man or nature, it is a structure of interrelationships created by the constant activity of its own elements, which somehow always form a pattern as long as the whole survives. Men's actions, men's ideas and the technological forces that they set in motion are all part of this whole, and their activity leads to further development. Freedom is not outside but within nature, Dewey has said. So, too, freedom does not exist apart from society. Planning is the self-consciousness of the human element in developing patterns of interrelation—a

6. Platt, *The Step to Man*, p. 183.

self-consciousness that alone makes control and therefore freedom possible. Control over the elements in the total system—human and nonhuman—is effected by a constant process of adjustment, pressures and signals. As in nature, cells die or are destroyed; sometimes as in cancer they multiply out of control until checked; often signals are blocked or short-circuited rather than amplified. But there is no need for postulating an overseer who directs from outside; every part of the whole has power and influence, every living particle is a source of direction and life. This diffusion of power runs the risk of becoming a dissipation of responsibility as well[7] unless each participant constantly holds himself responsible not only for the immediate results of his particular acts but also for their ultimate impact upon the shaping of the whole.

Technological man, imbued through education and constant experience with the conviction that this is what the universe is like, will discover techniques and construct guidelines for dealing with the problems created for humanity by the existential revolution. From this basic world view he can derive ethical norms that, channeled through reformed institutional structures, can become the basis for policies that will make survival possible.

What norms can guide technological man in this task? They are not all derived directly from his basic outlook, but are nonetheless compatible with it and rest upon the same sets of data about the universe. The first of these norms is that man is part of nature and therefore cannot be its conquerer, that indeed he owes it some respect. As Albert Schweitzer said, a morality that deals only with the relation of man to man and not of man to nature is only half a morality. Human self-knowledge is impossible in a world in which nature has been destroyed or so altered that it cannot speak to men. "Our goal," in the words of biologist Roger Revelle, chairman of the U.S. Committee for the International Biological Program, "should not be to conquer the natural world but to live in harmony with it."[8]

Secondly, ecological perspective dictates that man's economic and social life demands coordination if he is to survive, and his exploitation of natural resources must be determined by what is optimum for the total system. At the same time, the ability of the system to respond demands maximum freedom. Therefore, in purely cultural or individual matters where the linkage of

7. Cf. Warner R. Schilling, "The H-Bomb Decision: How To Decide Without Actually Choosing," *Political Science Quarterly,* 76 (1961), 24-46.

8. Quoted in "How Man Changes His World," New York *Times,* September 24, 1967.

behavior to the system is least direct, maximum freedom should be allowed. What this amounts to is combining economic and physical "planning" with cultural pluralism to the maximum extent possible.

On an even more basic level, man must maintain the distinction between himself and the machines of his creation. Since man is superior in complexity to the physical universe, some presumption exists that this complexity has an evolutionary meaning that should be preserved. Linkages of man to machines and technologies that would make him irrevocably dependent on lower orders of reality would be antievolutionary. The great strength of man throughout his evolutionary history has been the flexibility that has resulted from his variety and his complexity. He has triumphed not merely because of his intelligence but also because of his allied versatility. Human flesh is weak, but man avoided the "error" of the crustaceans in protecting themselves in a way that made future development impossible. The human individual is weak, but man has avoided the dead end of the social insects, who have created a marvelous structure in which the nothingness of the individual and the inability to change are opposite sides of the same coin. Man's destiny lies in continuing to exploit this "openness," rather than entering into a symbiotic relationship with the inorganic machine that, while it might bring immediate increments of power, would inhibit his development by chaining him to a system of lesser potentialities. The possibilities of man as a "soft machine" are far greater and as yet little explored.[9] Man must stand above his physical technologies if he is to avoid their becoming his shell and the principles of their organization his anthill.

But not only must man stand above the machine, he must be in control of his own evolution. Those who think of man's destiny as a mindless leap forward forget that man is not only the sole creature capable of being conscious of evolution but the only one capable of controlling it, and this control must include the power to slow down and stop evolution if he so desires. Actually, some elements of physical technology may be already peaking, at least as far as their effect on society and man is concerned. If the population explosion is brought under control we may enter what might be called a "steady-state" form, wherein the unplumbed future would lie in biological science, and in man's mind. The final step to man would have been taken.

In such a civilization man will have the task of finally finding himself, of fulfilling his role in the universe by becoming fully man. In the Old Testament,

9. The term comes from a different context, William Burroughs' novel, *The Soft Machine,* but is relevant here.

Yahweh reveals essentially nothing of Himself to the Hebrews save that "I am Who I am." Man if he is in any sense akin to divinity has as his role becoming himself, doing his own thing. This means that the conquest of outer space should take second place to furthering man's forward movement to the conquest of "inner space."

How man can best explore himself remains a question. Some see mind-expanding drugs as the way (a minor Hippie organ is called *Inner Space*). Arthur Koestler sees the primitive ape-brain as still existing as a "layer" of man's developed brain, and holds that only through drugs can the savage within us be sufficiently controlled so that we can avoid destroying ourselves, just as the Hippies hold that only thus can the bourgeoisie be "turned on." A score of mystic and cultural traditions argue otherwise. But one thing is certain: in a world in which man controls his environment so as to provide for his physical needs and to conquer hunger and disease, the new frontier will be within.

Genetic engineering may have a role to play in perfecting the human body, but the untapped frontiers of knowledge and action lie in the mysterious and versatile computer that is the human brain. Much of what it can do in relation to the body and the external environment by the use of tools we already know through existent technology, but of what it can do directly we may have only an inkling. Newton was the last of the magicians, it has been said; in the world of technological man everyone would be a magician even by Newton's standards. But the basic point is that man's role is not to create a new creature, a new mutation of himself physically, but to exploit this still-unleashed marvel of flesh and bone and synapses that we hardly know. . . .

THE NEED FOR CONTROLS

Continuity of the species means some continuity of social and cultural institutions and processes. Too rapid change leads to disorientation. If the future is absolutely unpredictable, any meaningful activity becomes impossible, and perhaps we should seek to slow down the rate of social and cultural change, as men such as Arnold Toynbee have advocated. On the other hand, certain things are changing inevitably anyway: short of sterilizing half of those now living we cannot prevent a substantially larger population in the near future. Since civilization is an interrelated whole, if we wish to retain other elements of human culture we must make some adjustments to the changes we cannot prevent. This need to adjust in order to preserve is something a wise conservatism has always known, and is what has distinguished it from sheer inertia and obscurantism.

Certain controls may be necessary if we are to preserve any freedom at all. Of paramount importance is the control of technological and economic innovation. Control does not mean that new techniques will not be introduced, but rather that they will be channeled in such a way as to serve the general rather than simply a private good. A society where talent produces new goods for sale and new means of destruction while cities decay and children baffle the educational system is no more innovative than one in which technological resources are devoted to the development of the depressed segments of the population and to enhancing the environment. Means must be found to channel technological advance into areas where it has the greatest potential for social usefulness.

This may not be as difficult as might be imagined. Government already directly or indirectly controls most research and technical innovation even in capitalist nations; the problem is to put technological men in power rather than men of a previous breed who do not have any sense of how these scientific resources might be used. Paradoxically, the control of technological change might be the supreme opportunity that technology affords for human progress. If technology compels men "to be more men" and "reveals the nature of nature more clearly," as one philosopher of science puts it, it does so by calling forth our highest powers, forcing us to use reason to decide what nature is and what it is for. But this is a challenge that the race cannot shirk. "To despair of reason is to despair of man."[10] Controlling technology in all its ramifications may be the supreme test of our species' adulthood.

Several conflicting priorities exist in the use of space and the oceans. Some access to nature in an untouched state is a scientific as well as a spiritual need. Both space and the oceans—especially the latter—must be used in such a way that they are not turned into mere dump heaps. Economic exploitation of both must serve the common good of the race. The oceans must be used in a way that benefits not alone the richer nations, best equipped technologically to exploit them, but the poor as well. Treaties for international control must aim not merely at orderly exploitation but at the principle that the oceans are a common world resource, to be used to equalize living standards rather than to perpetuate or accentuate conditions of economic inequality.

The economic problem of space exploration does not stem primarily from

10. Andreas G. Van Melsen, *Science and Technology* (Pittsburgh: Duquesne University Press, 1961), Vol. 2, pp. 306–308.

the need to distribute its potential economic benefits, which have been grossly exaggerated at least as far as any immediate future is concerned, but rather lies in the alternative use of resources now devoted to space exploration. A less feverish and costly endeavor would make possible division of resources—including scarce scientific talent—elsewhere. A planet that spends billions to put one or two men on another planet while children starve, not only in India but within the borders of the major powers, has carried the antientropic drive too far and perhaps should consolidate before moving onward.

Population control, conservation not of natural resources but of nature itself, and biogenetic policy are closely interrelated issues. The problems presented by the population explosion are so dramatic as to have already excited widespread popular concern throughout the world. It is quite possible that total world population could increase several times over and high living standards in terms of food and material artifacts be maintained within the developed areas of the world. Severe famines and widespread poverty can exist in the poorer nations without necessarily disturbing living standards elsewhere. The notion that the "Third World," the "nonwhite" races or the "underdeveloped" will rise up in wrath against the rich is largely a propaganda cliché. In a world of nuclear weapons, population size loses most of its meaning as a factor in national power and the rich would undoubtedly defend themselves against despoliation to the death.

But even if most or part of the world can keep on multiplying without famine becoming universal, sooner or later growth must stop. Even if the world becomes a mere anthill, using the most advanced technology imaginable to recycle every bit of air for breathing, creating food out of rocks and energy out of sea water, the sheer mass of flesh will ultimately make further growth impossible. We will have reached "standing room only," and interplanetary or interstellar migration offers little hope of a solution. Growth will have to stop and a steady state be achieved wherein death and birth rates are equal, as they have probably been throughout most of human history. But long before this point is reached, man will have destroyed every vestige of his natural environment, completely lost touch with his animal heritage and changed from an individual into a social insect in all but appearance.

Since putting an end to growth is inevitable, the only question is when. Given the laws of compound interest, it will not be too many generations before stoppage becomes mandatory. The problem therefore is one of whether we can halt population growth prior to the total destruction of man's relationship with nature and before his historic culture becomes meaningless. There is a "wisdom in wildness," writes Charles Lindbergh (himself a distinguished contributor to science and technology), and a technological man would agree.[11] If wilderness is necessary to the human spirit, we face a problem of crisis proportions. But even if the problem is reduced to one of simply carrying off wastes that pollute water and air and endanger life, health or economic efficiency, it is still a serious one, all psychological and aesthetic questions aside.

Yet it is easy to understand why resistance to controls exists. The more fundamental habits of behavior are the more resistant they are to change. Procreation, especially, involves intimate individual concerns. Any social policies in this area will mean, for modern Western man, a sharp break with tradition. Advocates of population control have suggested a variety of ways in which this might be accomplished. Some would use punitive sanctions such as a negative income tax or, in the case of those too poor to pay taxes, sterilization after they produce children beyond their quota. Others look to positive means, such as a bonus for not having children, on the theory that it is less onerous to choose between two goods—a child or financial gain—than between a child and financial loss—a good and an evil. The solution advanced by the economist Kenneth Boulding . . . is that each human being at birth should be given the right to have one child, and that these rights could be used, bought or sold.[12] This proposal would maximize choice, but Boulding ignores the problem of those who produce outside the system and the punitive sanctions necessary to underpin it.

It has also been suggested that technological means could be used, such as putting contraceptive substances into the water supply, thereby making the having of a child require special permission by placing control of the antidote under public auspices. These suggestions are not all as outlandish as they seem. Most human societies, including our own, arranged marriages until recently. In the West the combination of the tradition that no one married until he could support a wife—which meant owning land in some areas—with severe penalties for illegitimacy, were an effective social mechanism of population control. In Victorian England mass infanticide was practiced by consciously tolerating and even encouraging high infant mortality rates, especially in foundling homes. In recent years large numbers of couples in Western society who have adopted children have accepted the intrusion of social inspection

11. Charles A. Lindbergh, "The Wisdom of Wildness." *Life,* 63 (December 22, 1967), 8–10.

12. Kenneth Boulding, "Where Are We Going If Anywhere? A Look at Post-Civilization," *Human Organization,* 21 (1962), 166–167.

and decision with regard to their fitness to be parents with minimal after-effects.

Yet there is no question that a general and rigorous and open policy of population control would be regarded by most people as revolutionary, especially since many of them do not yet find the consequences of unlimited growth impossible to bear and have little regard for or knowledge about the future. Present evidence indicates that most prosperous Westerners now want families of about three or four children which would constantly refuel the population explosion. Therefore family planning, to be an effective check on growth, will require some degree of social control.

If population growth is not checked, then every other aspect of life will necessarily have to undergo revolutionary change simply to insure human survival over the next several generations. Societies that refuse to change their breeding habits will have to change how they eat, dwell, work and use their leisure, and freedom of procreation will be paid for by a loss of other freedoms. Here is an area where even an enlightened conservative might feel that one alteration in existing patterns was a cheap price to pay to prevent the total restructuring of human life.

If population growth in the developed nations posed an obvious threat to economic growth and material living standards, it might be relatively easy to elicit popular support for measures to curb the birth rate. But what if the result of uncontrolled growth is instead the overcrowding of cities, highways, and recreational facilities, and the destruction of humanity's age-old contract with the natural environment that gave our species birth? Then the political problem becomes more difficult. An aesthetic attachment to privacy, solitude, and the wilderness is a minority position in bourgeois civilization. In any democratic system, these values will have to be maintained by complicated political maneuvering—through convincing the majority that minority tastes have economic benefits for the whole, by trading off concessions in some areas of policy for preservation of what cannot be replaced and similar stratagems. But these are stopgap measures. Unless technological man assumes a steady state as an optimum for population growth and manifests a reverence for wilderness and history as necessary elements in total culture, postindustrial society will become an anthill society. Fortunately, the scientific community has been generally ardent in support of pollution controls and conservation, and an increase in scientific comprehension by the public may cause this attitude to spread.

Feelings about genetic controls, however, are more divided. The scientific community, even more perhaps than other professional groups, is suspicious of lay controls; this despite the many scientific activities that are supported by public funds. The medical profession, especially, enjoys an elite status that in capitalist nations has led them to try to maintain control not only of the content but of the financing and distribution of medical care. Most scientists have rejected suggestions—inspired by . . . publicity over the synthesis of DNA and the rash of heart transplants—that in the United States a commission be set up on the ethical and social aspects of biological research. This is in partial contrast to the widespread support that scientists have given to American participation in the International Biological Commission, which is concerned with maintaining the quality of the world environment.

This apparent inconsistency in scientists' attitudes stems from the fact that scientific discovery and its consequences are separated in the thinking of most scientists. Research must remain under the control of scientists rather than laymen. But for obvious economic and legal reasons the consequences of research may be subject to social controls; some scientists have even taken the position that what the military do with their discoveries is none of the scientists' concern. But the distinction between discovery and its application may be an unreal one in practice, even if we deny the conclusion of men such as Ellul that all knowledge will eventually be used.

If human beings are involved in biological research—having their organs transplanted, being administered new drugs—the very act of experimentation has social consequences;[13] the first test-tube baby will be a human being with a claim on citizenship. Biological research can enable mankind to determine its own genetic future. Obviously, a society that does not control these developments has lost control of itself. Just as war is too important, in Clemenceau's oft-quoted phrase, to be left to the generals so the future form of the race is too important to be left to the professionals in the life sciences.

Technological man has yet to emerge. Bourgeois man still dominates the world—just as much in nominally socialist as in capitalist nations. Industrial society is not so much being transformed into a postindustrial, technological society as it is breaking down—economically, politically and culturally. Rigidities in social institutions and attitudes create a society comparable to a geological formation with fault lines where slippage is inhibited and great earth-

13. On experimentation on humans see M. H. Pappworth, *Human Guinea Pigs* (Boston: Beacon Press, 1968); Bernard Barber, "Experimenting with Humans," *The Public Interest,* 6 (Winter, 1967), 91–102; Walter Goodman, "Doctors Must Experiment with Humans," New York *Times Magazine* (July 2, 1967), 12–13+; P. B. Medewar, "Science and the Sanctity of Life," *Encounter,* 27 (June, 1966), 96–104; and Edward Shils, "The Sanctity of Life," *Encounter,* 27 (January, 1967), 39–49.

quakes therefore necessarily build up. The existential revolution is building up pressures that can lead to cataclysm, or it can be converted into what Platt calls a "cultural shock-front," after the passage of which man will enter upon a new and stable plateau of existence where he can finally become Man.[14] If technological man comes into existence not only among scientists and technologists but in all walks of life in all advanced nations—and there are signs that he is emerging, like the seed beneath the snow—the existential revolution can become an instrument for liberation rather than destruction.

A world society could be based upon a realization that man is part of nature, yet something special in it—a mere reed, in Pascal's words—but a thinking reed, and that his problem is not to overcome nature but to live in a more subtle and conscious harmony with it, not to transcend his animal nature but to recognize that spirit and flesh are one and that the total human being must be activated and developed to new intensities and planes of activity. Such a world could become the launching pad for the next and final step in man's evolutionary process, where he becomes not a new creature but finally fully himself. For his destiny is not to become enslaved by his own creations or to lose himself in some cosmic nirvana, but to exploit fully all the intricacies of his individual self. It is to complexity, to individuation and to a new and more inclusive unity that the universe moves—to the transfiguration rather than the loss of identity of the individual human and the species. If technological man can create a world society wherein man and his environment are in balance, man can abandon the age-old fight against nature for survival and accept nature as a companion, just as an adolescent can abandon the struggle against his parents to assert his adulthood and in time can become their friend. Then man can turn to his real purposes, which are play and cultivation of the deeps of the inner space of the individual and society.

Technological man will be his own master. Prior to his emergence, the outlines of technological civilization must remain dim save for the knowledge that it will have to rest upon a unified view of the universe, on ecological balance and on fidelity to the essential identity of the human species. Technological man will create his own future, and it may contain some surprises even for him. The Dominican mystic Meister Eckhart wrote at the beginning of the long journey that brought Western man from the cocoon of medievalism through industrial civilization to our own day and its choice between chaos and transfiguration, but his words have timeless meaning: "There is no stopping place in this life—no, nor was there ever one for any man, no matter how

14. Platt, *The Step to Man*, p. 195.

far along his way he'd gone. This above all, then, be ready at all times for the gifts of God, and always for new ones."[15]

The new gifts are all about us today, and the newer ones in store are unpredictable in their nature and their timing. Upon man's ability to recognize them for what they are and to convert them into what his development requires rests not only his future but, for all we know, that of all creation.

15. Quoted in Huston Smith, "The New Age," *University of Chicago Magazine,* 59 (May, 1967), 18. Eckhart lived circa 1260–1328.

3

An Attempt
at Synthesis

The unquestioned importance as well as the intellectual complexity of the questions involved in unravelling the technology-society interface have attracted some of the most penetrating and creative minds of our age. In the readings of the first two parts, we have seen how these minds have been led in remarkably different directions according to their expectations, the aspects of reality they chanced to examine and reflect upon, and the values they placed on different qualities of human existence. Given the apparently enormous gulf between, for example, the President's Task Force on Science Policy and Jacques Ellul, one is tempted to ask whether it is possible to turn the tools of research upon technology itself and empirically examine technology's impact on society. In one sense, because of technology's broad permeation of the fabric of society, a great deal of contemporary social-science research is, in effect, examining the impact of technology. On the other hand, direct attempts to study technology's impact in a broad and systematic fashion have been relatively few and far between. Part 3 opens with a report summarizing the progress of one such attempt, quite probably the most important on the contemporary scene. Complementing the report are two essays, the first of which directly challenges the central assumptions of the report, and the second of which deals with some related questions in a theological analogy.

In 1964 the IBM Corporation announced a grant of $5 million to Harvard University for the establishment of a program to study the impact of technology on society. The grant was to run for a period of ten years, during which time the program would "undertake an inquiry in depth into the effects of technological change on the economy, on public policies, and on the character of the society, as well as into the reciprocal effects of social progress on the nature, dimension, and directions of scientific and technological developments." Dr. Emmanuel G. Mesthene was chosen to head the program. Mesthene elected to conduct the program by financing various relevant research projects both inside and outside the Harvard community and synthesizing from their results an overview of the problem.[1]

Each year, the program has issued an annual report outlining the progress it has made. Of these annual reports, the fourth, covering the 1967–68 period, is probably the best known. The report consists of two parts. First, a brief individual description of progress is given for each of the program's research projects. Sixteen such efforts are described under the headings, "Technology and Social Change," "Technology and Values," and "Technology and Political Organization." In the second part of the report, there is an essay by Mesthene in which he attempts to set forth for the first time a general statement of what the program has learned about the implications of technological change for society. We have reprinted this essay in its entirety.

Mesthene sees two mechanisms through which technology appears to induce social change. Simply put, technology creates new opportunities and also generates new problems for men and societies. "It has both positive and negative effects, and it usually has the two *at the same time and in virtue of each other.*" This somewhat paradoxical phenomenon results from the following sequence of events: "(1) technological advance creates a new opportunity to achieve some desired goal; (2) this requires (except in trivial cases) alterations in social organization if advantage is to be taken of the new opportunity; (3) which means that the functions of existing social structures will be interfered with; (4) with the result that the other goals which were served by the older structures are now only inadequately achieved." One kind of problem arises when society is unable to exploit a technological opportunity because of inadequacies in social structure. Other problems arise when negative side-effects of new technologies are not controlled "because it has not been anybody's explicit business to foresee and anticipate them."

The relationship of technology to social change cannot be fully understood without exploring technology's effect upon social and individual values. By enlarging the realm of goal choice, or by altering the relative costs associated with the implementation of different values, technology can induce value change. Mesthene's essay deals briefly with the value implications of eco-

1. The relationship among IBM, Harvard, and the program has never been a comfortable one, and in June 1971 Harvard announced that the program would be terminated at the end of the 1971–72 academic year.

nomic change, the impact of technology on religion, and the impact of technology on individual man. In all these areas, technology is seen to have two faces, one positive and one negative.

Ultimately, through changes in social structure and values, technology creates problems that must be considered political. Of central importance, according to Mesthene, is the fact that "technological change has the effect of enhancing the importance of public decision-making in society. . . ." Not only must more decisions be made in a public manner, but because of technological change, any decision once made is likely to require reevaluation sooner than was previously the case. Given that framework, Mesthene explores problems raised for the economic market system by technological change and the shift in demand toward public goods and services. He also examines the implications of new information-handling devices and scientific decision-making techniques for the political process, in light of the program's research. Finally, he deals with the "need to develop new institutional forms and new mechanisms to replace established ones that can no longer deal effectively with the new kinds of problems with which we are increasingly faced." Institutional innovation, says Mesthene, is one area where the program's work may produce direct inputs into the solution of current problems.

Several months after the report containing Mesthene's essay was released, a sharply critical essay-review by John McDermott appeared in the *New York Review of Books.* McDermott's review, entitled "Technology: The Opiate of the Intellectuals," is not a point-by-point analysis or rebuttal of the Mesthene work. Rather, it is an attempt to critique the entire point of view that McDermott sees as epitomized by Mesthene—"a not new but . . . newly aggressive right wing ideology in this country." In dissecting Mesthene's belief structure, McDermott focuses upon the notion of *"laissez innover,"* a modern equivalent of the old *laissez faire* principle in economics.

Laissez innover holds that technology is a "self-correcting system" and that we mortals should not attempt to restrict its free play. Mesthene is said to find this principle acceptable because he defines technology in an abstract sense as "organized knowledge for practical purposes." McDermott rejects *laissez innover* because he claims to see certain very specific trends and characteristics in contemporary technology which overshadow the importance of technology as an abstraction. Concentrating upon the application of technology to the war in Vietnam—"the very frontier of American technology"—McDermott performs an "empirical" examination of the nature of technology, from which he concludes that "technology, in its concrete, empirical meaning, refers fundamentally to systems of rationalized control over large groups of men, events and machines by small groups of technically skilled men operating through organizational hierarchy."

This definition is the crux of McDermott's analysis, and basing his essay upon it, he proceeds to discuss the social effect of modern technology in America. A major factor in the spread of the democratic ethos during the seventeenth, eighteenth, and nineteenth centuries was the closing of the gap in political culture between the masses and the ruling population. This resulted from the spread of literacy as well as from improved transportation and communication, all of which produced a greater similarity in social experience between the upper and lower classes. One of the major effects of today's technology, however, has been to reverse this trend and begin increasing the gap. The vast majority of the American public today is not at all literate in the political and social character of modern technology. McDermott sees the growth of "social irrationality" as an outcome of the social organization of today's technology, since it "systematically denie[s] to the general population experiences which are analogous to those of its higher management."

In McDermott's analysis, the technological society is governed by "altruistic bureaucrats," a select class which possesses the skills needed to run society. The equality of opportunity that exists in this kind of skill-oriented system does not necessarily imply an egalitarian society, since society's rewards are still distributed inequitably. In fact, what equality of opportunity does assure, through the elevation of "trained talent" into " 'key decision making' slots," is the preservation of the present social system and its inequities. The ideology of *laissez innover* is attractive to those in power since they are in a position to reap technology's benefits while avoiding its costs. Thus, in attacking Mesthene's treatment of the dual nature of technology, McDermott observes that "those technological effects which are sought either as positive opportunities and those which are dismissed as negative externalities are decisively influenced by the fact that this distinction between positive and negative within advanced technological organizations, tends to be made among the planners and managers themselves."

McDermott concludes by citing a set of hypotheses which he feels should be better guides to empirical investigation of technology than Mesthene's abstractions: (1) Technology should be viewed as an institutional system; (2) The most important dimension of advanced technological institutions is social—these institutions are instruments of centralized and intensive social control; (3) Profound social antagonisms exist in technological society; and

(4) "Technology is creating the basis for new and sharp class conflict in our society," and *laissez innover* is the ideology of the right wing of this conflict.

The third and final article of this section is in one sense a response to McDermott. In a footnote within his essay, McDermott expresses his pessimism about the possibility of creating a humane technology out of our present system: "Any discussion of the reorganization of technology to serve human needs seems, at this point, so Utopian that it robs one of the conviction necessary to shape a believable vision." Rejecting the seeming hopelessness of this position, Paul Goodman asks in the title of his article, "Can Technology Be Humane?" In developing his response to this question, Goodman admits that there is no certainty that technology *will* become humane. Yet, in the classic style of a prophet—partly predictive and partly prescriptive—he asserts that our society is "on the eve of a new protestant Reformation, and no institution or status will go unaffected." At the same time, he offers a number of suggestions for channeling the energies of this Reformation into directions which he sees as critical to its success.

Goodman's initial frame of reference is somewhat more limited than that of Mesthene or McDermott; he approaches technology primarily through the research and development enterprise, its structure and impact on society. Many of our problems stem from the fact that the vast amount of money and manpower currently invested in such activities is not at all aimed at increasing the sum of human happiness. Rather, "it is dominated by producing hardware, figuring logistics, and devising salable novelties." As a consequence, science and scientific technology which for three hundred years had "an unblemished and justified reputation as a wonderful adventure," are increasingly seen as the source of new human woes. In order to deal with the historical and religious crisis of which this questioning is a part, Goodman believes it will be necessary "to alter the entire relationship of science, technology, and social needs both in men's minds and in fact."

The types of changes Goodman envisions fall into three general categories. First, he speaks of the need for "prudence"—caution, foresight, and modesty—in the application of technology. The pace of innovation must be slowed and its trend must be turned away from increasing complexity and toward simplification. Second, the ecological viewpoint, with its emphases on balances and interdependence of a system's parts, must come to dominate technological affairs. Third, the institutions of technological society, particularly the research and development enterprise, ought to be widely decentralized. All of these notions are seen as constituting a return to the "pure faith," the basic tradition of science and technology. Goodman develops his Reformation analogy in some detail, but concludes, finally, that he does not know if it will actually occur. Everywhere, he says, there are contradictory signs and dilemmas.

The Role of Technology in Society

EMMANUEL G. MESTHENE

SOCIAL CHANGE

Three Unhelpful Views about Technology. While a good deal of research
is aimed at discerning the particular effects of technological change on industry, government, or education, systematic inquiry devoted to seeing these
effects together and to assessing their implications for contemporary society
as a whole is relatively recent and does not enjoy the strong methodology and
richness of theory and data that mark more established fields of scholarship.
It therefore often has to contend with facile or one-dimensional views about
what technology means for society. Three such views, which are prevalent at
the present time, may be mildly caricatured somewhat as follows.

The first holds that technology is an unalloyed blessing for man and society. Technology is seen as the motor of all progress, as holding the solution to
most of our social problems, as helping to liberate the individual from the
clutches of a complex and highly organized society, and as the source of permanent prosperity; in short, as the promise of utopia in our time. This view
has its modern origins in the social philosophies of such 19th-century thinkers
as Saint-Simon, Karl Marx, and Auguste Comte. It tends to be held by many
scientists and engineers, by many military leaders and aerospace industrialists,
by people who believe that man is fully in command of his tools and his destiny, and by many of the devotees of modern techniques of "scientific management."

A second view holds that technology is an unmitigated curse. Technology
is said to rob people of their jobs, their privacy, their participation in democratic government, and even, in the end, their dignity as human beings. It is
seen as autonomous and uncontrollable, as fostering materialistic values and
as destructive of religion, as bringing about a technocratic society and bureaucratic state in which the individual is increasingly submerged, and as threatening, ultimately, to poison nature and blow up the world. This view is akin to
historical "back-to-nature" attitudes toward the world and is propounded
mainly by artists, literary commentators, popular social critics, and existen-
tialist philosophers. It is becoming increasingly attractive to many of our
youth, and it tends to be held, understandably enough, by segments of the

population that have suffered dislocation as a result of technological change.

The third view is of a different sort. It argues that technology as such is not worthy of special notice, because it has been well recognized as a factor in social change at least since the Industrial Revolution, because it is unlikely that the social effects of computers will be nearly so traumatic as the introduction of the factory system in 18th-century England, because research has shown that technology has done little to accelerate the rate of economic productivity since the 1880s, because there has been no significant change in recent decades in the time period between invention and widespread adoption of new technology, and because improved communications and higher levels of education make people much more adaptable than heretofore to new ideas and to new social reforms required by technology.

While this view is supported by a good deal of empirical evidence, however, it tends to ignore a number of social, cultural, psychological, and political effects of technological change that are less easy to identify with precision. It thus reflects the difficulty of coming to grips with a new or broadened subject matter by means of concepts and intellectual categories designed to deal with older and different subject matters. This view tends to be held by historians, for whom continuity is an indispensable methodological assumption, and by many economists, who find that their instruments measure some things quite well while those of the other social sciences do not yet measure much of anything.

Stripped of caricature, each of these views contains a measure of truth and reflects a real aspect of the relationship of technology and society. Yet they are oversimplifications that do not contribute much to understanding. One can find empirical evidence to support each of them without gaining much knowledge about the actual mechanism by which technology leads to social change or significant insight into its implications for the future. All three remain too uncritical or too partial to guide inquiry. Research and analysis lead to more differentiated conclusions and reveal more subtle relationships.

Some Countervailing Considerations. Two of the projects of the Harvard University Program on Technology and Society serve, respectively, to temper some exaggerated claims made for technology and to replace gloom with balanced judgment. Professor Anthony G. Oettinger's study of information technology in education[1] has shown that, in the schools at least, technology is not

---

1. Unless otherwise noted, studies such as Oettinger's which are referred to in this article are described in the Fourth Annual Report (1967–68) of the Harvard University Program on Technology and Society.

likely to bring salvation with it quite so soon as the U.S. Office of Education, leaders of the education industry, and enthusiastic computermen and systems analysts might wish. Neither educational technology nor the school establish-ment seems ready to consummate the revolution in learning that will bring in-dividualized instruction to every child, systematic planning and uniform stan-dards across 25,000 separate school districts, an answer to bad teachers and unmovable bureaucracies, and implementation of a national policy to educate every American to his full potential for a useful and satisfying life. Human fallibility and political reality are still here to keep utopia at bay, and neither promises soon to yield to a quick technological fix. Major institutional change that can encourage experimentation, flexibility, variety, and competition among educational institutions seems called for before the new technology can contribute significantly to education. Application of the technology it-self, moreover, poses problems of scale-up, reliability, and economics that have scarcely been faced as yet.

By contrast, Professor Manfred Stanley's study of the value presupposi-tions that underlie the pessimistic arguments about technology suggests that predictions of inevitable doom are premature and that a number of different social outcomes are potential in the process of technological change. In other words, the range of possibility and of human choice implicit in technology is much greater than most critics assume. The problem—here, as well as in the application of educational technology—is how to organize society to free the possibility of choice.

Finally, whether modern technology and its effects constitute a subject matter deserving of special attention is largely a matter of how technology is defined. The research studies of the Harvard Program on Technology and Society reflect an operating assumption that the meaning of technology in-cludes more than machines. As most serious investigators have found, under-standing is not advanced by concentrating single-mindedly on such narrowly drawn yet imprecise questions as "What are the social implications of com-puters, or lasers, or space technology?" Society and the influences of tech-nology upon it are much too complex for such artificially limited approaches to be meaningful. The opposite error, made by some, is to define technology too broadly by identifying it with rationality in the broadest sense. The term is then operationally meaningless and unable to support fruitful inquiry.

We have found it more useful to define technology as tools in a general sense, including machines, but also including linguistic and intellectual tools and contemporary analytic and mathematical techniques. That is, we define technology as the organization of knowledge for practical purposes. It is in this broader meaning that we can best see the extent and variety of the effects of technology on our institutions and values. Its pervasive influence on our very culture would be unintelligible if technology were understood as no more than hardware.

It is in the pervasive influence of technology that our contemporary situation seems qualitatively different from that of past societies, for three reasons. (1) Our tools are more powerful than any before. The rifle wiped out the buffalo, but nuclear weapons can wipe out man. Dust storms lay whole regions waste, but too much radioactivity in the atmosphere could make the planet uninhabitable. The domestication of animals and the invention of the wheel literally lifted the burden from man's back, but computers could free him from all need to labor. (2) This quality of finality of modern technology has brought our society, more than any before, to explicit awareness of technology as an important determinant of our lives and institutions. (3) As a result, our society is coming to a deliberate decision to understand and control technology to good social purpose and is therefore devoting significant effort to the search for ways to measure the full range of its effects rather than only those bearing principally on the economy. It is this prominence of technology in many dimensions of modern life that seems novel in our time and deserving of explicit attention.

How Technological Change Impinges on Society. It is clearly possible to sketch a more adequate hypothesis about the interaction of technology and society than the partial views outlined above. Technological change would appear to induce or "motor" social change in two principal ways. New technology creates new opportunities for men and societies, and it also generates new problems for them. It has both positive and negative effects, and it usually has the two *at the same time and in virtue of each other.* Thus, industrial technology strengthens the economy, as our measures of growth and productivity show. As Dr. Anne P. Carter's study on structural changes in the American economy has helped to demonstrate, however, it also induces changes in the relative importance of individual supplying sectors in the economy as new techniques of production alter the amounts and kinds of materials, parts and components, energy, and service inputs used by each industry to produce its output. It thus tends to bring about dislocations of businesses and people as a result of changes in industrial patterns and in the structure of occupations.

The close relationship between technological and social change itself helps to explain why any given technological development is likely to have both positive and negative effects. The usual sequence is that (1) technological advance creates a new opportunity to achieve some desired goal; (2) this requires (except in trivial cases) alterations in social organization if advantage is to be taken of the new opportunity, (3) which means that the functions of existing social structures will be interfered with, (4) with the result that other goals which were served by the older structures are now only inadequately achieved.

As the Meyer-Kain study has shown, for example, improved transportation technology and increased ownership of private automobiles have increased the mobility of businesses and individuals. This has led to altered patterns of industrial and residential location, so that older unified cities are being increasingly transformed into larger metropolitan complexes. The new opportunities for mobility are largely denied to the poor and black populations of the core cities, however, partly for economic reasons, and partly as a result of restrictions on choice of residence by Negroes, thus leading to persistent Negro unemployment despite a generally high level of economic activity. Cities are thus increasingly unable to perform their traditional functions of providing employment opportunities for all segments of their populations and an integrated social environment that can temper ethnic and racial differences. The new urban complexes are neither fully viable economic units nor effective political organizations able to upgrade and integrate their core populations into new economic and social structures. The resulting instability is further aggravated by modern mass communications technology, which heightens the expectations of the poor and the fears of the well-to-do and adds frustration and bitterness to the urban crisis.

An almost classic example of the sequence in which technology impinges on society is provided by Professor Mark Field's study of changes in the system and practice of medical care. Recent advances in biomedical science and technology have created two new opportunities: (1) they have made possible treatment and cures that were never possible before, and (2) they provide a necessary condition for the delivery of adequate medical care to the population at large as a matter of right rather than privilege. In realization of the first possibility, the medical profession has become increasingly differentiated and specialized and is tending to concentrate its best efforts in a few major, urban centers of medical excellence. This alters the older social organization of medicine that was built around the general practitioner. The second possibility has led to big increases in demand for medical services, partly because a healthy population has important economic advantages in a highly industrialized society. This increased demand accelerates the process of differentiation and multiplies the levels of paramedical personnel between the physician at the top and the patient at the bottom of the hospital pyramid.

Both of these changes in the medical system are responsive to the new opportunities for technical excellence that have been created by biomedical technology. Both also involve a number of well-known costs in terms of some older desiderata of medical care. The increasing scarcity of the general practitioner in many sections of the country means that people in need often have neither easy access to professional care nor the advantage of a "medical general manager" who can direct them to the right care at the right place at the right time, which can result both in poor treatment and a waste of medical resources. Also, too exclusive a concentration on technical excellence can lead to neglect of the patient's psychological well-being, and even the possibility of technical error increases as the "medical assembly line" gets longer.

The pattern illustrated by the preceding examples tends to be the general one. Our most spectacular technological successes in America in the last quarter of a century have been in national defense and in space exploration. They have brought with them, however, enthusiastic advocates and vested interests who claim that the development of sophisticated technology is an intrinsic good that should be pursued for its own sake. They thus contribute to the self-reinforcing quality of technological advance and raise fears of an autonomous technology uncontrollable by man. Mass communications technology has also made rapid strides since World War II, with great benefit to education, journalism, commerce, and sheer convenience. It has also been accompanied by an aggravation of social unrest, however, and may help to explain the singular rebelliousness of a youth that can find out what the world is like from television before home and school have had the time to instill some ethical sense of what it could or should be like.

In all such cases, technology creates a new opportunity and a new problem at the same time. That is why isolating the opportunity or the problem and construing it as the whole answer is ultimately obstructive of rather than helpful to understanding.

How Society Reacts to Technological Change. The heightened prominence of technology in our society makes the interrelated tasks of profiting from its opportunities and containing its dangers a major intellectual and political challenge of our time.

Failure of society to respond to the opportunities created by new technology means that much actual or potential technology lies fallow, that is, is not used at all or is not used to its full capacity. This can mean that potentially solvable problems are left unsolved and potentially achievable goals unachieved, because we waste our technological resources or use them inefficiently. A society has at least as much stake in the efficient utilization of technology as in that of its natural or human resources.

There are often good reasons, of course, for not developing or utilizing a particular technology. The mere fact that it can be developed is not sufficient reason for doing so. The costs of development may be too high in the light of the expected benefits, as in the case of the project to develop a nuclear-powered aircraft. Or, a new technological device may be so dangerous in itself or so inimical to other purposes that it is never developed, as in the cases of Herman Kahn's "Doomsday Machine" and the recent proposal to "nightlight" Vietnam by reflected sunlight.

But there are also cases where technology lies fallow because existing social structures are inadequate to exploit the opportunities it offers. This is revealed clearly in the examination of institutional failure in the ghetto by Professor Richard S. Rosenbloom and his colleagues. At point after point, their analyses confirm what has been long suspected, that is, that existing institutions and traditional approaches are by and large incapable of coming to grips with the new problems of our cities—many of them caused by technological change, as the Meyer-Kain study has reminded us—and unable to realize the possibilities for resolving them that are also inherent in technology. Vested economic and political interests serve to obstruct adequate provision of low-cost housing. Community institutions wither for want of interest and participation by residents. City agencies are unable to marshal the skills and take the systematic approach needed to deal with new and intensified problems of education, crime control, and public welfare. Business corporations, finally, which are organized around the expectation of private profit, are insufficiently motivated to bring new technology and management know-how to bear on urban projects where the benefits will be largely social. All these factors combine to dilute what may otherwise be a genuine desire to apply our best knowledge and adequate resources to the resolution of urban tensions and the eradication of poverty in the nation.

There is also institutional failure of another sort. Government in general and agencies of public information in particular are not yet equipped for the massive task of public education that is needed if our society is to make full use of its technological potential, although the federal government has been making significant strides in this direction in recent years. Thus, much potentially valuable technology goes unused because the public at large is insufficiently informed about the possibilities and their costs to provide support for appropriate political action. As noted, we have done very well with our tech-

nology in the face of what were or were believed to be crisis situations, as
with our military technology in World War II and with our space efforts when
beating the Russians to the moon was deemed a national goal of first priority.
We have also done very well when the potential benefits of technology were
close to home or easy to see, as in improved health care and better and more
varied consumer goods and services. We have done much less well in developing and applying technology where the need or opportunity has seemed neither so clearly critical nor so clearly personal as to motivate political action,
as in the instance of urban policy already cited. Technological possibility continues to lie fallow in those areas where institutional and political innovation
is a precondition of realizing it.

Containing the Negative Effects of Technology. The kinds and magnitude
of the negative effects of technology are no more independent of the institutional structures and cultural attitudes of society than is realization of the
new opportunities that technology offers. In our society, there are individuals
or individual firms always on the lookout for new technological opportunities, and large corporations hire scientists and engineers to invent such opportunities. In deciding whether to develop a new technology, individual entrepreneurs engage in calculations of expected benefits and expected costs to
themselves, and proceed if the former are likely to exceed the latter. Their
calculations do not take adequate account of the probable benefits and costs
of the new developments to others than themselves or to society generally.
These latter are what economists call external benefits and costs.

The external benefits potential in new technology will thus not be realized by the individual developer and will rather accrue to society as a result of
deliberate social action, as has been argued above. Similarly with the external
costs. In minimizing only expected costs to himself, the individual decision
maker helps to contain only some of the potentially negative effects of the
new technology. The external costs and therefore the negative effects on society at large are not of principal concern to him and, in our society, are not
expected to be.

Most of the consequences of technology that are causing concern at the
present time—pollution of the environment, potential damage to the ecology
of the planet, occupational and social dislocations, threats to the privacy and
political significance of the individual, social and psychological malaise—are
negative externalities of this kind. They are with us in large measure because
it has not been anybody's explicit business to foresee and anticipate them.
They have fallen between the stools of innumerable individual decisions to
develop individual technologies for individual purposes without explicit atten-

tion to what all these decisions add up to for society as a whole and for people as human beings. This freedom of individual decision making is a value that we have cherished and that is built into the institutional fabric of our society. The negative effects of technology that we deplore are a measure of what this traditional freedom is beginning to cost us. They are traceable, less to some mystical autonomy presumed to lie in technology, and much more to the autonomy that our economic and political institutions grant to individual decision making.

When the social costs of individual decision making in the economic realm achieved crisis proportions in the great depression of the 1930s, the federal government introduced economic policies and measures many of which had the effect of abridging the freedom of individual decision. Now that some of the negative impacts of technology are threatening to become critical, the government is considering measures of control that will have the analogous effect of constraining the freedom of individual decision makers to develop and apply new technologies irrespective of social consequence. Congress is actively seeking to establish technology-assessment boards of one sort or another which it hopes may be able to foresee potentially damaging effects of technology on nature and man. In the executive branch, attention is being directed (1) to development of a system of social indicators to help gauge the social effects of technology, (2) to establishment of some body of social advisers to the president to help develop policies in anticipation of such effects, and generally (3) to strengthening the role of the social sciences in policy making.

Measures to control and mitigate the negative effects of technology, however, often appear to threaten freedoms that our traditions still take for granted as inalienable rights of men and good societies, however much they may have been tempered in practice by the social pressures of modern times: the freedom of the market, the freedom of private enterprise, the freedom of the scientist to follow truth wherever it may lead, and the freedom of the individual to pursue his fortune and decide his fate. There is thus set up a tension between the need to control technology and our wish to preserve our values, which leads some people to conclude that technology is inherently inimical to human values. The political effect of this tension takes the form of inability to adjust our decision-making structures to the realities of technology so as to take maximum advantage of the opportunities it offers and so that we can act to contain its potential ill effects before they become so pervasive and urgent as to seem uncontrollable.

To understand why such tensions are so prominent a social consequence of technological change, it becomes necessary to look explicitly at the effects of technology on social and individual values.

VALUES

Technology's Challenge to Values. Despite the practical importance of the techniques, institutions, and processes of knowledge in contemporary society, political decision making and the resolution of social problems are clearly not dependent on knowledge alone. Numerous commentators have noted that ours is a "knowledge" society, devoted to rational decision making and an "end of ideology," but none would deny the role that values play in shaping the course of society and the decisions of individuals. On the contrary, questions of values become more pointed and insistent in a society that organizes itself to control technology and that engages in deliberate social planning. Planning demands explicit recognition of value hierarchies and often brings into the open value conflicts which remain hidden in the more impersonal working of the market.

In economic planning, for example, we have to make choices between the values of leisure and increased productivity, without a common measure to help us choose. In planning education, we come face to face with the traditional American value dilemma of equality versus achievement: do we opt for equality and nondiscrimination and give all students the same basic education, or do we foster achievement by tailoring education to the capacity for learning, which is itself often conditioned by socioeconomic background?

The new science-based decision-making techniques also call for clarity: in the specification of goals, thus serving to make value preferences explicit. The effectiveness of systems analysis, for example, depends on having explicitly stated objectives and criteria of evaluation to begin with, and the criteria and objectives of specific actions invariably relate to the society's system of values. That, incidentally, is why the application of systems analysis meets with less relative success in educational or urban planning than in military planning: the value conflicts are fewer in the latter and the objectives and criteria easier to specify and agree on. This increased awareness of conflicts among our values contributes to a general questioning attitude toward traditional values that appears to be endemic to a high-technology, knowledge-based society: "A society in which the store of knowledge concerning the consequences of action is large and is rapidly increasing is a society in which received norms and their 'justifying' values will be increasingly subjected to questioning and reformulation."[2]

This is another way of pointing to the tension alluded to earlier, between the need for social action based on knowledge on the one hand, and the pull of our traditional values on the other. The increased questioning and reformulation of values that Williams speaks of, coupled with a growing awareness that our values are in fact changing under the impact of technological change, leads many people to believe that technology is by nature destructive of values. But this belief presupposes a conception of values as eternal and unchanging and therefore tends to confuse the valuable with the stable. The fact that values come into question as our knowledge increases and that some traditional values cease to function adequately when technology leads to changes in social conditions does not mean that values per se are being destroyed by knowledge and technology.

What does happen is that values change through a process of accommodation between the system of existing values and the technological and social changes that impinge on it. The projects of the Harvard Program in the area of technology and values are devoted to discovering the specific ways in which this process of accommodation occurs and to tracing its consequences for value changes in contemporary American society. The balance of this section is devoted to a more extended discussion of the first results of these projects.

Technology as a Cause of Value Change. Technology has a direct impact on values by virtue of its capacity for creating new opportunities. By making possible what was not possible before, it offers individuals and society new options to choose from. For example, space technology makes it possible for the first time to go to the moon or to communicate by satellite and thereby adds those two new options to the spectrum of choices available to society. By adding new options in this way, technology can lead to changes in values in the same way that the appearance of new dishes on the heretofore standard menu of one's favorite restaurant can lead to changes in one's tastes and choices of food. Specifically, technology can lead to value change either (1) by bringing some previously unattainable goal within the realm of choice or (2) by making some values easier to implement than heretofore, that is, by changing the costs associated with realizing them.

2. Robin Williams, "Individual and Group Values," *Annals of the American Academy of Political and Social Science* 37 (May 1967): 30.

Dr. Irene Taviss is exploring the ways in which technological change affects intrinsic sources of tension and potential change in value systems. When technology facilitates implementation of some social ideal and society fails to act upon this new possibility, the conflict between principle and practice is sharpened, thus leading to new tensions. For example, the economic affluence that technology has helped to bring to American society makes possible fuller implementation than heretofore of our traditional values of social and economic equality. Until it is acted upon, that possibility gives rise to the tensions we associate with the rising expectations of the underprivileged and provokes both the activist response of the radical left and the hippie's rejection of society as "hypocritical."

Another example related to the effect of technological change on values is implicit in our concept of democracy. The ideal we associate with the old New England town meeting is that each citizen should have a direct voice in political decisions. Since this has not been possible, we have elected representatives to serve our interests and vote our opinions. Sophisticated computer technology, however, now makes possible rapid and efficient collection and analysis of voter opinion and could eventually provide for "instant voting" by the whole electorate on any issue presented to it via television a few hours before. It thus raises the possibility of instituting a system of direct democracy and gives rise to tensions between those who would be violently opposed to such a prospect and those who are already advocating some system of participatory democracy.

This new technological possibility challenges us to clarify what we mean by democracy. Do we construe it as the will of an undifferentiated majority, as the resultant of transient coalitions of different interest groups representing different value commitments, as the considered judgment of the people's elected representatives, or as by and large the kind of government we actually have in the United States, minus the flaws in it that we would like to correct? By bringing us face to face with such questions, technology has the effect of calling society's bluff and thereby preparing the ground for changes in its values.

In the case where technological change alters the relative costs of implementing different values, it impinges on inherent contradictions in our value system. To pursue the same example, modern technology can enhance the values we associate with democracy. But it can also enhance another American value—that of "secular rationality," as sociologists call it—by facilitating the use of scientific and technical expertise in the process of political decision making. This can in turn further reduce citizen participation in the democratic process. Technology thus has the effect of facing us with contradictions in our own value system and of calling for deliberate attention to their resolution.

The Value Implications of Economic Change. In addition to the relatively direct effects of technology on values, as illustrated above, value change often comes about through the intermediation of some more general social change produced by technology, as in the tension imposed on our individualistic values by the external benefits and costs of technological development that was alluded to in the earlier discussion of the negative effects of technology. Professor Nathan Rosenberg is exploring the closely allied relationship between such values and the need for society to provide what economists call public goods and services.

As a number of economists have shown, such public goods differ from private consumer goods and services in that they are provided on an all-or-none basis and consumed in a joint way, so that more for one consumer does not mean less for another. The clearing of a swamp or a flood-control project, once completed, benefits everyone in the vicinity. A meteorological forecast, once made, can be transmitted by word of mouth to additional users at no additional cost. Knowledge itself may thus be thought of as the public good par excellence, since the research expenses needed to produce it are incurred only once, unlike consumer goods of which every additional unit adds to the cost of production.

As noted earlier, private profit expectation is an inadequate incentive for the production of such public goods, because their benefit is indiscriminate and not fully appropriate to the firm or individual that might incur the cost of producing them. Individuals are therefore motivated to dissimulate by understating their true preferences for such goods in the hope of shifting their cost to others. This creates a "free-loader" problem, which skews the mechanism of the market. The market therefore provides no effective indication of the optimal amount of such public commodities from the point of view of society as a whole. If society got only as much public health care, flood control, or knowledge as individual profit calculations would generate, it would no doubt get less of all of them than it does now or than it expresses a desire for by collective political action.

This gap between collective preference and individual motivation imposes strains on a value system, such as ours, which is primarily individualistic rather than collective or "societal" in its orientation. That system arose out of a simpler, more rustic, and less affluent time, when both benefits and costs were of a much more private sort than now. It is no longer fully adequate for our society, which industrial technology has made productive enough to allocate significant resources to the purchase of public goods and services, and in which modern transportation and communications as well as the absolute magnitude of technological effects lead to extensive ramifications of individual actions on other people and on the environment.

The response to this changed experience on the part of the public at large generally takes the form of increased government intervention in social and economic affairs to contain or guide these wider ramifications, as noted previously. The result is that the influence of values associated with the free reign of individual enterprise and action tends to be counteracted, thus facilitating a change in values. To be sure, the tradition that ties freedom and liberty to a laissez-faire system of decision making remains very strong, and the changes in social structures and cultural attitudes that can touch it at its foundations are still only on the horizon.

Religion and Values. Much of the unease that our society's emphasis on technology seems to generate among various sectors of society can perhaps be explained in terms of the impact that technology has on religion. The formulations and institutions of religion are not immune to the influences of technological change, for they too tend toward an accommodation to changes in the social milieu in which they function. But one way in which religion functions is as an ultimate belief system that provides legitimation, that is, a "meaning" orientation, to moral and social values. This ultimate meaning orientation, according to Professor Harvey Cox, is even more basic to human existence than the value orientation. When the magnitude or rapidity of social change threatens the credibility of that belief system, therefore, and when the changes are moreover seen as largely the results of technological change, the meanings of human existence that we hold most sacred seem to totter and technology emerges as the villain.

Religious change thus provides another mediating mechanism through which technology affects our values. That conditions are ripe for religious change at the present time has been noted by many observers, who are increasingly questioning whether our established religious syntheses and symbol systems are adequate any longer to the religious needs of a scientific and secular society that is changing so fundamentally as to strain traditional notions of eternity. If they are not, how are they likely to change? Professor Cox is addressing himself to this problem with specific attention to the influence of technology in guiding the direction of change.

He notes that religion needs to come to terms with the pluralism of belief systems that is characteristic of the modern world. The generation of knowledge and the use of technology are so much a part of the style and self-image of our own society that men begin to experience themselves, their power, and their relationships to nature and history in terms of open possibility, hope, action, and self-confidence. The symbolism of such traditional religious postures as subservience, fatefulness, destiny, and suprarational faith begin then to seem irrelevant to our actual experience. They lose credibility, and their religions function is weakened. Secular belief systems arise to compete for the allegiance of men: political belief systems, such as communism; or scientific ones, such as modern-day humanism; or such inexplicit, noninstitutionalized belief complexes as are characteristic of agnosticism.

This pluralism poses serious problems for the ultimate legitimation or "meaning" orientation for moral and social values that religion seeks to provide, because it demands a religions synthesis that can integrate the fact of variant perspectives into its own symbol system. Western religions have been notoriously incapable of performing this integrating function and have rather gone the route of schism and condemnation of variance as heresy. The institutions and formulations of historical Christianity in particular, which once served as the foundations of Western society, carry the added burden of centuries of conflict with scientific world views as these have competed for ascendancy in the same society. This makes it especially difficult for traditional Christianity to accommodate to a living experience so infused by scientific knowledge and attitudes as ours and helps explain why its adequacy is coming under serious question at the present time.

Cox notes three major traditions in the Judeo-Christian synthesis and finds them inconsistent in their perceptions of the future: an "apocalyptic" tradition foresees imminent catastrophe and induces a negative evaluation of this world; a "teleological" tradition sees the future as the certain unfolding of a fixed purpose inherent in the universe itself; a "prophetic" tradition, finally, sees the future as an open field of human hope and responsibility and as becoming what man will make of it.[3]

Technology, as noted, creates new possibilities for human choice and action but leaves their disposition uncertain. What its effects will be and what ends it will serve are not inherent in the technology, but depend on what man will do with technology. Technology thus makes possible a future of open-ended options that seems to accord well with the presuppositions of the prophetic tradition. It is in that tradition above others, then, that we may seek

3. See Harvey Cox, "Tradition and the Future," pts. 1 and 2, in *Christianity and Crisis* 27, nos. 16 and 17 (October 2 and 16, 1968): 218–20 and 227–31.

the beginnings of a religious synthesis that is both adequate to our time and continuous with what is most relevant in our religious history. But this requires an effort at deliberate religious innovation for which Cox finds insufficient theological ground at the present time. Although it is recognized that religions have changed and developed in the past, conscious innovation in religion has been condemned and is not provided for by the relevant theologies. The main task that technological change poses for theology in the next decades, therefore, is that of deliberate religious innovation and symbol reformulation to take specific account of religious needs in a technological age.

What consequences would such changes in religion have for values? Cox approaches this question in the context of the familiar complaint that, since technology is principally a means, it enhances merely instrumental values at the expense of expressive, consummatory, or somehow more "real" values. The appropriate distinction, however, is not between technological instrumental values and nontechnological expressive values, but among the expressive values that attach to different technologies. The horse-and-buggy was a technology too, after all, and it is not prima facie clear that its charms were different in kind or superior to the sense of power and adventure and the spectacular views that go with jet travel.

Further, technological advance in many instances is a condition for the emergence of new creative or consummatory values. Improved sound boxes in the past and structural steel and motion photography in the present have made possible the artistry of Jascha Heifetz, Frank Lloyd Wright, and Charles Chaplin, which have opened up wholly new ranges of expressive possibility without, moreover, in any way inhibiting a concurrent renewal of interest in medieval instruments and primitive art. If religious innovation can provide a meaning orientation broad enough to accommodate the idea that new technology can be creative of new values, a long step will have been taken toward providing a religious belief system adequate to the realities and needs of a technological age.

Individual Man in a Technological Age. What do technological change and the social and value changes that it brings with it mean for the life of the individual today? It is not clear that their effects are all one-way. For example, we are often told that today's individual is alienated by the vast proliferation of technical expertise and complex bureaucracies, by a feeling of impotence in the face of "the machine," and by a decline in personal privacy. It is probably true that the social pressures placed on individuals today are more complicated and demanding than they were in earlier times. Increased geographical and occupational mobility and the need to function in large organizations place difficult demands on the individual to conform or "adjust." It is also evident that the privacy of many individuals tends to be encroached upon by sophisticated eavesdropping and surveillance devices, by the accumulation of more and more information about individuals by governmental and many private agencies, and by improvements in information-handling technologies such as the proposed institution of centralized statistical data banks. There is little doubt, finally, that the power, authority, influence, and scope of government are greater today than at any time in the history of the United States.

But, as Professor Edward Shils points out in his study on technology and the individual, there is another, equally compelling side of the coin. First, government seems to be more shy and more lacking in confidence today than ever before. Second, while privacy may be declining in the ways indicated above, it also tends to decline in a sense that most individuals are likely to approve. The average man in Victorian times, for example, probably "enjoyed" much more privacy than today. No one much cared what happened to him, and he was free to remain ignorant, starve, fall ill, and die in complete privacy; that was the "golden age of privacy," as Shils puts it. Compulsory universal education, social security legislation, and public health measures—indeed, the very idea of a welfare state—are all antithetical to privacy in this sense, and it is the rare individual today who is loath to see that kind of privacy go.

It is not clear, finally, that technological and social complexity must inevitably lead to reducing the individual to "mass" or "organization" man. Economic productivity and modern means of communication allow the individual to aspire to more than he ever could before. Better and more easily available education not only provides him with skills and with the means to develop his individual potentialities, but also improves his self-image and his sense of value as a human being. This is probably the first age in history in which such high proportions of people have *felt* like individuals; no 18th-century English factory worker, so far as we know, had the sense of individual worth that underlies the demands on society of the average resident of the black urban ghetto today. And, as Shils notes, the scope of individual choice and action today are greater than in previous times, all the way from consumer behavior to political or religious allegiance. Even the much-maligned modern organization may in fact "serve as a mediator or buffer between the individual and the full raw impact of technological change," as an earlier study supported by the Harvard Program has concluded.

Recognition that the impact of modern technology on the individual has two faces, both negative and positive, is consistent with the double effect of technological change that was discussed above. It also suggests that appreciation of that impact in detail may not be achieved in terms of old formulas, such as more or less privacy, more or less government, more or less individuality. Professor Shils is therefore attempting to couch his inquiry in terms of the implications of technological change for the balance that every individual must strike between his commitment to private goals and satisfactions and his desires and responsibilities as a public citizen. The citizens of ancient Athens seem to have been largely public beings in this sense, while certain segments of today's hippie population seem to pursue mainly private gratifications. The political requirements of our modern technological society would seem to call for a relatively greater public commitment on the part of individuals than has been the case in the past, and it is by exploring this hypothesis that we may enhance our understanding of what technology does to the individual in present-day society. . . .

ECONOMIC AND POLITICAL ORGANIZATION

The Enlarged Scope of Public Decision Making. When technology brings about social changes (as described in the first section of this essay) which impinge on our existing system of values (in ways reviewed in the second section), it poses for society a number of problems that are ultimately political in nature. The term "political" is used here in the broadest sense: it encompasses all of the decision-making structures and procedures that have to do with the allocation and distribution of wealth and power in society. The political organization of society thus includes not only the formal apparatus of the state but also industrial organizations and other private institutions that play a role in the decision-making process. It is particularly important to attend to the organization of the entire body politic when technological change leads to a blurring of once clear distinctions between the public and private sectors of society and to changes in the roles of its principal institutions.

It was suggested above that the political requirements of our modern technological society call for a relatively greater public commitment on the part of individuals than in previous times. The reason for this, stated most generally, is that technological change has the effect of enhancing the importance of public decision making in society, because technology is continually creating new possibilities for social action as well as new problems that have to be dealt with.

A society that undertakes to foster technology on a large scale, in fact, commits itself to social complexity and to facing and dealing with new problems as a normal feature of political life. Not much is yet known with any precision about the political imperatives inherent in technological change, but one may nevertheless speculate about the reasons why an increasingly technological society seems to be characterized by enlargement of the scope of public decision making.

For one thing, the development and application of technology seems to require large-scale, and hence increasingly complex, social concentrations, whether these be large cities, large corporations, big universities, or big government. In instances where technological advance appears to facilitate reduction of such first-order concentrations, it tends instead to enlarge the relevant *system* of social organization, that is, to lead to increased centralization. Thus, the physical dispersion made possible by transportation and communications technologies, as Meyer and Kain have shown, enlarges the urban complex that must be governed as a unit.

A second characteristic of advanced technology is that its effects cover large distances, in both the geographical and social senses of the term. Both its positive and negative features are more extensive. Horsepowered transportation technology was limited in its speed and capacity, but its nuisance value was also limited, in most cases to the owner and to the occupant of the next farm. The supersonic transport can carry hundreds across long distances in minutes, but its noise and vibration damage must also be suffered willy-nilly by everyone within the limits of a swath 3,000 miles long and several miles wide.

The concatenation of increased density (or enlarged system) and extended technological "distance" means that technological applications have increasingly wider ramifications and that increasingly large concentrations of people and organizations become dependent on technological systems. A striking illustration of this was provided by the widespread effects of the power blackout in the northeastern part of the United States. The result is not only that more and more decisions must be social decisions taken in public ways, as already noted, but that, once made, decisions are likely to have a shorter useful life than heretofore. That is partly because technology is continually altering the spectrum of choices and problems that society faces, and partly because any decision taken is likely to generate a need to take ten more.

These speculations about the effects of technology on public decision making raise the problem of restructuring our decision-making mechanisms—including the system of market incentives—so that the increasing number and importance of social issues that confront us can be resolved equitably and effectively.

Private Firms and Public Goods. Among these issues, as noted earlier, is that created by the shift in the composition of demand in favor of public goods and services—such as education, health, transportation, slum clearance, and recreational facilities—which, it is generally agreed, the market has never provided effectively and in the provision of which government has usually played a role of some significance. This shift in demand raises serious questions about the relationship between technological change and existing decision-making structures in general and about the respective roles of government and business in particular. [A] project initiated . . . under the direction of Dr. Robin Marris is designed to explore those questions in detail.

In Western industrialized countries, new technological developments generally originate in and are applied through joint stock companies whose shares are widely traded on organized capital markets. Corporations thus play a dominant role in the development of new methods of production, of new methods of satisfying consumer wants, and even of new wants. Most economists appear to accept the thesis originally proposed by Schumpeter that corporations play a key role in the actual process of technological innovation in the economy. Marris himself has recently characterized this role as a perceiving of latent consumer needs and of fostering and regulating the rate at which these are converted into felt wants.[4]

There is no similar agreement about the implications of all this for social policy. J. K. Galbraith, for example, argues that the corporation is motivated by the desire for growth subject to a minimum profit constraint and infers (1) a higher rate of new-want development than would be the case if corporations were motivated principally to maximize profit, (2) a bias in favor of economic activities heavy in "technological content" in contrast to activities requiring sophisticated social organization, and (3) a bias in the economy as a whole in favor of development and satisfaction of private needs to the neglect of public needs and at the cost of a relatively slow rate of innovation in the public sector.

But Galbraith's picture is not generally accepted by economists, and his model of the corporation is not regarded as established economic theory. There is, in fact, no generally accepted economic theory of corporate behavior, as Marris points out, so that discussions about the future of the system of corporate enterprise usually get bogged down in an exchange of unsubstantiated assertions about how the existing system actually operates. What seems needed at this time, then, is less a new program of empirical research than an attempt to synthesize what we know for the purpose of arriving at a more

4. Robin Marris, *The Economic Theory of "Managerial" Capitalism* (New York, 1964).

adequate theory of the firm. This is the objective of phase 1 of the Marris project.

On the basis of the resulting theoretical clarification, phase 2 will go on to address such questions as (1) the costs of a policy of economic growth, (2) the incommensurability of individual incentive and public will, (3) the desirable balance between individual and social welfare when the two are inconsistent with each other, (4) changes in the roles of government and industrial institutions in the political organization of American society, and (5) the consequences of those changes for the functions of advertising and competing forms of communication in the process of public education. In particular, attention will be directed to whether existing forms of company organization are adequate for marshaling technology to social purposes by responding to the demand for public goods and services, or whether new productive institutions will be required to serve that end.

We can hope to do no more than raise the level of discussion of such fundamental and difficult questions, of course, but even that could be a service.

The Promise and Problems of Scientific Decision Making. There are two further consequences of the expanding role of public decision making. The first is that the latest information-handling of devices and techniques tend to be utilized in the decision-making process. This is so (1) because public policy can be effective only to the degree that it is based on reliable knowledge about the actual state of the society, and thus requires a strong capability to collect, aggregate, and analyze detailed data about economic activities, social patterns, popular attitudes, and political trends, and (2) because it is recognized increasingly that decisions taken in one area impinge on and have consequences for other policy areas often thought of as unrelated, so that it becomes necessary to base decisions on a model of society that sees it as a system and that is capable of signaling as many as possible of the probable consequences of a contemplated action.

As Professor Alan F. Westin points out, reactions to the prospect of more decision making based on computerized data banks and scientific management techniques run the gamut of optimism to pessimism mentioned in the opening of this essay. Negative reactions take the form of rising political demands for greater popular participation in decision making, for more equality among different segments of the population, and for greater regard for the dignity of individuals. The increasing dependence of decision making on scientific and technological devices and techniques is seen as posing a threat to these goals, and pressures are generated in opposition to further "rationalization" of decision-making processes. These pressures have the paradoxical effect, however, not of deflecting the supporters of technological decision making from their course, but of spurring them on to renewed effort to save the society before it explodes under planlessness and inadequate administration.

The paradox goes further, and helps to explain much of the social discontent that we are witnessing at the present time. The greater complexity and the more extensive ramifications that technology brings about in society tend to make social processes increasingly circuitous and indirect. The effects of actions are widespread and difficult to keep track of, so that experts and sophisticated techniques are increasingly needed to detect and analyze social events and to formulate policies adequate to the complexity of social issues. The "logic" of modern decision making thus appears to require greater and greater dependence on the collection and analysis of data and on the use of technological devices and scientific techniques. Indeed, many observers would agree that there is an "increasing relegation of questions which used to be matters of political debate to professional cadres of technicians and experts which function almost independently of the democratic political process."[5] In recent times, that process has been most noticeable, perhaps, in the areas of economic policy and national security affairs.

This "logic" of modern decision making, however, runs counter to that element of traditional democratic theory that places high value on direct participation in the political processes and generates the kind of discontent referred to above. If it turns out on more careful examination that direct participation is becoming less relevant to a society in which the connections between causes and effects are long and often hidden—which is an increasingly "indirect" society, in other words—elaboration of a new democratic ethos and of new democratic processes more adequate to the realities of modern society will emerge as perhaps the major intellectual and political challenge of our time.

The Need for Institutional Innovation. The challenge is, indeed, already upon us, for the second consequence of the enlarged scope of public decision making is the need to develop new institutional forms and new mechanisms to replace established ones that can no longer deal effectively with the new kinds of problems with which we are increasingly faced. Much of the political ferment of the present time—over the problems of technology assessment, the introduction of statistical data banks, the extension to domestic problems of techniques of analysis developed for the military services, and the modifica-

5. Harvey Brooks, "Scientific Concepts and Cultural Change," in G. Holton, ed., *Science and Culture* (Boston, 1965), p. 71.

tion of the institutions of local government—is evidence of the need for new institutions. It will be recalled that Professor Oettinger's study concludes that innovation is called for in the educational establishment before instructional technology can realize the promise that is potential in it. Our research in the biomedical area has repeatedly confirmed the need for institutional innovation in the medical system, and Marris has noted the evolution that seems called for in our industrial institutions. The Rosenbloom research group, finally, has documented the same need in the urban area and is exploring the form and course that the processes of innovation might take.

Direct intervention by business or government to improve ghetto conditions will tend to be ineffective until local organizations come into existence which enable residents to participate in and control their own situation. Such organizations seem to be a necessary condition for any solution of the ghetto problem that is likely to prove acceptable to black communities. Professors Richard S. Rosenbloom, Paul R. Lawrence, and their associates are therefore engaged in the design of two types of organization suited to the peculiar problems of the modern ghetto. These are (1) a state- or area-wide urban development corporation in which business and government join to channel funds and provide technical assistance to (2) a number of local development corporations, under community control, which can combine social service with sound business management.

Various "ghetto enrichment" strategies are being proposed at the present time, all of which stress the need for institutional innovation of some kind and in many of which creation of one sort or another of community development corporation is a prominent feature. In none of these respects does our approach claim any particular originality. What does seem promising, however, is our effort to design a local development corporation that is at once devoted to social service and built on sound business principles.

These characteristics point to large and powerful organizations that can serve as engines of indigenous ghetto development. They would of course interact with "outside" institutions, not only those at various levels of government, but especially their counterpart state or area urban development corporations. They would not be dependent principally on such outside institutions, however, since they would be engines that, once started, could keep running largely on their own power. In economic terms, the local development corporations would become "customers" of business. In political terms, they would be partners of existing governmental structures. In broader social terms, they could become vehicles for integrating underprivileged urban communities into the mainstream of American society.

The design for the state or area urban development corporation, in Professor Rosenbloom's description, would be a new form of public-private partnership serving to pull together the resources and programs of the business sector, of universities and research institutions, of public agencies, and of community organizations. This corporation could act as a surrogate for the "invisible hand" of the market, able to reward the successes of the local development corporations through command of a pool of unrestricted funds. Since there is no necessary relationship between profitability and social benefit for economic ventures in the ghetto, however, success would need to be measured, not in usual profit-and-loss terms, but in terms of such social indicators as employment levels, educational attainment, health statistics, and the like.

The collaborative arrangements we have entered into in New Jersey and in Boston offer us a welcome opportunity to test and develop some of our hypotheses and designs. In both of these programs, our research group is in a position to contribute know-how and advice, based on its understanding of organizational and corporate behavior, and to acquire insight and primary data for research that can prove useful in other contexts. As long ago as our first annual report, we announced the hope and expectation that the Harvard Program could supplement its scholarly production by adding a dimension of action research. New Jersey and Boston are providing us with our first opportunity to realize that objective.

CONCLUSION

As we review what we are learning about the relationship of technological and social change, a number of conclusions begin to emerge. We find, on the one hand, that the creation of new physical possibilities and social options by technology tends toward and appears to require the emergence of new values, new forms of economic activity, and new political organizations. On the other hand, technological change also poses problems of social and psychological displacement.

The two phenomena are not unconnected, nor is the tension between them new: man's technical prowess always seems to run ahead of his ability to deal with and profit from it. In America, especially, we are becoming adept at extracting the new techniques, the physical power, and the economic productivity that are inherent in our knowledge and its associated technologies. Yet we have not fully accepted the fact that our progress in the technical realm does not leave our institutions, values, and political processes unaffected. Individuals will be fully integrated into society only when we can extract from our knowledge not only its technological potential but also its implications for a system of values and a social, economic, and political organization appropriate to a society in which technology is so prevalent. . . .

Technology: The Opiate
of the Intellectuals

JOHN MCDERMOTT

If religion was formerly the opiate of the masses, then surely technology is the opiate of the educated public today, or at least of its favorite authors. No other single subject is so universally invested with high hopes for the improvement of mankind generally and of Americans in particular. The content of these millennial hopes varies somewhat from author to author, though with considerable overlap. A representative but by no means complete list of these promises and their prophets would include: an end to poverty and the inauguration of permanent prosperity (Leon Keyserling), universal equality of opportunity (Zbigniew Brzezinski), a radical increase in individual freedom (Edward Shils), the replacement of work by leisure for most of mankind (Robert Theobald), fresh water for desert dwellers (Lyndon Baines Johnson), permanent but harmless social revolution (Walt Rostow), the final comeuppance of Mao Tse-tung and all his ilk (same prophet), the triumph of wisdom over power (John Kenneth Galbraith), and, lest we forget, the end of ideology (Daniel Bell).

These hopes for mankind's, or technology's, future, however, are not unalloyed. Technology's defenders, being otherwise reasonable men, are also aware that the world population explosion and the nuclear missiles race are also the fruit of the enormous advances made in technology during the past half century or so. But here too a cursory reading of their literature would reveal widespread though qualified optimism that these scourges too will fall before technology's might. Thus population (and genetic) control and permanent peace are sometimes added to the already imposing roster of technology's promises. What are we to make of such extravagant optimism?

[In early 1968] Harvard University's Program on Technology and Society, ". . . an inquiry in depth into the effects of technological change on the economy, on public policies, and on the character of society, as well as into the reciprocal effects of social progress on the nature, dimension, and directions of scientific and technological development," issued its Fourth Annual Report to the accompaniment of full front-page coverage in *The New York Times* (January 18). Within the brief (fewer than 100) pages of that report and most clearly in the concluding essay by the Program's Director, Emmanuel G. Mesthene, one can discern some of the important threads of belief which bind together much current writing on the social implications of technology. Mesthene's essay is worth extended analysis because these beliefs are of interest in themselves and, of greater importance, because they form the basis not of a new but of a newly aggressive right-wing ideology in this country, an ideology whose growing importance was accurately measured by the magnitude of the *Times*'s news report.

At the very beginning of Mesthene's essay, which attempts to characterize the relationships between technological and social change, the author is careful to dissociate himself from what he believes are several extreme views of those relationships. For example, technology is neither the relatively "unalloyed blessing" which, he claims, Marx, Comte, and the Air Force hold it to be, nor an unmitigated curse, a view he attributes to "many of our youth." (This is but the first of several reproofs Mesthene casts in the direction of youth.) Having denounced straw men to the right and left of him he is free to pursue that middle or moderate course favored by virtually all political writers of the day. This middle course consists of an extremely abstract and—politically speaking—sanitary view of technology and technological progress.

For Mesthene, it is characteristic of technology that it:

. . . creates new possibilities for human choice and action but leaves their disposition uncertain. What its effects will be and what ends it will serve are not inherent in the technology, but depend on what man will do with technology. Technology thus makes possible a future of open-ended options . . . .

This essentially optimistic view of the matter rests on the notion that technology is merely ". . . the organization of knowledge for practical purposes . . ." and therefore cannot be purely boon or wholly burden. The matter is somewhat more complex:

New technology creates new opportunities for men and societies and it also generates new problems for them. It has both positive and negative effects, and it usually has the two *at the same time and in virtue of each other.*

This dual effect he illustrates with an example drawn from the field of medicine. Recent advances there

have created two new opportunities: (1) they have made possible treatment and cures that were never possible before, and (2) they provide a necessary condition for the delivery of adequate medical care to the population at large as a matter of right rather than privilege.

Because of the first, however,

the medical profession has become increasingly differentiated and specialized and is tending to concentrate its best efforts in a few major, urban centers of medical excellence.

Mesthene clearly intends but does not state the corollary to this point, namely that the availability of adequate medical care is declining elsewhere.[1] Moreover, because of the second point, there have been

... big increases in demand for medical services, partly because a healthy population has important economic advantages in a highly industrialized society. This increased demand accelerates the process of differentiation and multiplies the levels of paramedical personnel between the physician at the top and the patient at the bottom of the hospital pyramid.

Similarly, Mesthene points out that marvelous improvements in auto and air transportation have aggravated social and other problems in the inner city. Furthermore,

Mass communications technology has also made rapid strides since World War II, with great benefit to education, journalism, commerce and sheer convenience. It has also been accompanied by an aggravation of social unrest, however, and may help to explain the singular rebelliousness of a youth that can find out what the world is like from television before home and school have had the time to instill some ethical sense of what it could or should be like.

Mesthene believes there are two distinct problems in technology's relation to society, a positive one of taking full advantage of the opportunities it offers

1. This is almost certainly true of persons living in rural areas or in smaller towns and cities. However, a New York based New Left project, the Health-Policy Advisory Center, has argued with considerable documentation, that roughly half of New York City's population is now medically indigent and perhaps 80 percent of the population is indigent with respect to major medical care.

and the negative one of avoiding unfortunate consequences which flow from the exploitation of those opportunities. Positive opportunities may be missed because the costs of technological development outweigh likely benefits (e.g., Herman Kahn's "Doomsday Machine"). Mesthene seems convinced, however, that a more important case is that in which

> ... technology lies fallow because existing social structures are inadequate to exploit the opportunities it offers. This is revealed clearly in the examination of institutional failure in the ghetto carried on by [the Program]. At point after point, ... analyses confirm ... that existing institutions and traditional approaches are by and large incapable of coming to grips with the new problems of our cities—many of them caused by technological change ... —and unable to realize the possibilities for resolving them that are also inherent in technology. Vested economic and political interests serve to obstruct adequate provision of low-cost housing. Community institutions wither for want of interest and participation by residents. City agencies are unable to marshall the skills and take the systematic approach needed to deal with new and intensified problems of education, crime control, and public welfare. Business corporations, finally, which are organized around the expectation of private profit, are insufficiently motivated to bring new technology and management know-how to bear on urban projects where the benefits will be largely social.

His diagnosis of these problems is generous in the extreme:

> All these factors combine to dilute what may be otherwise a genuine desire to apply our best knowledge and adequate resources to the resolution of urban tensions and the eradication of poverty in the nation.

Moreover, because government and the media ". . . are not yet equipped for the massive task of public education that is needed . . ." if we are to exploit technology more fully, many technological opportunities are lost because of the lack of public support. This too is a problem primarily of "institutional innovation."

Mesthene believes that institutional innovation is no less important in combatting the negative effects of technology. Individuals or individual firms which decide to develop new technologies normally do not take "adequate account" of their likely social benefits or costs. His critique is anti-capitalist in spirit, but lacks bite, for he goes on to add that

> ... [most of the negative] consequences of technology that are causing concern at the present time—pollution of the environment, potential damage to the ecology of the planet, occupational and social dislocations, threats to the privacy and political significance of the individual, social and psychological malaise—are *negative externalities of this kind.* They are with us in large measure because it has not been anybody's explicit business to foresee and anticipate them. [Italics added.]

Mesthene's abstract analysis and its equally abstract diagnosis in favor of "institutional innovation" places him in a curious and, for us, instructive position. If existing social structures are inadequate to exploit technology's full potential, or if, on the other hand, so-called negative externalities assail us because it is nobody's business to foresee and anticipate them, doesn't this say that we should apply technology to this problem too? That is, we ought to apply and organize the appropriate *organizational* knowledge for the practical purpose of solving the problems of institutional inadequacy and "negative externalities."[2] Hence, in principle, Mesthene is in the position of arguing that the cure for technology's problems, whether positive or negative, is still more technology. This is the first theme of the technological school of writers and its ultimate First Principle.

Technology, in their view, is a self-correcting system. Temporary oversight or "negative externalities" will and should be corrected by technological means. Attempts to restrict the free play of technological innovation are, in the nature of the case, self-defeating. Technological innovation exhibits a distinct tendency to work for the general welfare in the long run. *Laissez innover!*

I have so far deliberately refrained from going into any greater detail than does Mesthene on the empirical character of contemporary technology (see below) for it is important to bring out the force of the principle of *laissez innover* in its full generality. Many writers on technology appear to deny in their definition of the subject—organized knowledge for practical purposes—that contemporary technology exhibits distinct trends which can be identified or projected. Others, like Mesthene, appear to accept these trends, but

---

2. Practicing what it preaches, the Program sponsors a Research Project on Technology, Business, and the City which has begun for urban areas ". . . an exploration into what organizational innovations might produce the social and economic development programs that might take maximum advantage of the opportunities offered by modern technology while exploiting the advantages and *reducing the weaknesses of both traditional business institutions and traditional government organizations*" (italics added). The Project has proposed ". . . (1) a state- or area-wide Urban Development Corporation in which business and government join to channel funds and provide technical assistance to (2) a number of Local Development Corporations, *under community control,* which can *combine social service with sound business management*" (italics added).

Mesthene comments that the Urban Development Corporation ". . . could act as a surrogate for the 'invisible hand' of the market, able to reward the success of the Local Development Corporation through command of a pool of unrestricted funds." Community control is to be strengthened and business weaknesses reduced by linking the two together and providing the latter with a "pool of unrestricted funds." It's all very participatory, though a trifle weak on democracy.

then blunt the conclusion by attributing to technology so much flexibility and "scientific" purity that it becomes an abstraction infinitely malleable in behalf of good, pacific, just, and egalitarian purposes. Thus the analogy to the *laissez-faire* principle of another time is quite justified. Just as the market or the free play of competition provided in theory the optimum long-run solution for virtually every aspect of virtually every social and economic problem, so too does the free play of technology, according to its writers. Only if technology or innovation (or some other synonym) is allowed the freest possible reign, they believe, will the maximum social good be realized.

What reasons do they give to believe that the principle of *laissez innover* will normally function for the benefit of mankind rather than, say, merely for the benefit of the immediate practitioners of technology, their managerial cronies, and for the profits accruing to their corporations? As Mesthene and other writers of his school are aware, this is a very real problem, for they all believe that the normal tendency of technology is, and ought to be, the increasing concentration of decision-making power in the hands of larger and larger scientific-technical bureaucracies. *In principle,* their solution is relatively simple, though not often explicitly stated.[3]

Their argument goes as follows: the men and women who are elevated by technology into commanding positions within various decision-making bureaucracies exhibit no generalized drive for power such as characterized, say, the landed gentry of pre-industrial Europe or the capitalist entrepreneur of the last century. For their social and institutional position and its supporting culture as well are defined solely by the fact that these men are problem solvers. (Organized knowledge for practical purposes again.) That is, they gain advantage and reward only to the extent that they can bring specific technical knowledge to bear on the solution of specific technical problems. Any more general drive for power would undercut the bases of their usefulness and legitimacy.

Moreover their specific training and professional commitment to solving technical problems creates a bias against ideologies in general which inhibits any attempts to formulate a justifying ideology for the group. Consequently, they do not constitute a class and have no general interests antagonistic to those of their problem-beset clients. We may refer to all of this as the disinterested character of the scientific-technical decision-maker, or, more briefly and cynically, as the principle of the Altruistic Bureaucrat.

---

3. For a more complete statement of the argument which follows, see Suzanne Keller, *Beyond the Ruling Class* (Random House, 1963).

As if not satisfied by the force of this (unstated) principle, Mesthene like many of his school fellows spends many pages commenting around the belief that the concentration of power at the top of technology's organizations is a problem, but that like other problems technology should be able to solve it successfully through institutional innovation. You may trust in it; the principle of *laissez innover* knows no logical or other hurdle.

This combination of guileless optimism with scientific toughmindedness might seem to be no more than an eccentric delusion were the American technology it supports not moving in directions that are strongly antidemocratic. To show why this is so we must examine more closely Mesthene's seemingly innocuous distinction between technology's positive opportunities and its "negative externalities." In order to do this I will make use of an example drawn from the very frontier of American technology, the Vietnam War.

II

At least two fundamentally different bombing programs [have been] carried out in South Vietnam. There are fairly conventional attacks against targets which consist of identified enemy troops, fortifications, medical centers, vessels, and so forth. The other program is quite different and, at least since March, 1968, infinitely more important. With some oversimplification it can be described as follows:

Intelligence data is gathered from all kinds of sources, of all degrees of reliability, on all manner of subjects, and fed into a computer complex located, I believe, at Bien Hoa. From this data and using mathematical models developed for the purpose, the computer then assigns probabilities to a range of potential targets, probabilities which represent the likelihood that the latter contain enemy forces or supplies. These potential targets might include: a canal-river crossing known to be used occasionally by the NLF; a section of trail which would have to be used to attack such and such an American base, now overdue for attack; a square mile of plain rumored to contain enemy troops; a mountainside from which camp fire smoke was seen rising. Again using models developed for the purpose, the computer divides pre-programmed levels of bombardment among those potential targets which have the highest probability of containing actual targets. Following the raids, data provided by further reconnaissance is fed into the computer and conclusions are drawn (usually optimistic ones) on the effectiveness of the raids. This estimate of effectiveness then becomes part of the data governing current and future operations, and so on.

Two features must be noted regarding this program's features which are superficially hinted at but fundamentally obscured by Mesthene's distinction between the abstractions of positive opportunity and "negative externality." First, when considered from the standpoint of its planners, the bombing program is extraordinarily rational, for it creates previously unavailable "opportunities" to pursue their goals in Vietnam. It would make no sense to bomb South Vietnam simply at random, and no serious person or Air Force General would care to mount the effort to do so. So the system employed in Vietnam significantly reduces, though it does not eliminate, that randomness. That canal-river crossing which is bombed at least once every eleven days or so is a very poor target compared to an NLF battalion observed in a village. But it is an infinitely more promising target than would be selected by throwing a dart at a grid map of South Vietnam. In addition to bombing the battalion, why not bomb the canal crossing to the frequency and extent that it *might* be used by enemy troops?

Even when we take into account the crudity of the mathematical models and the consequent slapstick way in which poor information is evaluated, it is a "good" program. No single raid will definitely kill an enemy soldier but a whole series of them increases the "opportunity" to kill a calculable number of them (as well, of course, as a calculable but not calculated number of non-soldiers). This is the most rational bombing system to follow if American lives are very expensive and American weapons and Vietnamese lives very cheap. Which, of course, is the case.

Secondly, however, considered from the standpoint of goals and values not programmed in by its designers, the bombing program is incredibly irrational. In Mesthene's terms, these "negative externalities" would include, in the present case, the lives and well-being of various Vietnamese as well as the feelings and opinions of some less important Americans. Significantly, this exclusion of the interests of people not among the managerial class is based quite as much on the so-called technical means being employed as on the political goals of the system. In the particular case of the Vietnamese bombing system, the political goals of the bombing system clearly exclude the interests of certain Vietnamese. After all, the victims of the bombardment are communists or their supporters, they are our enemies, they resist US intervention. In short, their interests are fully antagonistic to the goals of the program and simply must be excluded from consideration. The technical reasons for this exclusion require explanation, being less familiar and more important, especially in the light of Mesthene's belief in the malleability of technological systems.

Advanced technological systems such as those employed in the bombardment of South Vietnam make use not only of extremely complex and expensive equipment but, quite as important, of large numbers of relatively scarce and expensive-to-train technicians. They have immense capital costs; a thousand aircraft of a very advanced type, literally hundreds of thousands of spare parts, enormous stocks of rockets, bombs, shells and bullets, in addition to tens of thousands of technical specialists; pilots, bombardiers, navigators, radar operators, computer programmers, accountants, engineers, electronic and mechanical technicians, to name only a few. In short, they are "capital intensive."

Moreover, the coordination of this immense mass of esoteric equipment and its operators in the most effective possible way depends upon an extremely highly developed technique both in the employment of each piece of equipment by a specific team of operators and in the management of the program itself. Of course, all large organizations standardize their operating procedures, but it is peculiar to advanced technological systems that their operating procedures embody a very high degree of information drawn from the physical sciences, while their managerial procedures are equally dependent on information drawn from the social sciences. We may describe this situation by saying that advanced technological systems are both "technique intensive" and "management intensive."

It should be clear, moreover, even to the most casual observer that such intensive use of capital, technique, and management spills over into almost every area touched by the technological system in question. An attack program delivering 330,000 tons of munitions more or less selectively to several thousand different targets monthly would be an anomaly if forced to rely on sporadic intelligence data, erratic maintenance systems, or a fluctuating and unpredictable supply of heavy bombs, rockets, jet fuel, and napalm tanks. Thus it is precisely because the bombing program requires an intensive use of capital, technique, and management that the same properties are normally transferred to the intelligence, maintenance, supply, coordination and training systems which support it. Accordingly, each of these supporting systems is subject to sharp pressures to improve and rationalize the performance of its machines and men, the reliability of its techniques, and the efficiency and sensitivity of the management controls under which it operates. Within integrated technical systems, higher levels of technology drive out lower, and the normal tendency is to integrate systems.

From this perverse Gresham's Law of Technology follow some of the main social and organizational characteristics of contemporary technological systems:

the radical increase in the scale and complexity of operations that they demand and encourage; the rapid and widespread diffusion of technology to new areas; the great diversity of activities which can be directed by central management; an increase in the ambition of management's goals; and, as a corollary, especially to the last, growing resistance to the influence of so-called negative externalities.

Complex technological systems are extraordinarily resistant to intervention by persons or problems operating outside or below their managing groups, and this is so regardless of the "politics" of a given situation. Technology creates its own politics. The point of such advanced systems is to minimize the incidence of personal or social behavior which is erratic or otherwise not easily classified, of tools and equipment with poor performance, of improvisory techniques, and of unresponsiveness to central management.

For example, enlisted men who are "unrealistically soft" on the subject of civilian casualties and farmers in contested districts pose a mortal threat to the integral character of systems like that used in Vietnam. In the case of the soldier this means he must be kept under tight military discipline. In the case of the farmer, he must be easily placed in one of two categories; collaborator or enemy. This is done by assigning a probability to him, his hamlet, his village, or his district, and by incorporating that probability into the targeting plans of the bombing system. Then the enlisted man may be controlled by training and indoctrination as well as by highly developed techniques of command and coercion, and the farmers may be bombed according to the most advanced statistical models. In both cases the system's authority over its farmer subjects or enlisted men is a technical one. The technical means which make that system rational and efficient in its aggregate terms, i.e., as viewed from the top, themselves tend by design to filter out the "non-rational" or "non-efficient" elements of its components and subjects, i.e., those rising from the bottom.

To define technology so abstractly that it obscures these observable characteristics of contemporary technology—as Mesthene and his school have done—makes no sense. It makes even less sense to claim some magical malleability for something as undefined as "institutional innovation." Technology, in its concrete, empirical meaning, refers fundamentally to systems of rationalized control over large groups of men, events, and machines by small groups of technically skilled men operating through organizational hierarchy. The latent "opportunities" provided by that control and its ability to filter out discordant "negative externalities" are, of course, best illustrated by extreme cases. Hence the most instructive and accurate example should be of a technology able to suppress the humanity of its rank-and-file and to commit genocide as a by-product of its rationality. The Vietnam bombing program fits technology to a "T."

III

It would certainly be difficult to attempt to translate in any simple and direct way the social and organizational properties of highly developed technological systems from the battlefields of Vietnam to the different cultural and institutional setting of the US. Yet before we conclude that any such attempt would be futile or even absurd, we might consider the following story.

In early 1967 I stayed for several days with one of the infantry companies of the US Fourth Division whose parent battalion was then based at Dau Tieng. From the camp at Dau Tieng the well-known Black Lady Mountain, sacred to the Cao Dai religious sect, was easily visible and in fact dominated the surrounding plain and the camp itself. One afternoon when I began to explain the religious significance of the mountain to some GI friends, they interrupted my somewhat academic discourse to tell me a tale beside which even the strange beliefs of the Cao Dai sect appeared prosaic.

According to GI reports which the soldiers had heard and believed, the Viet Cong had long ago hollowed out most of the mountain in order to install a very big cannon there. The size of the cannon was left somewhat vague—"huge, fucking . . ."—but clearly the GI's imagined that it was in the battleship class. In any event, this huge cannon had formerly taken a heavy toll of American aircraft and had been made impervious to American counterattacks by the presence of two—"huge, fucking"—sliding steel doors, behind which it retreated whenever the Americans attacked. Had they seen this battleship cannon, and did it ever fire on the camp, which was easily within its range? No, they answered, for a brave flyer, recognizing the effectiveness of the cannon against his fellow pilots, had deliberately crashed his jet into those doors one day, jamming them, and permitting the Americans to move into the area unhindered.

I had never been in the army, and at the time of my trip to Vietnam had not yet learned how fantastic GI stories can be. Thus I found it hard to understand how they could be convinced of so improbable a tale. Only later, after talking to many soldiers and hearing many other wild stories from them as well, did I realize what the explanation for this was. Unlike officers and civilian correspondents who are almost daily given detailed briefings on a unit's situation capabilities and objectives, GI's are told virtually nothing of this sort by the Army. They are simply told what to do, where, and how, and it is a rare officer, in my experience anyway, who thinks they should be told any more than this. Officers don't think soldiers are stupid; they simply assume it, and act accordingly. For the individual soldier's personal life doesn't make too much difference; he still has to deal with the facts of personal feelings, his own well-being, and that of his family.

But for the soldier's group life this makes a great deal of difference. In their group life, soldiers are cut off from sources of information about the situation of the group and are placed in a position where their social behavior is governed largely by the principle of blind obedience. Under such circumstances, reality becomes elusive. Because the soldiers are not permitted to deal with facts in their own ways, facts cease to discipline their opinions. Fantasy and wild tales are the natural outcome. In fact, it is probably a mark of the GI's intelligence to fantasize, for it means that he has not permitted his intellectual capacity to atrophy. The intelligence of the individual is thus expressed in the irrationality of the group.

It is this process which we may observe when we look to the social effect of modern technological systems in America itself. Here the process is not so simple and clear as in Vietnam, for it involves not simply the relations of to-day's soldiers to their officers and to the Army but the historical development of analogous relations between the lower and upper orders of our society. Moreover, these relations are broadly cultural rather than narrowly social in nature. It is to a brief review of this complex subject that I now wish to turn.

IV

Among the conventional explanations for the rise and spread of the democratic ethos in Europe and North America in the seventeenth, eighteenth, and nineteenth centuries, the destruction of the gap in political culture between the mass of the population and that of the ruling classes is extremely important. There are several sides to this explanation. For example, it is often argued that the invention of the printing press and the spread of Protestant Christianity encouraged a significant growth in popular literacy. In its earliest phases this literacy was largely expended on reading the Old and New Testaments, but it quickly broadened to include other religious works such as Bunyan's *Pilgrim's Progress*, and after that to such secular classics as *Gulliver's Travels*. The dating of these developments is, in the nature of the case, somewhat imprecise. But certainly by the middle of the eighteenth century, at least in Britain and North America, the literacy of the population was sufficient to support a variety of newspapers and periodicals not only in the larger cities but in the smaller provincial towns as well. The decline of Latin as the first language of politics and religion paralleled this development, of course. Thus, even before the advent of Tom Paine, Babeuf, and other popular tribunes, literacy and the information it carried were widely and securely spread throughout the population and the demystification of both the religious and the political privileges of the ruling classes was well developed. Common townsmen had closed at least one of the cultural gaps between themselves and the aristocracy of the large cities.

Similarly, it is often argued that with the expansion and improvement of road and postal systems, the spread of new tools and techniques, the growth in the number and variety of merchants, the consequent invigoration of town life, and other numerous and familiar related developments, the social experiences of larger numbers of people became richer, more varied, and similar in fact to those of the ruling classes. This last, the growth in similarity of the social experiences of the upper and lower classes, is especially important. Social skills and experiences which underlay the monopoly of the upper classes over the processes of law and government were spreading to important segments of the lower orders of society. For carrying on trade, managing a commercial—not a subsistence—farm, participating in a vestry of workingmen's guild, or working in an up-to-date manufactory or business, unlike the relatively narrow existence of the medieval serf or artisan, were experiences which contributed to what I would call the social rationality of the lower orders.

Activities which demand frequent intercourse with strangers, accurate calculation of near means and distant ends, and a willingness to devise collective ways of resolving novel and unexpected problems demand and reward a more discriminating attention to the realities and deficiencies of social life, and provide thereby a rich variety of social experiences analogous to those of the governing classes. As a result not only were the processes of law and government, formerly treated with semi-religious veneration, becoming demystified but, equally important, a population was being fitted out with sufficient skills and interests to contest their control. Still another gap between the political cultures of the upper and lower ends of the social spectrum was being closed.

The same period also witnesses a growth in the organized means of popular expression. In Britain, these would include the laboring people's organizations whose development is so ably described in Edward Thompson's *The Making of the English Working Class.* In America, the increase in the organized power of the populace was expressed not only in the growing conflict between the colonies and the Crown but more sharply and fundamentally in the continuous antagonism between the coastal areas and the backwoods, expressed, for example, in Shay's rebellion in western Massachusetts in 1786. Clearly these organizational developments were related to the two foregoing as both cause and effect. For the English workingmen's movement and the claims to local self-government in America spurred, and were spurred by, the growth in individual literacy and in social rationality among the lower classes. They were in fact its organizational expression.

These same developments were also reflected in the spread of egalitarian and republican doctrines such as those of Richard Price and Thomas Paine, which pointed up the arbitrary character of what had heretofore been considered the rights of the higher orders of society, and thus provided the popular ideological base which helped to define and legitimate lower-class demands.[4]

4. Mesthene is blind on this point. He writes, for example, that "This is probably the first age in history in which such high proportions of people have *felt* like individuals; no eighteenth century English factory worker, so far as we know, had the sense of individual worth that underlies the demands on society of the average resident of the black urban ghetto today." Contrast the following account from Edward Thompson's *The Making of the English Working Class* (Vintage Books, 1967), one of several hundred of the same character.

During a wave of repression against various workingmen's organizations in May, 1794, Prime Minister William Pitt himself, in the presence of the Lord Chancellor, the Home Secretary and, we may presume, a full battery of police spies and other officials, interrogated a number of Jacobite working men. Thompson relates that at one point Pitt ". . . summoned for interrogation a fourteen-year-old lad, Henry Eaton, who had been living with [the family of one of the accused]. But the boy stood his ground and [as a contemporary account relates] " 'entered into a political harangue, in which he used very harsh language against Mr. Pitt; upbraiding him with having taxed the people to an enormous extent. . . .' " (p. 19).

As Thompson richly documents, the boy was not speaking out of personal cheek. He was part of a movement of Englishmen of the lower orders whose culture had long been developing broad conceptions of working-class rights and dignity in opposition to the repressive culture of the aristocracy and the bourgeoisie. The sources of that culture were very diverse and included religious elements as well as political ones. Thompson shows, for example, that the religious traditions of some lower-class Britons included the view that worldly success was a mark of the Devil, and poverty often a sign of virtue. Thus no very great effort was required to see through the social, no less than the religious, legitimacy of the upper classes. Only a slight shift of understanding was required to change sin into social vice and the Devil himself into the capitalist system, while the poor's sense of their own moral worth became a fundamental support of their belief in the rightness and worth of the working class movement.

One wonders just what Mesthene's conception of the history of the rise of the democratic ethos consists in. I suspect that he, like many other intellectuals, assumed without thinking that its impulse derives more from blind developments in technology and from ideological inputs from elite intellectuals, than from any processes which exemplify merit and intelligence in the lower classes. How flattering to intellectuals to assume that their benevolence is more important in these matters than the labors, struggles, and experiences of vital popular cultures.

This description by no means does justice to the richness and variety of the historical process underlying the rise and spread of what has come to be called the democratic ethos. But it does, I hope, isolate some of the important structural elements and, moreover, it enables us to illuminate some important ways in which the new technology, celebrated by Mesthene and his associates for its potential contributions to democracy, contributes instead to the erosion of that same democratic ethos. For if, in an earlier time, the gap between the political cultures of the higher and lower orders of society was being widely attacked and closed, this no longer appears to be the case. On the contrary, I am persuaded that the direction has been reversed and that we now observe evidence of a growing separation between ruling and lower-class culture in America, a separation which is particularly enhanced by the rapid growth of technology and the spreading influence of its *laissez innover* ideologues.

Certainly, there has been a decline in popular literacy, that is to say, in those aspects of literacy which bear on an understanding of the political and social character of the new technology. Not one person in a hundred is even aware of, much less understands, the nature of technologically highly advanced systems such as are used in the Vietnam bombing program. People's ignorance in these things is revealed in their language. No clearer illustration of this ignorance is needed than the growing and already enormous difference between the speech of organizational and technical specialists and that of the man in the street, including many of the educated ones. To the extent that technical forms of speech within which the major business of American society is carried on are not understood or are poorly understood, there is a decline in one of the essentials of democracy.

This is not to say that the peculiar jargon which characterizes the speech of, say, aerospace technicians, crisis managers, or economic mandarins is intrinsically superior to the vocabulary of ordinary conversation, though sometimes this is indeed the case. What is important about technical language is that the words, being alien to ordinary speech, hide their meaning from ordinary speakers; terms like foreign aid or technical assistance have a good sound in ordinary speech; only the initiate recognizes them as synonyms for the old-fashioned, nasty word, imperialism. Such instances can be corrected but when almost all of the public's business is carried on in specialized jargon correction makes little difference. Like Latin in the past, the new language of social and technical organization is divorced from the general population, which continues to speak in the vulgar tongue of, say, *The New Republic,* the *Saturday Review of Literature,* or *The Reader's Digest.*

Secondly, the social organization of this new technology, by systematically denying to the general population experiences which are analogous to those of its higher management, contributes very heavily to the growth of social irrationality in our society. For example, modern technological organization defines the roles and values of its members, not vice versa. An engineer or a sociologist is one who does all those things but only those things called for by the "table of organization" and the "job description" used by his employer. Professionals who seek self-realization through creative and autonomous behavior without regard to the defined goals, needs, and channels of their respective departments have no more place in a large corporation or government agency than squeamish soldiers in the Army. Naturally some tolerance would normally be extended to very gifted or personable individuals. This is especially true in universities. But for the common garden variety employee (or junior faculty member) company sanctions on job behavior, style of work, and related matters must have the force of law.

However, those at the top of technology's more advanced organizations hardly suffer the same experience. For reasons which are clearly related to the principle of the Altruistic Bureaucracy the psychology of an individual's fulfillment through work has been incorporated into management ideology. As the pages of *Fortune, Time,* or *Business Week* or the memoirs of out-of-office Kennedyites serve to show, the higher levels of business and government are staffed by men and women who spend killing hours looking after the economic welfare and national security of the rest of us. The rewards of this life are said to be very few: the love of money would be demeaning and, anyway, taxes are said to take most of it; its sacrifices are many, for failure brings economic depression to the masses or gains for communism as well as disgrace to the erring managers. Even the essential high-mindedness or altruism of our managers earns no reward, for the public is distracted, fickle, and, on occasion, vengeful. (The extensive literature on the "ordeal" of Lyndon Johnson is a case in point.) Hence for these "real revolutionaries of our time," as Walt Rostow has called them, self-fulfillment through work and discipline is the only reward. The managerial process is seen as an expression of the vital personalities of our leaders and the right to it an inalienable right of the national elite.

In addition to all of this, their lonely and unrewarding eminence in the face of crushing responsibility, etc., tends to create an air of mystification around technology's managers. When the august mystery of science and the perquisites of high office are added to their halos, they glow very blindingly indeed. Thus, in ideology as well as in reality and appearance, the experiences of the higher managers tend to separate and isolate themselves from those of the managed. Again the situation within the US is not so severe nor so stark as in the Army in Vietnam but the effect on those who are excluded from self-management is very similar. Soldiers in Vietnam are not alone in believing huge, secret guns threaten them from various points; that same feeling is a national malady in the US.

It seems fundamental to the social organization of modern technology that the quality of the social experience of the lower orders of society declines as the level of technology grows no less than does their literacy. And, of course, this process feeds on itself, for with the consequent decline in the real effectiveness and usefulness of local and other forms of organization open to easy and direct popular influence their vitality declines still further, and the cycle is repeated.

The normal life of men and women in the lower and, I think, middle levels of American society now seems cut off from those experiences in which near social means and distant social ends are balanced and rebalanced, adjusted, and readjusted. But it is from such widespread experience with effective balancing and adjusting that social rationality derives. To the degree that it is lacking, social irrationality becomes the norm, and social paranoia a recurring phenomenon.

Those who seek an explanation for the infatuation of local government with anti-fluoridation campaigns several years ago need look no further. A similar irrationality is now being exhibited toward the war in Vietnam and the anti-war Movement. With no great effort and using no great skill, Presidents Johnson and Nixon have managed to direct disorganized popular frustration over the continuation of the war and popular abhorrence over its unremitting violence on to precisely that element in the population most actively and effectively opposed to the war and its violence. As for paranoia, consider the widespread reaction of whites to the murder of Dr. King. Their demand for force and more force to be used against the Black population was consistent only with the hypothesis that Dr. King murdered James Earl Ray, just as SNCC members had lynched Klansmen only a few years before.

People often say that America is a sick society when what they really mean is that it has lots of sick individuals. But they were right the first time: the society is so sick that individual efforts to right it and individual rationality come to be expressed in fundamentally sick ways. Like the soldiers in Vietnam, we try to avoid atrophy of our social intelligence only to be led into fantasy and, often, violence. It is a good thing to want the war in Vietnam over for, as everyone now recognizes, it hurts us almost as much as the Vietnamese who are its intended victims. But for many segments of our population, especially those cut off from political expression because of their own social disorganization, the rationality of various alternatives for ending the war is fundamentally obscure. Thus their commendable desire to end the war is expressed in what they believe is the clearest and most certain alternative: use the bomb!

Mesthene himself recognizes that such "negative externalities" are on the increase. His list includes ". . . pollution of the environment, potential damage to the ecology of the planet, occupational and social dislocations, threats to the privacy and political significance of the individual, social and psychological malaise. . . ." Minor matters all, however, when compared to the marvelous opportunities *laissez innover* holds out to us: more GNP, continued free world leadership, supersonic transports, urban renewal on a regional basis, institutional innovation, and the millennial promises of his school.

This brings us finally to the ideologies and doctrines of technology and their relation to what I have argued is a growing gap in political culture between the lower and upper classes in American society. Even more fundamentally than the principles of *laissez innover* and the altruistic bureaucrat, technology in its very definition as the organization of knowledge for practical purposes assumes that the primary and really creative role in the social processes consequent on technological change is reserved for a scientific and technical elite, the elite which presumably discovers and organizes that knowledge. But if the scientific and technical elite and their indispensable managerial cronies are the really creative (and hardworking and altruistic) element in American society, what is this but to say that the common mass of men are essentially drags on the social weal? This is precisely the implication which is drawn by the *laissez innover* school. Consider the following quotations from an article which appeared in *The New Republic* in December 1967, written by Zbigniew Brzezinski, one of the intellectual leaders of the school.

Brzezinski is describing a nightmare which he calls the "technetronic society" (the word like the concept is a pastiche of technology and electronics). This society will be characterized, he argues, by the application of ". . . the principle of equal opportunity for all but . . . special opportunity for the singularly talented few." It will thus combine ". . . continued *respect* for the popular will with an increasing *role* in the key decision-making institutions of individuals with special intellectual and scientific attainments." (Italics added.) Naturally, "The educational and social systems [will make] it increasingly attractive and easy for those meritocratic few to develop to the fullest of their special potential."

However, while it will be ". . . necessary to require everyone at a sufficiently responsible post to take, say, two years of [scientific and technical]
retraining every ten years . . . ," the rest of us can develop a new ". . . interest
in the cultural and humanistic aspects of life, *in addition to purely hedonistic
preoccupations.*" (Italics added.) The latter, he is careful to point out, "would
serve as a social valve, reducing tensions and political frustration."

Is it not fair to ask how much *respect* we carefree pleasure lovers and culture consumers will get from the hard-working bureaucrats, going to night
school two years in every ten, while working like beavers in the "key decision-
making institutions"? The altruism of our bureaucrats has a heavy load to
bear.

Stripped of their euphemisms these are simply arguments which enhance
the social legitimacy of the interests of new technical and scientific elites and
detract from the interests of the rest of us; that is to say, if we can even formulate those interests, blinded as we will be by the mad pursuit of pleasures
(and innovation??!) heaped up for us by advanced technology. Mesthene and
his schoolfellows try to argue around their own derogation of the democratic
ethos by frequent references, as we have seen, to their own fealty to it. But it
is instructive in this regard to note that they tend, with Brzezinski, to find the
real substance of that democratic ethos in the principle of the equality of opportunity. Before we applaud, however, we ought to examine the role which
that principle plays within the framework of the advanced technological society they propose.

As has already been made clear the *laissez innover* school accepts as inevitable and desirable the centralizing tendencies of technology's social organization, and they accept as well the mystification which comes to surround
the management process. Thus equality of opportunity, as they understand it,
has precious little to do with creating a more egalitarian society. On the contrary, it functions as an indispensable feature of the highly stratified society
they envision for the future. For in their society of meritocratic hierarchy,
equality of opportunity assures that talented young meritocrats (the word is
no uglier than the social system it refers to) will be able to climb into the
"key decision-making" slots reserved for trained talent, and thus generate the
success of the new society, and its cohesion against popular "tensions and
political frustration."

The structures which formerly guaranteed the rule of wealth, age, and
family will not be destroyed (or at least not totally so). They will be firmed
up and rationalized by the perpetual addition of trained (and, of course, ac-
culturated) talent. In technologically advanced societies, equality of oppor-

tunity functions as a hierarchical principle, in opposition to the egalitarian social goals it pretends to serve. To the extent that it has already become the kind of "equality" we seek to institute in our society, it is one of the main factors contributing to the widening gap between the cultures of upper- and lower-class America.

V

Approximately a century ago, the philosophy of *laissez faire* began its period of hegemony in American life. Its success in achieving that hegemony clearly had less to do with its merits as a summary statement of economic truth than with its role in the social struggle of the time. It helped to identify the interests of the institutions of entrepreneurial capitalism for the social classes which dominated them and profited from them. Equally, it sketched in bold strokes the outlines of a society within which the legitimate interests of all could supposedly be served only by systematic deference to the interests of entrepreneurial capitalists, their institutions, and their social allies. In short, the primary significance of *laissez faire* lay in its role as ideology, as the cultural or intellectual expression of the interests of a class.

Something like the same thing must be said of *laissez innover*. As a summary statement of the relationship between social and technological change it obscures far more than it clarifies, but that is often the function and genius of ideologues. *Laissez innover* is now the premier ideology of the technological impulse in American society, which is to say, of the institutions which monopolize and profit from advanced technology and of the social classes which find in the free exploitation of *their* technology the most likely guarantee of their power, status, and wealth.

This said, it is important to stress both the significance and limitations of what has in fact been said. Here Mesthene's distinction between the positive opportunities and negative "externalities" inherent in technological change is pivotal; for everything else which I've argued follows inferentially from the actual social meaning of that distinction. As my analysis of the Vietnam bombing program suggested, those technological effects which are sought after as positive opportunities and those which are dismissed as negative externalities are decisively influenced by the fact that this distinction between positive and negative within advanced technological organizations tends to be made among the planners and managers themselves. Within these groups there are, as was pointed out, extremely powerful organizational, hierarchical, doctrinal, and other *"technical"* factors, which tend by design to filter out "irrational" demands from below, substituting for them the "rational" demands of technology itself. As a result, technological rationality is as socially neutral today as market rationality was a century ago.

Turning from the inner social logic of advanced technological organizations and systems to their larger social effect, we can observe a significant convergence. For both the social tendency of technology and the ideology (or rhetoric) of the *laissez innover* school converge to encourage a political and cultural gap between the upper and lower ends of American society. As I have pointed out, these can now be characterized as those who manage and those who are managed by advanced technological systems.

This analysis lends some weight (though perhaps no more than that) to a number of wide-ranging and unorthodox conclusions about American society today and the directions in which it is tending. It may be useful to sketch out the most important of those conclusions in the form of a set of linked hypotheses, not only to clarify what appear to be the latent tendencies of America's advanced technological society but also to provide more useful guides to the investigation of the technological impulse than those offered by the obscurantism and abstractions of the school of *laissez innover.*

First, and most important, technology should be considered as an institutional system, not more and certainly not less. Mesthene's definition of the subject is inadequate, for it obscures the systematic and decisive social changes, especially their political and cultural tendencies, that follow the widespread application of advanced technological systems. At the same time, technology is less than a social system per se, though it has many elements of a social system, viz., an elite, a group of linked institutions, an ethos, and so forth. Perhaps the best summary statement of the case resides in an analogy— with all the vagueness and precision attendant on such things: today's technology stands in relation to today's capitalism as, a century ago, the latter stood to the free market capitalism of the time.

The analogy suggests, accurately enough I believe, the likelihood that the institutional links and shared interests among the larger corporations, the federal government, especially its military sector, the multiversity and the foundations, will grow rather than decline. It suggests further a growing entanglement of their elites, probably in the neo-corporations of technology, such as urban development corporations and institutes for defense analysis, whose importance seems likely to increase markedly in the future.

Finally, it suggests a growing convergence in the ethos and ideology of technology's leading classes along lines which would diminish slightly the relative importance of rhetoric about "property" and even about "national security," while enhancing the rhetoric of *laissez innover*. This does not necessarily imply any sacrifice in the prerogatives of either the private sector or of the crisis managers and the military, for one can readily understand how the elite strictures of *laissez innover* may be applied to strengthen the position of the corporate and military establishments.[5]

A word about the elites: a number of writers of the *laissez innover* school, for example, J. K. Galbraith in his *The New Industrial State,* have argued that the enhanced importance of scientific and technical knowledge within advanced technological systems implies an enhanced socio-political power for the people who have such knowledge. Galbraith in particular has argued that these people, whom he calls "the educational and scientific estate," now constitute an elite class whose interests diverge quite sharply from those of other elites. Since I have argued at length elsewhere against this view,[6] let me limit myself here to only a few critical observances.

5. An interesting illustration of this point is provided by the major change in national security policy brought about in the first years of the Kennedy Administration, a change in which many *laissez innover* writers—Walt Rostow comes immediately to mind—played a prominent intellectual and policy-making role. One of the goals of the new policy was to assign an enhanced importance to American efforts to aid in the development of the so-called underdeveloped world. The leading ideas of the policy were very much influenced by *laissez innover*, for the process of development in the third world nations was largely conceived of as a process of nurturing a technologically advanced sector in the host economy to the point at which it would be able to dominate, economically, socially, politically the remainder of the society. At that "take-off" point American efforts could presumably be relaxed for the further development of the country would be assured, along with its integration into an international economy dominated by the US.

Superficially this might appear as a policy change in which the interests of the American military were sacrificed, at least partially, to those of AID and the State Department. Certainly, slogans to that effect—"less military aid; more economic aid"—seemed to indicate this. But in practice the nation-builders quickly found that the military of the third world nations were their best allies. Theory was quickly adjusted to the needs of practice.

The military in a non-industrialized economy have an abiding interest in the development of a modern economic infrastructure, not least because such an infrastructure is essential to support the modern weaponry amply supplied by the US—a fact about social leverage not lost on our policymakers. The social cohesion even of a swollen officers corps tends to offset the general social fractionation resulting from the changes of modernization and, of course, officers tend to be stalwartly anti-communist.

Thus, in spite of a change in rhetoric under Kennedy, the reality of the AID program very much served the interests of our own military; by strengthening the military capacity of other nations, by providing an expanding advisory role for our officers corps, and, not least important, by maintaining a growing market for American military equipment, both new and used. As an added fillip, the burst of nation-building activity under Kennedy also provided, as in Vietnam, a host of new overseas "commitments," which of course necessitated a major rearmament program for our conventional (i.e., limited war) forces.

6. "Knowledge is Power," *The Nation,* April 14, 1969. Galbraith's "educational and scientific estate" seems but a variant of Keller's strategic elites. . . . In fairness to Gal-

Galbraith's concept of an "educational and scientific" elite class overlooks the peculiar relationship which the members of that supposed class have to advanced technology. Specifically, it overlooks the fact that most technical, scientific, and educational people are employed at relatively specialized tasks within very large organizations whose managing and planning levels are hardly less insulated from their influence than from the influence of the technically unskilled.

The obvious growth in status and, I think, power of such men as Ithiel de Sola Pool, Herman Kahn, Samuel Huntington, Daniel Patrick Moynihan, Henry Kissinger, Charles Hitch, and Paul Samuelson hardly represents the triumph of wisdom over power—an implication not absent from Galbraith's analysis. An examination of the role which these men now play in our national life should emphasize that they are scientific and technical entrepreneurs whose power is largely based on their ability to mobilize *organized* intellectual, scientific, and technical manpower and other resources, including foundation grants and university sponsorship, in behalf of the objectives of going institutions. They are much more like managers than like intellectuals, much more like brokers than like analysts.

The same hardly applies to the thousands of E.E.'s, Ph.D.'s, M.S.'s, and so forth who make up the resources over which these mandarins preside and whose skills are so much at their disposal. But in recognizing the managerial and brokerage functions which predominate in the mandarin role we must also recognize that mandarin interests are more likely than not to converge

braith it should be pointed out that he too is concerned with the authoritarianism and anti-humanism of the technology. His "educational and scientific estate" is supposed to reintroduce democratic and humanist values into society because it, being highly educated, has these things in overabundance. On the whole this seems a dubious proposition. Democracy is vital only when it expresses some sort of social equilibrium; elite ideologies attack the legitimacy of social equilibrium and reduce democracy or democratic values thereby to some sort of elite benevolence toward the unwashed. Similarly, a humanist technology seems not likely to come from a class of humanist masters of technology. Mastership usually interferes with humanism in such cases. Humanist values become like Sunday School values; very good in themselves but not much in use during the week.

Any discussion of a reorganization of technology to serve human needs seems, at this point, so utopian that it robs one of the conviction necessary to shape a believable vision. Perhaps in a period of greater technological stability it would be possible to conjure up an alternate vision, but now, when the rush to technological centralization is so powerful and rapid the task seems beyond us.

My own feeling is that the fundamental point to take account of in constructing an alternate vision is the fact that technology itself and its need for a skilled and knowledgeable population has created within the population ample resources for self-management even of the most complicated activities. For further discussion of this basic contradiction, see below.

toward the interests of other segments of the national elite. This conclusion is diametrically opposed to the one argued by Galbraith.

A second major hypothesis would argue that the most important dimension of advanced technological institutions is the social one, that is, the institutions are agencies of highly centralized and intensive social control. Technology conquers nature, as the saying goes. But to do so it must first conquer man. More precisely, it demands a very high degree of control over the training, mobility, and skills of the work force. The absence (or decline) of direct controls or of coercion should not serve to obscure from our view the reality and intensity of the social controls which are employed (such as the internalized belief in equality of opportunity, indebtedness through credit, advertising, selective service channeling, and so on).

Advanced technology has created a vast increase in occupational specialties, many of them requiring many, many years of highly specialized training. It must motivate this training. It has made ever more complex and "rational" the ways in which these occupational specialties are combined in our economic and social life. It must win passivity and obedience to this complex activity. Formerly, technical rationality had been employed only to organize the production of rather simple physical objects, for example, aerial bombs. Now technical rationality is increasingly employed to organize all of the processes necessary to the utilization of physical objects, such as bombing systems. For this reason it seems a mistake to argue that we are in a "post-industrial" age, a concept favored by the *laissez innover* school. On the contrary, the rapid spread of technical rationality into organizational and economic life and, hence, into social life is more aptly described as a second and much more intensive phase of the industrial revolution. One might reasonably suspect that it will create analogous social problems.

Accordingly, a third major hypothesis would argue that there are very profound social antagonisms or contradictions not less sharp or fundamental than those ascribed by Marx to the development of nineteenth-century industrial society. The general form of the contradictions might be described as follows: a society characterized by the employment of advanced technology requires an ever more socially disciplined population, yet retains an ever declining capacity to enforce the required discipline.

One may readily describe four specific forms of the same general contradiction. Occupationally, the work force must be over-trained and under-utilized. Here, again, an analogy to classical industrial practice serves to shorten and simplify the explanation. I have in mind the assembly line. As a device in the organization of the work process the assembly line is valuable mainly in that it gives management a high degree of control over the pace of the work and, more to the point in the present case, it divides the work process into units so simple that the quality of the work performed is readily predictable. That is, since each operation uses only a small fraction of a worker's skill, there is a very great likelihood that the operation will be performed in a minimally acceptable way. Alternately, if each operation taxed the worker's skill there would be frequent errors in the operation, frequent disturbance of the work flow, and a thoroughly unpredictable quality to the end product. The assembly line also introduces standardization in work skills and thus makes for a high degree of interchangeability among the work force.

For analogous reasons the work force in advanced technological systems must be relatively over-trained or, what is the same thing, its skills relatively under-used. My impression is that this is no less true now of sociologists than of welders, of engineers than of assemblers. The contradiction emerges when we recognize that technological progress requires a continuous increase in the skill levels of its work force, skill levels which frequently embody a fairly rich scientific and technical training, while at the same time the advance of technical rationality in work organization means that those skills will be less and less fully used.

Economically, there is a parallel process at work. It is commonly observed that the work force within technologically advanced organizations is asked to work not less hard but more so. This is particularly true for those with advanced training and skills. Brzezinski's conjecture that technical specialists undergo continuous retraining is off the mark only in that it assumes such retraining only for a managing elite. To get people to work harder requires growing incentives. Yet the prosperity which is assumed in a technologically advanced society erodes the value of economic incentives (while of course, the values of craftsmanship are "irrational"). Salary and wage increases and the goods they purchase lose their over-riding importance once necessities, creature comforts, and an ample supply of luxuries are assured. As if in confirmation of this point, *Fortune* has pointed out (January 1969) that among young people one can already observe a radical weakening in the power of such incentives as money, status, and authority.

Politically, the advance of technology tends to concentrate authority within its managing groups in the ways I have described. But at the same time the increasing skill and educational levels of the population create latent capacities for self-management in the work place and in society. This aspect of the contradictions inherent in technology seems especially noteworthy in much of the current dissent within the armed forces. Of course, there has al-

ways been griping in the Army, but the fact that the griping now attaches itself to political problems—the war, the rights of servicemen, and so on—clearly
speaks to the fact that GI educational levels have increased very radically.

A similar explanation casts light on the campus revolt. As Lionel Trilling
has pointed out (*Partisan Review,* Summer 1968), the cultural and intellectual
level of today's university students is far higher than that of their predeces-
sors, if only because of television and the fact that a good part of traditional
college work is now completed in the better high schools. The claim to greater
self-management by university students is the natural outcome of this change.
At the same time, however, the university has been developing the power and
status of its own elites. These include the research elites whose power and
status are based on consultantships, on their ability to win research grants and
contracts and thus prestige for their universities, as well as the more general
category of professional elite, i.e., those whose power within the university is
buttressed by their prestige in the national professional associations and expressed in their control of the major academic departments. In spite of the
apparent decentralization within the university organization, one must recognize that there has been a very tangible increase in the influence of these
elites. Within the university (as elsewhere) power has become more centralized, that is, it has gravitated toward an identifiable collection of research and
professional mandarins. It is the power of the latter over curriculum, admissions, research and consulting policy, hiring and advancement that is being
challenged by student dissidence.[7]

It should be added here that even the "irrationality" of the student revolt
is clarified by the general lines of this explanation, i.e., its common failure to
formulate coherent social programs and its tendency to enter battle under extremely vague symbolic banners. As we have seen social irrationality can be

7. The foregoing explanation is confirmed, I believe, by some salient aspects of the history of the student movement. Most of the radical student groups began and grew to
prominence on elite campuses, i.e., on campuses where the contradiction between the
cultural level of the students and the institutional power of the mandarins was most
sharp. The New Left began at the University of Michigan and, after winning control over
the SDS organization, organized first at Harvard, Swarthmore, Chicago, Berkeley, and
other elite campuses. Only in the past two years has it reached out in any significant degree to non-elite campuses and in this it was very much aided by its militant stand against
the war and the draft. Even today, *on attitudes toward the university* (as opposed to the
war or racism, etc.) the most militant chapters are found in elite schools, Columbia, Chicago, Berkeley, and Harvard. The major exception to this statement is in California, especially San Francisco State, and my impression is that this has to do with the fact that the
California system of higher education is, in general, at a further stage of development
toward institutional hierarchy than those of most other states.

explained as a normal effect of the social and organizational patterns of advanced technological systems and, if anything, is increased by the personal intelligence of the people trapped in those systems.

Finally, there is a profound social contradiction between the highly stratified society implicit in, say, Brzezinski's meritocracy and the spread of educational opportunity. Yet each appears equally required by advanced technology.

These are brief and, I believe, barely adequate reviews of extremely complex hypotheses. But, in outline, each of these contradictions appears to bear on roughly the same group of the American population, a technological underclass. If we assume this to be the case, a fourth hypothesis would follow, namely that technology is creating the basis for new and sharp class conflict in our society. That is, technology is creating its own working and managing classes just as earlier industrialization created its working and owning classes. Perhaps this suggests a return to the kind of class-based politics which characterized the US in the last quarter of the nineteenth century, rather than the somewhat more ambiguous politics which was a feature of the second quarter of this century. I am inclined to think that this is the case, though I confess the evidence for it is as yet inadequate.

This leads to a final hypothesis, namely that *laissez innover* should be frankly recognized as a conservative or right-wing ideology. This is an extremely complex subject for the hypothesis must confront the very difficult fact that the intellectual genesis of *laissez innover* is traceable much more to leftist and socialist theorizing on the wonders of technical rationality and social planning than it is to the blood politics of a De Maistre or the traditionalism of a Burke. So be it. Much more important is the fact that *laissez innover* is now the most powerful and influential statement of the demands and program of the technological impulse in our society, an impulse rooted in its most powerful institutions. More than any other statement, it succeeds in identifying and rationalizing the interests of the most authoritarian elites within this country, and the expansionism of their policies overseas. Truly it is no accident that the leading figures of *laissez innover,* the Rostows, Kahn, Huntington, Brzezinski, to name but a few, are among the most unreconstructed cold warriors in American intellectual life.

The point of this final hypothesis is not primarily to re-impress the language of European politics on the American scene. Rather it is to summarize the fact that many of the forces in American life hostile to the democratic ethos have enrolled under the banner of *laissez innover.* Merely to grasp this is already to take the first step toward a politics of radical reconstruction and against the malaise, irrationality, powerlessness, and official violence that characterize American life today.

Can Technology Be Humane?

PAUL GOODMAN

On March 4, 1969 there was a "work stoppage" and teach-in initiated by dissenting professors at the Massachusetts Institute of Technology, and followed at thirty other major universities and technical schools across the country, against misdirected scientific research and the abuse of scientific technology. Here I want to consider this event in a broader context than the professors did, indeed as part of a religious crisis. For an attack on the American scientific establishment is an attack on the world-wide system of belief. I think we are on the eve of a new protestant Reformation, and no institution or status will go unaffected.

March 4 was, of course, only [one] of a series of protests in the [over] twenty-five years since the Manhattan Project to build the atom bomb, during which time the central funding of research and innovation has grown so enormously and its purposes have become so unpalatable. In 1940 the Federal budget for research and development was less than 100 million dollars, in 1967, 17 billion. Hitler's war was a watershed of modern times. We are accustomed, as H. R. Trevor-Roper has pointed out, to write Hitler off as an aberration, of little political significance. But, in fact, the military emergency that he and his Japanese allies created confirmed the worst tendencies of the giant states, till now they are probably irreversible by ordinary political means.

After Hiroshima, there was the conscience-stricken movement of the Atomic Scientists and the founding of their Bulletin. The American Association for the Advancement of Science pledged itself to keep the public informed about the dangerous bearings of new developments. There was the Oppenheimer incident. Ads of the East Coast scientists successfully stopped the bomb shelters, warned about the fall-out, and helped produce the test ban. There was a scandal about the bombardment of the Van Allen belt. Scientists and technologists formed a powerful (and misguided) *ad hoc* group for Johnson in the 1964 election. In some universities, sometimes with bitter struggle, classified contracts have been excluded. There is a Society for Social Responsibility in Science. Rachel Carson's book on the pesticides caused a stir, until the Department of Agriculture rescued the manufacturers and plantation-owners. Ralph Nader has been on his rampage. Thanks to spectacular abuses like smog, strip-mining, asphalting, pesticides, and oil pollution, even ecologists and conservationists have been getting a hearing. Protest against the boom has slowed up the development of the supersonic transport[, particularly in the United States]. Most recent has been the concerted outcry against the anti-ballistic missiles.

. The target of protest has become broader and the grounds of complaint deeper. The target is now not merely the military, but the universities, commercial corporations, and government. It is said that money is being given by the wrong sponsors to the wrong people for the wrong purposes. In some of the great schools, such funding is the main support, e.g., at MIT, 90 percent of the research budget is from the government, and 65 percent of that is military.

Inevitably, such funding channels the brainpower of most of the brightest science students, who go where the action is, and this predetermines the course of American science and technology for the foreseeable future. At present nearly 200,000 American engineers and scientists spend all their time making weapons, which is a comment on, and perhaps explanation for, the usual statement that more scientists are now alive than since Adam and Eve. And the style of such research and development is not good. It is dominated by producing hardware, figuring logistics, and devising salable novelties. Often there is secrecy, always nationalism. Since the grants go overwhelmingly through a very few corporations and universities, they favor a limited number of scientific attitudes and preconceptions, with incestuous staffing. There is a premium on "positive results"; surprising "failures" cannot be pursued, so that science ceases to be a wandering dialogue with the unknown.

The policy is economically wasteful. A vast amount of brains and money is spent on crash programs to solve often essentially petty problems, and the claim that there is a spin-off of useful discoveries is derisory, if we consider the sums involved. The claim that research is neutral, and it doesn't matter what one works on, is shabby, if we consider the heavy funding in certain directions. Social priorities are scandalous: money is spent on overkill, supersonic planes, brand-name identical drugs, annual model changes of cars, new detergents, and color television, whereas water, air, space, food, health, and foreign aid are neglected. And much research is morally so repugnant, e.g., chemical and biological weapons, that one dares not humanly continue it.

The state of the behavioral sciences is, if anything, worse. Their claim to moral and political neutrality becomes, in effect, a means of diverting attention from glaring social evils, and they are in fact used—or would be if they worked—for warfare and social engineering, manipulation of people for the political and economic purposes of the powers that be. This is an especially sad betrayal since, in the not-too-distant past, the objective social sciences were developed largely to dissolve orthodoxy, irrational authority, and taboo. They were heretical and intellectually revolutionary, as the physical sciences had been in their own Heroic Age, and they weren't getting government grants.

This is a grim indictment. Even so, I do not think the dissenting scientists understand how deep their trouble is. They still take themselves too much for granted. Indeed, a repeated theme of the March 4 [1969] complaints was that the science budget was being cut back, especially in basic research. The assumption was that though the sciences are abused, Science would rightly maintain and increase its expensive pre-eminence among social institutions. Only Science could find the answers.

But underlying the growing dissent there is an historical crisis. There has been a profound change in popular feeling, more than among the professors. Put it this way: Modern societies have been operating as if religion were a minor and moribund part of the scheme of things. But this is unlikely. Men do not do without a system of "meanings" that everybody believes and puts his hope in even if, or especially if, he doesn't know anything about it; what Freud called a "shared psychosis," meaningful because shared, and with the power that resides in dream and longing. In fact, in advanced countries it is science and technology themselves that have gradually and finally triumphantly become the system of mass faith, not disputed by various political ideologies and nationalism that have also been mass religions. Marxism called itself "scientific socialism" as against moral and utopian socialisms; and movements of national liberation have especially promised to open the benefits of industrialization and technological progress when once they have gotten rid of the imperialists.

For three hundred years, science and scientific technology had an unblemished and justified reputation as a wonderful adventure, pouring out practical benefits, and liberating the spirit from the errors of superstition and traditional faith. During this century they have finally been the only generally credited system of explanation and problem-solving. Yet in our generation they have come to seem to many, and to very many of the best of the young, as essentially inhuman, abstract, regimenting, hand-in-glove with Power, and even diabolical. Young people say that science is anti-life, it is a Calvinist obsession, it has been a weapon of white Europe to subjugate colored races, and manifestly—in view of recent scientific technology—people who think that way become insane. With science, the other professions are discredited; and the academic "disciplines" are discredited.

The immediate reasons for this shattering reversal of values are fairly obvious. Hitler's ovens and his other experiments in eugenics, the first atom bombs and their frenzied subsequent developments, the deterioration of the physical environment and the destruction of the biosphere, the catastrophes impending over the cities because of technological failures and psychological stress, the prospect of a brainwashed and drugged 1984. Innovations yield diminishing returns in enhancing life. And instead of rejoicing, there is now widespread conviction that beautiful advances in genetics, surgery, computers, rocketry, or atomic energy will surely only increase human woe.

In such a crisis, in my opinion, it will not be sufficient to ban the military from the universities; and it will not even be sufficient, as liberal statesmen and many of the big corporations envisage, to beat the swords into ploughshares and turn to solving problems of transportation, desalinization, urban renewal, garbage disposal, and cleaning up the air and water. If the present difficulty is religious and historical, it is necessary to alter the entire relationship of science, technology, and social needs both in men's minds and in fact. This involves changes in the organization of science, in scientific education, and in the kinds of men who make scientific decisions.

In spite of the fantasies of hippies, we are certainly going to continue to live in a technological world. The question is a different one: is that workable?

PRUDENCE

Whether or not it draws on new scientific research, technology is a branch of moral philosophy, not of science. It aims at prudent goods for the commonweal and to provide efficient means for these goods. At present, however, "scientific technology" occupies a bastard position in the universities, in funding, and in the public mind. It is half tied to the theoretical sciences and half treated as mere know-how for political and commercial purposes. It has no principles of its own. To remedy this—so Karl Jaspers in Europe and Robert Hutchins in America have urged—technology must have its proper place on the faculty as a learned profession important in modern society, along with medicine, law, the humanities, and natural philosophy, learning from them and having something to teach them. As a moral philosopher, a technician should be able to criticize the programs given him to implement. As a professional in a community of learned professionals, a technologist must have a different kind of training and develop a different character than we see at present among technicians and engineers. He should know something of the social sciences, law, the fine arts, and medicine, as well as relevant natural sciences.

Prudence is foresight, caution, utility. Thus it is up to the technologists, not to regulatory agencies of the government, to provide for safety and to think about remote effects. This is what Ralph Nader is saying and Rachel Carson used to ask. An important aspect of caution is flexibility, to avoid the pyramiding catastrophe that occurs when something goes wrong in interlocking technologies, as in urban power failures. Naturally, to take responsibility for such things often requires standing up to the front office and urban politicians, and technologists must organize themselves in order to have power to do it.

Often it is clear that a technology has been oversold, like the cars. Then even though the public, seduced by advertising, wants more, technologists must balk, as any professional does when his client wants what isn't good for him. We are now repeating the same self-defeating congestion with the planes and airports: the more the technology is oversold, the less immediate utility it provides, the greater the costs, and the more damaging the remote effects. As this becomes evident, it is time for technologists to confer with sociologists and economists and ask deeper questions. Is so much travel necessary? Are there ways to diminish it? Instead, the recent history of technology has consisted largely of a desperate effort to remedy situations caused by previous over-application of technology.

Technologists should certainly have a say about simple waste, for even in an affluent society there are priorities—consider the supersonic transport, which has little to recommend it. But the moon shot has presented the more usual dilemma of authentic conflicting claims. I myself believe that space exploration is a great human adventure, with immense aesthetic and moral benefits, whatever the scientific or utilitarian uses. Yet it is amazing to me that the scientists and technologists involved have not spoken more insistently for international cooperation instead of a puerile race. But I have heard some say that except for this chauvinist competition, Congress would not vote any money at all.

Currently, perhaps the chief moral criterion of a philosophic technology is modesty, having a sense of the whole and not obtruding more than a particular function warrants. Immodesty is always a danger of free enterprise, but when the same disposition is financed by big corporations, technologists rush into production with neat solutions that swamp the environment. This applies to packaging products and disposing of garbage, to freeways that bulldoze neighborhoods, high-rises that destroy landscape, wiping out a species for a passing fashion, strip mining, scrapping an expensive machine rather than making a minor repair, draining a watershed for irrigation because (as in Southern California) the cultivable land has been covered by asphalt. Given this disposition, it is not surprising that we defoliate a forest in order to expose a guerrilla and spray teargas from a helicopter on a crowded campus.

Since we are technologically over-committed, a good general maxim in advanced countries at present is to innovate in order to simplify the technical system, but otherwise to innovate as sparingly as possible. Every advanced country is over-technologized; past a certain point, the quality of life diminishes with new "improvements." Yet no country is rightly technologized, making efficient use of available techniques. There are ingenious devices for unimportant functions, stressful mazes for essential functions, and drastic dislocation when anything goes wrong, which happens with increasing frequency. To add to the complexity, the mass of people tend to become incompetent and dependent on repairmen—indeed, unrepairability except by experts has become a desideratum of industrial design.

When I speak of slowing down or cutting back, the issue is not whether research and making working models should be encouraged or not. They should be, in every direction, and given a blank check. The point is to resist the temptation to apply every new device without a second thought. But the big corporate organization of research and development makes prudence and modesty very difficult; it is necessary to get big contracts and rush into production in order to pay the salaries of the big team. Like other bureaucracies, technological organizations are run to maintain themselves but they are more dangerous because, in capitalist countries, they are in a competitive arena.

I mean simplification quite strictly, to simplify the *technical* system. I am unimpressed by the argument that what is technically more complicated is really economically or politically simpler, e.g., by complicating the packaging we improve the supermarkets; by throwing away the machine rather than repairing it, we give cheaper and faster service all around; or even by expanding the economy with trivial innovations, we increase employment, allay discontent, save on welfare. Such ideas may be profitable for private companies or political parties, but for society they have proved to be an accelerating rat race. The technical structure of the environment is too important to be a political or economic pawn; the effect on the quality of life is too disastrous; and the hidden social costs are not calculated, the auto graveyards, the torn-up streets, the longer miles of commuting, the advertising, the inflation, etc. As I pointed out in *People or Personnel,* a country with a fourth of our per capita income, like Ireland, is not necessarily less well off; in some respects it is much richer, in some respects a little poorer. If possible, it is better to solve political problems by political means. For instance, if teaching machines and audio-visual aids are indeed educative, well and good; but if they are used just to save money on teachers, then not good at all—nor do they save money.

Of course, the goals of right technology must come to terms with other values of society. I am not a technocrat. But the advantage of raising technology to be a responsible learned profession with its own principles is that it can have a voice in the debate and argue for *its* proper contribution to the community. Consider the important case of modular sizes in building, or prefabrication of a unit bathroom: these conflict with the short-run interests of manufacturers and craft-unions, yet to deny them is technically an abomination. The usual recourse is for a government agency to set standards; such agencies accommodate to interests that have a strong voice, and at present technologists have no voice.

The crucial need for technological simplification, however, is not in the advanced countries—which can afford their clutter and probably deserve it—but in underdeveloped countries which must rapidly innovate in order to diminish disease, drudgery, and deepening starvation. They cannot afford to make mistakes. It is now widely conceded that the technological aid we have given to such areas according to our own high style—a style usually demanded by the native ruling groups—has done more harm than good. Even when, as frequently if not usually, aid has been benevolent, without strings attached, not military, and not dumping, it has nevertheless disrupted ways of life, fomented tribal wars, accelerated urbanization, decreased the food supply, gone wasted for lack of skills to use it, developed a do-nothing élite.

By contrast, a group of international scientists called Intermediate Technology argue that what is needed is techniques that use only native labor, resources, traditional customs, and teachable know-how, with the simple aim of remedying drudgery, disease, and hunger, so that people can then develop further in their own style. This avoids cultural imperialism. Such intermediate techniques may be quite primitive, on a level unknown among us for a couple of centuries, and yet they may pose extremely subtle problems, requiring exquisite scientific research and political and human understanding, to devise a very simple technology. Here is a reported case (which I trust I remember accurately): In Botswana, a very poor country, pasture was over-grazed, but the economy could be salvaged if the land were fenced. There was no local material for fencing, and imported fencing was prohibitively expensive. The solution was to find the formula and technique to make posts out of mud, and a pedagogic method to teach people how to do it.

In *The Two Cultures,* C. P. Snow berated the humanists for their irrelevance when two-thirds of mankind are starving and what is needed is science and technology. They have perhaps been irrelevant; but unless technology is itself more humanistic and philosophical, it is of no use. There is only one culture.

Finally, let me make a remark about amenity as a technical criterion. It is discouraging to see the concern about beautifying a highway and banning billboards, and about the cosmetic appearance of the cars, when there is no regard for the ugliness of bumper-to-bumper traffic and the suffering of the drivers. Or the concern for preserving an historical landmark while the neighborhood is torn up and the city has no shape. Without moral philosophy, people have nothing but sentiments.

ECOLOGY

The complement to prudent technology is the ecological approach to science. To simplify the technical system and modestly pinpoint our artificial intervention in the environment makes it possible for the environment to survive in its complexity evolved for a billion years, whereas the overwhelming instant intervention of tightly interlocked and bulldozing technology has already disrupted many of the delicate sequences and balances. The calculable consequences are already frightening, but of course we don't know enough, and won't in the foreseeable future, to predict the remote effects of much of what we have done. The only possible conclusion is to be prudent; when there is serious doubt, to do nothing.

Cyberneticists—I am thinking of Gregory Bateson—come to the same cautious conclusion. The use of computers has enabled us to carry out crashingly inept programs on the bases of willful analyses. But we have also become increasingly alert to the fact that things respond, systematically, continually, cumulatively; they cannot simply be manipulated or pushed around. Whether bacteria or weeds or bugs or the technologically unemployed or unpleasant thoughts, they cannot be eliminated and forgotten; repressed, the nuisances return in new forms. A complicated system works most efficiently if its parts readjust themselves decentrally, with a minimum of central intervention or control, except in case of breakdown. Usually there is an advantage in a central clearing house of information about the gross total situation, but decision and execution require more minute local information. The fantastically simulated moon landing hung on a last split-second correction on the spot. In social organization, deciding in headquarters means relying on information that is cumulatively abstract and irrelevant, and chain-of-command execution applies standards that cumulatively do not fit the concrete situation. By and large it is better, given a sense of the whole picture, for those in the field to decide what to do and do it (cf. *People or Personnel,* Chapter 3).

But with organisms too, this has long been the bias of psychosomatic medicine, the Wisdom of the Body, as Cannon called it. To cite a classical experiment of Ralph Hefferline of Columbia: a subject is wired to suffer an annoying regular buzz, which can be delayed and finally eliminated if he makes a precise but unlikely gesture, say by twisting his ankle in a certain way; then it is found that he adjusts quicker if he is *not* told the method and it is left to his spontaneous twitching than if he is told and tries deliberately to help himself. He adjusts better without conscious control, his own or the experimenter's.

Technological modesty, fittingness, is not negative. It is the ecological wisdom of cooperating with Nature rather than trying to master her. (The personification of "Nature" is linguistic wisdom.) A well-known example is the long-run superiority of partial pest-control in farming by using biological deterrents rather than chemical ones. The living defenders work harder, at the right moment, and with more pin-pointed targets. But let me give another example because it is so lovely—though I have forgotten the name of my informant: A tribe in Yucatan educates its children to identify and pull up all weeds in the region; then what is left is a garden of useful plants that have chosen to be there and now thrive.

In the life sciences there is at present a suggestive bifurcation in methodology. The rule is still to increase experimental intervention, but there is also a considerable revival of old-fashioned naturalism, mainly watching and thinking, with very modest intervention. Thus, in medicine, there is new diagnostic machinery, new drugs, spectacular surgery; but there is also a new respect for family practice with a psychosomatic background, and a strong push, among young doctors and students, for a social-psychological and sociological approach, aimed at preventing disease and building up resistance. In psychology, the operant conditioners multiply and refine their machinery to give maximum control of the organism and the environment (I have not heard of any dramatic discoveries, but perhaps they have escaped me). On the other hand, the most interesting psychology in recent years has certainly come from animal naturalists, e.g., pecking order, territoriality, learning to control aggression, language of the bees, overcrowding among rats, trying to talk to dolphins.

On a fair judgment, both contrasting approaches give positive results. The logical scientific problem that arises is, What is there in the nature of things that makes a certain method, or even moral attitude, work well or poorly in a given case? This question is not much studied. Every scientist seems to know what "the" scientific method is.

Another contrast of style, extremely relevant at present, is that between Big Science and old-fashioned shoe-string science. There is plenty of research, with corresponding technology, that can be done only by Big Science; yet much, and perhaps most, of science will always be shoe-string science, for which it is absurd to use the fancy and expensive equipment that has gotten to be the fashion.

Consider urban medicine. The problem, given a shortage of doctors and facilities, is how to improve the level of mass health, the vital statistics, and yet to practice medicine, which aims at the maximum possible health for each person. Perhaps the most efficient use of Big Science technology for the general health would be compulsory biennial checkups, as we inspect cars, for early diagnosis and to forestall chronic conditions with accumulating costs. Then an excellent machine would be a total diagnostic bus to visit the neighborhoods, as we do chest X-rays. On the other hand, for actual treatment and especially for convalescence, the evidence seems to be that small personalized hospitals are best. And to revive family practice, maybe the right idea is to offer a doctor a splendid suite in a public housing project.

Our contemporary practice makes little sense. We have expense technology stored in specialists' offices and big hospitals, really unavailable for mass use in the neighborhoods; yet every individual, even if he is quite rich, finds it almost impossible to get attention to himself as an individual whole organism in his setting. He is sent from specialist to specialist and exists as a bag of symptoms and a file of test scores.

In automating there is an analogous dilemma of how to cope with masses of people and get economies of scale, without losing the individual at great consequent human and economic cost. A question of immense importance for the immediate future is, Which functions should be automated or organized to use business machines, and which should not? This question also is not getting asked, and the present disposition is that the sky is the limit for extraction, refining, manufacturing, processing, packaging, transportation, clerical work, ticketing, transactions, information retrieval, recruitment, middle management, evaluation, diagnosis, instruction, and even research and invention. Whether the machines can do all these kinds of jobs and more is partly an empirical question, but it also partly depends on what is meant by doing a job. Very often, e.g., in college admissions, machines are acquired for putative economies (which do not eventuate); but the true reason is that an overgrown and overcentralized organization cannot be administered without them. The technology conceals the essential trouble, e.g., that there is no community of scholars and students are treated like things. The function is badly performed, and finally the system breaks down anyway. I doubt that enterprises in which interpersonal relations are important are suited to much programming.

But worse, what can happen is that the real function of the enterprise is subtly altered so that it is suitable for the mechanical system. (E.g., "information retrieval" is taken as an adequate replacement for critical scholarship.) Incommensurable factors, individual differences, the local context, the weighting of evidence are quietly overlooked though they may be of the essence. The system, with its subtly transformed purposes, seems to run very smoothly; it is productive, and it is more and more out of line with the nature of things and the real problems. Meantime it is geared in with other enterprises of society, e.g., major public policy may depend on welfare or unemployment statistics which, as they are tabulated, are blind to the actual lives of poor families. In such a case, the particular system may not break down, the whole society may explode.

I need hardly point out that American society is peculiarly liable to the corruption of inauthenticity, busily producing phony products. It lives by public relations, abstract ideals, front politics, show-business communications, mandarin credentials. It is preeminently overtechnologized. And computer technologists especially suffer for the euphoria of being in a new and rapidly expanding field. It is so astonishing that the robot can do the job at all or seem to do it, that it is easy to blink at the fact that he is doing it badly or isn't really doing quite that job.

DECENTRALIZATION

The current political assumption is that scientists and inventors, and even social scientists, are "value-neutral," but their discoveries are "applied" by those who make decisions for the nation. Counter to this, I have been insinuating a kind of Jeffersonian democracy or guild socialism, that scientists and inventors and other workmen are responsible for the uses of the work they do, and ought to be competent to judge these uses and have a say in deciding them. They usually are competent. To give a striking example, Ford assembly line workers, according to Harvey Swados, who worked with them, are accurately critical of the glut of cars, but they have no way to vent their dissatisfactions with their useless occupation except to leave nuts and bolts to rattle in the body.

My bias is also pluralistic. Instead of the few national goals of a few decision-makers, I propose that there are many goods of many activities of life, and many professions and other interest groups each with its own criteria and goals that must be taken into account. A society that distributes power widely is superficially conflictful but fundamentally stable.

Research and development ought to be widely decentralized, the national fund for them being distributed through thousands of centers of initiative and decision. This would not be chaotic. We seem to have forgotten that for four hundred years Western science majestically progressed with no central direction whatever, yet with exquisite international coordination, little duplication, almost nothing getting lost, in constant communication despite slow facilities. The reason was simply that all scientists wanted to get on with the same enterprise of testing the boundaries of knowledge, and they relied on one another.

What is as noteworthy is that something similar holds also in invention and innovation, even in recent decades when there has been such a concentration of funding and apparent concentration of opportunity. The majority of big advances have still come from independents, partnerships, and tiny companies. (Evidence published by the Senate Sub-Committee on Antitrust and Monopoly, May 1965.) To name a few, jet engines, xerography, automatic transmission, cellophane, air-conditioning, quick freeze, antibiotics, and tranquilizers. The big technological teams must have disadvantages that outweigh their advantages, like lack of singlemindedness, poor communications, awkward scheduling. Naturally, big corporations have taken over the innovations, but the Senate evidence is that 90 percent of the government subsidy has gone for last-stage development for production, which they ought to have paid out of their own pockets.

We now have a theory that we have learned to learn, and that we can program technical progress, directed by a central planning board. But this doesn't make it so. The essence of the new still seems to be that nobody has thought of it, and the ones who get ideas are those in direct contact with the work. *Too precise* a preconception of what is wanted discourages creativity more than it channels it; and bureaucratic memoranda from distant directors don't help. This is especially true when, as at present, so much of the preconception of what is wanted comes from desperate political anxiety in emergencies. Solutions that emerge from such an attitude rarely strike out on new paths, but rather repeat traditional thinking with new gimmicks; they tend to compound the problem. A priceless advantage of widespread decentralization is that it engages more minds, and more mind, instead of a few panicky (or greedy) corporate minds.

A homespun advantage of small groups, according to the Senate testimony, is that co-workers can talk to one another, without schedules, reports, clock-watching, and face-saving.

An important hope from decentralizing science is to develop knowledgeable citizens, and provide not only a bigger pool of scientists and inventors but also a public better able to protect itself and know how to judge the enormous budgets asked for. The safety of the environment is too important to be left to scientists, even ecologists. During the last decades of the nineteenth century and the first decade of the twentieth, the heyday of public faith in the beneficent religion of science and invention, say from Pasteur and Huxley to Edison and the Wright Brothers, philosophers of science had a vision of a "scientific way of life," one in which people would be objective, respectful of evidence, accurate, free of superstition and taboo, immune to irrational authority, experimental. All would be well, is the impression one gets from Thomas Huxley, if everybody knew the splendid Ninth Edition of the *Encyclopaedia Britannica* with its articles by Darwin and Clerk Maxwell. Veblen put his faith in the modesty and matter-of-factness of engineers to govern. Sullivan and Frank Lloyd Wright spoke for an austere functionalism and respect for the nature of materials and industrial processes. Patrick Geddes thought that new technology would finally get us out of the horrors of the Industrial Revolution and produce good communities. John Dewey devised a system of education to rear pragmatic and experimental citizens to be at home in the new technological world rather than estranged from it. Now fifty years later, we are in the swamp of a scientific and technological environment and there are more scientists alive, etc., etc. But the mention of the "scientific way of life" seems like black humor.

Many of those who have grown up since 1945 and have never seen any other state of science and technology assume that rationalism itself is totally evil and dehumanizing. It is probably more significant than we like to think that they go in for astrology and the Book of Changes, as well as inducing psychedelic dreams by technological means. Jacques Ellul, a more philosophic critic, tries to show that technology is necessarily over-controlling, standardizing, and voraciously inclusive, so that there is no place for freedom. But I doubt that any of this is intrinsic to science and technology. The crude history has been, rather, that they have fallen willingly under the dominion of money and power. Like Christianity or communism, the scientific way of life has never been tried.

THE NEW REFORMATION

To satisfy the March 4 dissenters, to break the military-industrial corporations and alter the priorities of the budget, would be to restructure the American economy almost to a revolutionary extent. But to meet the historical crisis of science at present, for science and technology to become prudent, ecological, and decentralized requires a change that is even more profound, a kind of religious transformation. Yet there is nothing untraditional in what I have proposed; prudence, ecology, and decentralization are indeed the high tradition of science and technology. Thus the closest analogy I can think of is the Protestant Reformation, a change of moral allegiance, liberation from the Whore of Babylon, return to the pure faith.

Science has long been the chief orthodoxy of modern times and has certainly been badly corrupted, but the deepest flaw of the affluent societies that has alienated the young is not, finally, their imperialism, economic injustice, or racism, bad as these are, but their nauseating phoniness, triviality, and wastefulness, the cultural and moral scandal that Luther found when he went to Rome in 1510. And precisely science, which should have been the wind of truth to clear the air, has polluted the air, helped to brainwash, and provided weapons for war. I doubt that most young people today have even heard of the ideal of the dedicated researcher, truculent and incorruptible, and unrewarded, for instance the "German scientist" that Sinclair Lewis described in *Arrowsmith*. Such a figure is no longer believable. I don't mean, of course, that he doesn't exist; there must be thousands of him, just as there were good priests in 1510.

The analogy to the Reformation is even more exact if we consider the school system, from educational toys and Head Start up through the universities. This system is manned by the biggest horde of monks since the time of Henry VIII. It is the biggest industry in the country. I have heard the estimate that 40 percent of the national product is in the Knowledge Business. It is mostly hocus-pocus. Yet the belief of parents in this institution is quite delusional and school diplomas are in fact the only entry to licensing and hiring in every kind of job. The abbots of this system are the chiefs of science, e.g., the National Science Foundation, who talk about reform but work to expand the school budgets, step up the curriculum, and inspire the endless catechism of tests.

These abuses are international, as the faith is. For instance, there is no essential difference between the military-industrial or the school system, of the Soviet Union and the United States. There are important differences in way of life and standard of living, but the abuses of technology are very similar: pollution, excessive urbanization, destruction of the biosphere, weaponry, and disastrous foreign aid. Our protesters naturally single out our own country, and the United States is the most powerful country, but the corruption we are speaking of is not specifically American nor even capitalist; it is a disease of modern times.

But the analogy is to the Reformation, it is not to primitive Christianity or some other primitivism, the abandonment of technological civilization. There is indeed much talk about the doom of Western civilization, and a few Adamites actually do retire into the hills; but for the great mass of mankind, and myself, that's not where it's at. There is not the slightest interruption to the universalizing of Western civilization, including most of its delusions, into the so-called Third World. (If the atom bombs go off, however?)

Naturally the exquisitely interesting question is whether or not this Reformation will occur, how to make it occur, against the entrenched worldwide system of corrupt power that is continually aggrandizing itself. I don't know. In my analogy I have deliberately been choosing the date 1510, Luther in Rome, rather than 1517 when, in the popular story, he nailed his Theses on the cathedral door. There are everywhere contradictory signs and dilemmas. The new professional and technological class is more and more entangled in the work, statuses, and rewards of the system, and yet this same class, often the very same people, are more and more protestant. On the other hand, the dissident young, who are unequivocally for radical change, are so alienated from occupation, function, knowledge, or even concern, that they often seem to be simply irrelevant to the underlying issues of modern times. The monks keep "improving" the schools and getting bigger budgets to do so, yet it is clear that high schools will be burned down, twelve-year-olds will play truant in droves, and the taxpayers are already asking what goes on and voting down the bonds.

The interlocking of technologies and all other institutions makes it almost impossible to reform policy in any part; yet this very interlocking that renders people powerless, including the decision-makers, creates a remarkable resonance and chain-reaction if any determined group, or even determined individual, exerts force. In the face of overwhelmingly collective operations like the space exploration, the average man must feel that local or grassroots efforts are worthless, there is no science but Big Science, and no administration but the State. And yet there is a powerful surge of localism, populism, and community action, as if people were determined to be free even it it makes no sense. A mighty empire is stood off by a band of peasants, and *neither* can win—this is even more remarkable than if David beats Goliath; it means that neither principle is historically adequate. In my opinion, these dilemmas and impasses show that we are on the eve of a transformation of conscience.

4

The Movement
Toward Control:
Technology Assessment

Throughout the first three parts of this book we have examined, in a rather general fashion, the manifold relationships between technology and society. Our emphasis has been on developing an understanding of the perspectives that different thinkers have brought to bear on the subject. One dimension, however, has been largely lacking from these perspectives—the dimension of policy. It is the political system through which man aggregates and allocates the resources needed to develop and implement large-scale technology. Further, it is through the political system that the cost and benefits associated with technologies are distributed throughout society. Thus, if we are to alter significantly the present patterns of technology-society interaction, it is likely that the changes involved will begin with the political system.

At this point we must shift our attention from the general problem of technology-society interaction to the specific case of the United States in the final third of the twentieth century. We are not concerned with a political system in the abstract, but we are seeking policy directions in the context of modern American democracy, given the strengths and the weaknesses of our pluralist system. A broad range of political possibilities exists. Some writers have proposed (or forecast) the establishment of a "meritocracy," in which scientists and engineers, because of their deep familiarity with the tools needed to run the technological society, become "philosopher-kings" and are entrusted with most of the political power. Others, representing a polar extreme, have discussed the need for a violent revolution to overthrow the current technological system, feeling that the costs of such a revolution are justified by its ends. Between these extremes are movements that seek peaceful social revolution, including radical changes in the manner in which technology is governed, and proposals that describe evolutionary shifts in social and political institutions. The current policy discussions focusing about the awkwardly phrased concept "technology assessment" represent such a system of evolutionary change. Within the framework of these discussions, scholars and policy makers, for the past several years, have been seeking to develop an appropriate political mechanism for predicting and controlling the effects of technology on a broader basis than is currently possible.

Since World War II, American government, particularly at the federal level, has been increasingly concerned with the support and utilization of scientific research. Policy for science and technology as well as science and technology for policy have been the subjects of considerable thought. The concept of technology assessment has begun to emerge from this body of thought as policy makers have felt the pressure of increasing societal preoccupation with such problems as environmental deterioration. The kinds of new political patterns likely to emerge from implementation of a technology-assessment mechanism will not be capable of dealing with the whole technology-society problem as conceptualized by Marcuse or Ellul. Nor can they have much effect on perceptual or characterological changes in human beings produced by technology. On the other hand, technology assessment is perhaps the first serious attempt by the central institutions of our political system to deal with the problem of controlling technology in a general and systematic fashion. The papers collected here are some of the most important to emerge from the technology-assessment discussions; thus, they merit our attention not only for their immediate practical importance but also because they serve to highlight some of the most salient political issues involved in controlling technology.

The term "technology assessment" was coined in 1967 by Emilio Q. Daddario, at the time a Democratic Congressman from Connecticut and chairman of the House Subcommittee on Science, Research, and Development. Daddario saw the problem of managing the technology-society relationship as one of utmost gravity and devoted a major share of his energies as a Congressman to it. In March 1967, he introduced a bill calling on the federal government to establish a Technology Assessment Board, in order "to provide a method for identifying, assessing, publicizing, and dealing with the implications and effects of applied research and technology." Daddario did not regard this bill as a finished piece of legislation, but he hoped that it would be a "stimulant to discussion." Indeed, a significant discussion has ensued, as the balance of this section will show. Daddario's own statement, defining the concept of technology assessment and explaining his intent in pursuing this line of legislative inquiry, constitutes the first selection. In it, Daddario describes the reasons for which he feels some assessment mechanism is needed, provides an historical perspective on the subject, outlines the role of Congress, and defines the scope and meaning of the term. It is an important statement, not only for what it says but also for the vast influence it had on the many papers that followed.

Daddario's statement concludes with a description of his subcommittee's program for developing the technology-assessment idea. Among the planned activities, he lists studies by the National Academies of Sciences and Engineering (NAS and NAE). These two bodies are the formal honorary societies for their respective professions in the United States, and they are often called upon to undertake consultative tasks for Congress. Each academy did carry out such a study—the NAS under the title, "Technology: Processes of Assessment and Choice," and the NAE under the title, "A Study of Technology Assessment." The engineering academy, characteristically, set about to actually perform several pilot assessments. The NAS, on the other hand, produced a more contemplative report, examining the problem in depth and suggesting possible remedies. We have included material from both reports in this volume.

A summary of the NAS report appears first, co-authored by Harvey Brooks, chairman of the panel that prepared it, and Raymond Bowers, one of the panel members. Brooks, dean of engineering and applied physics at Harvard University, and Bowers, professor of physics at Cornell University, describe the intellectual path followed by the NAS panel and report on its conclusions. Technology assessment processes are constantly in operation, the authors observe, but since costs and benefits are assessed by those primarily concerned with exploiting a given technology, "the frame of reference for the assessment is often quite limited." The problem is one of allocating costs and benefits equitably to different interest groups, and this is fundamentally a political matter. Technology assessment can go only so far; its function is "to clarify the political choices rather than to come up with a final answer." Within this framework, the NAS report discusses those factors, both conceptual and institutional, that inhibit effective technology assessment. Among these are the lack of a method for measuring social costs and benefits, the inability of "diffuse and poorly articulated interests" to inject themselves into the decision-making process, and the absence of adequate assessment methodologies. The authors propose a "constellation of organizations" strategically located within the government which would provide a variety of functions related to technology assessment. On the whole, these institutional reforms are intended to increase the amount of information on the effects of technology and channel this information in such a manner as to insure its appropriate utilization.

The report of the National Academy of Engineering, "A Study of Technology Assessment," is an eminently practical piece with an action-oriented, no-nonsense approach. The NAE committee performed experimental assessments of: (1) the technology of teaching aids; (2) subsonic aircraft noise; and (3) multiphasic health screening. These assessments are rather technical and too long to be treated in the present volume. Instead, we have included three selections from the report—the introduction, the overall summary of findings, and an examination of the three experimental assessments, which describes the methodology used in them and analyzes the experience gained. The NAE found the conduct of technology assessment to be entirely feasible and likely to be of significant value to the congressional decision-making process. The report stresses that assessments should be made by expert task forces in a neutral, nonpolitical environment. It sets out guidelines for the selection of technologies to be assessed, as well as for the assembly of assessment task forces, and it explores, in some detail, methodologies applicable to assessment.

The proposals of the National Academy of Sciences, as well as the approach taken by the National Academy of Engineering, are subjected to strong criticism in a paper by Hugh Folk, professor of economics and labor and industrial relations at the University of Illinois (Champaign-Urbana). Folk sees the interplay of interests in the policy-making process as an inherently irrational phenomenon and berates the NAS and NAE panels for failing to recognize that simply introducing greater quantities of information into the system, on the assumption that it will be used rationally, will not solve the problem. Folk argues that you cannot separate assessment, no matter how "objective," from the interests it serves. Beyond this, he continues, experts in a given area of technology are generally closely involved with the promotion of that technology and, with all good intentions, tend to accept current institutional arrangements and balances of power ("political feasibility") as given. Folk's answer is "a responsible process of technological debate." Rather than looking for an impossible value-free assessment, he proposes the establishment of a responsible technological opposition, which would perform *counterassessments* of technologies and thus shape the policy-making process through a sort of adversary proceeding.

Harold Green, professor of law at George Washington University, elaborates on this idea in his paper, "The Adversary Process in Technology Assessment." Whereas the NAS panel sees the assessment function as one of clarifying political choices, Green contends that it is "properly concerned with balancing the benefits of the technology to the public against its costs (including risks) to the public and emerging with the conclusion as to what Government's role with respect to that technology should be." Since, in Green's view, it seeks to *balance* and because, as he points out, "there is never any lack of articulation of the benefits of a technology," a technology-assessment institution must first and foremost provide a means for exposing and articulating into the decision process the *negative* aspects of a technology. Green proceeds to describe in some detail his idea for a "devil's advocate agency," supporting his case by reference to the situation in nuclear power technology. It is interesting that Green's paper, initially presented at a seminar at George Washington University, immediately provoked a heated discussion. Some participants, in fact, accused Green of "putting them on" by presenting such an obviously outrageous idea. Green's proposal may indeed be unconventional, but the idea of an adversary process in technology assessments merits, and has subsequently received, serious discussion.

As the concluding article in this section, Kenneth Boulding's paper, "The Role of the Social Sciences in the Control of Technology," provides an overview, from the perspective of economics, which transcends the technology assessment debate. Professor Boulding, a noted economist from the University of Colorado, originally presented this paper at a symposium on "Technology Assessment and Human Possibilities" at the 1969 Convention of the American Association for the Advancement of Science. In it, he examines the relationship of technology to a basic dichotomy in economics—the *exchange* economy (roughly equivalent to the market economy as we know it) versus the *grants* economy (in which there is only a one-way transfer of an exchangeable). Boulding analyzes "pathological processes in the evolution of technologies" within both of these types of economies on the theory that if such pathological processes can be detected, it should be possible to treat them. He concludes that the pathological states of the exchange economy are correctable through the apparatus of the grants economy, but that "we do not have any apparatus for correcting the pathological states of the grants economy or of the public sector, apart from the classical notions of checks and balances." Boulding's recommendations for dealing with this problem are made at a rather general level. He concludes, however, with a strong call to the scientific community to think carefully about its ethical system and attempt in some manner to introduce into the interaction between research, technology, and the rest of society the same lofty qualities of truthfulness and personal integrity that govern its own subculture.

Technology Assessment

EMILIO Q. DADDARIO

A perceptive student of modern science and technology observes that "every major advance in the technological competence of man has enforced revolutionary changes in the economic and political structure of society."[1]

It is fundamentally for this reason, plus the extreme acceleration of contemporary applied science, that I feel compelled to make this statement.

This is consistent with our responsibilities for authorization, appropriation, and oversight. More specifically, Chairman George P. Miller announced objectives for the Science, Research, and Development Subcommittee, when it was formed on August 23, 1963, as follows:

"The strengthening of Congressional sources of information and advice in the fields of science and technology," and "the achievement of the most effective utilization of the scientific and engineering resources of the United States in the effort to accomplish national goals which affect the lives of all Americans."[2]

We have accepted this charter. The second progress report of the subcommittee, issued in October 1966, summarized our activities to that time and also attempted a look into the future as to what issues might confront the Congress. The report stated:

. . . that no matter how important the influence of science and technology upon society has been in the past, it is likely to prove but a pale shadow of the scale of influence we may expect in the future.

One thoughtful science administrator (Chairman Seaborg of the Atomic Energy Commission) has voiced the matter succinctly, at the same time putting his finger on a significant corollary:

"The scientific revolution is here to stay . . . indeed, it is only beginning. What we have seen in the past is as nothing compared to the future. We shall be found wanting if we do not plan with that thought in mind. Our success in achieving the objectives of creative evolution requires both an ever more vigorous effort in science and technology and an enormous improvement in techniques for integrating the products of science and technology into society."

1. Barry Commoner. *Science and Survival,* Viking Press, 1963.
2. U.S. Congress, House, Committee on Science and Astronautics Report of the Subcommittee on Science, Research, and Development "Government and Science, No. 1, A Statement of Purpose." 88th Cong., 1st sess., Serial C, p. 9.

Our inquiries made during the past 3½ years convince us of the hard truth of this postulation.

The Nation simply cannot solve the serious, even critical, problems facing it without the aid of additional science and technology. But our success in the development of such new knowledge must be accompanied by careful and improved methods of putting that knowledge to work. Otherwise we may strangle in the coils of unplanned, unwanted, but unstoppable technocracy.[3]

THE SPECIAL REQUIREMENTS
OF THE LEGISLATIVE BRANCH

On March 7, 1967, I introduced H. R. 6698 "to provide a method for identifying, assessing, publicizing, and dealing with the implications and effects of applied research and technology" by establishing a Technology Assessment Board.[4] The bill recognized both the need for "identifying the potentials of applied research and technology and promoting ways and means to accomplish their transfer into practical use, and identifying the undesirable by-products and side effects of such applied research and technology in advance of their crystallization and informing the public of their potential in order that appropriate steps may be taken to eliminate or minimize them."

This bill was introduced, not as a piece of perfected legislation, but as a stimulant to discussion. I have received many thoughtful comments, criticisms, and suggestions on the Technology Assessment Board concept. The discussions of the past few months have led to the decision that much more should be learned about the "how" of Technology Assessment before any permanent mechanism or organization was proposed. Therefore we on the Science committee are planning to undertake a long-range study of the concept of Technology Assessment. The subcommittee's intention is to employ a variety of information and advisory resources for the development of an optimum system.

A Technology Assessment capability for the legislative branch of our Government will enable us to deploy the finite scientific and engineering resources of money, facilities, and skilled manpower to take fullest advantage of the gains offered to society. At the same time, Technology Assessment can anticipate and minimize the unwanted side effects which so often accompany innovations. The purpose of the subcommittee study is to strengthen the role

3. U.S. Congress, House, Committee on Science and Astronautics, Second Progress Report. Subcommittee on Science, Research and Development "Inquiries, Legislation, Policy Studies Re: Science and Technology." 89th Cong., 2d sess., serial R, p. 21.
4. H. R. 6698, 90th Cong., 1st sess., Mar 7, 1967, Mr. Daddario.

of the Congress in making judgments among alternatives for putting science to work for human benefit.

THE CURRENT URGENCY OF ASSESSMENT

A capability for Technology Assessment is needed now in a new, different, and insistent way as compared to former times. Virtually all civilized activities are highly dependent on technology. A progressive society is venturesome —willing to take risks in order to achieve potential benefits. New applications of science and engineering continually present attractive solutions to social, economic, and political problems.

Economic growth is a major U.S. national goal which increasingly is accomplished through technological change. The marketplace acts to magnify and dramatize the economic benefits of new technology. Easily quantifiable social effects (unemployment, health, statistics, education factors, hourly productivity, etc.) are also efficiently appraised by society. Other results are not so easily calculated into the risk-benefit equations.

Technological change produces numerous and diverse effects—some recognizable before the fact, others not until later; some good and others bad; some never clearly established in a cause-and-effect relationship.

To maximize the standard of living, society needs to know as much as possible about the consequences of technological change. (This holds regardless of any disagreements as to what constitutes "progress" or what the collective tastes of a nation or region may set as standards.) Two new factors have made the assessment of technological alternatives more critical.

First, the increased worldwide population density (a result of technological advancements in itself) means that any activity is likely to affect a great many human beings. There is less uninhabited area in which to conduct risky ventures. There is less virgin land to move into if an activity deteriorates presently settled territory. Thus, the large, widespread world population has made the maintenance of environmental quality much more important today.

Second, the forces for change which are at the disposal of mankind, are very powerful. Biological, chemical, radiation, and energy effects are now available which can literally upset the so-called balance of the natural world. This means that unforeseen consequences are less likely to be confined locally, or detected under restricted conditions, where lessons can be learned before significant damage is done. On the constructive side, it means that society has opportunities for human betterment which can alleviate the very basic problems of the world—war, hunger, disease, and poverty.

A REDEFINITION OF PROGRESS

Technology Assessment could easily become a stifling influence on progress if the dangers are emphasized rather than the potentials for good. There is an innate conservatism in our culture which makes innovation difficult at the very best. History presents many familiar examples of the entrepreneur being ridiculed and frustrated by a society which clung to the status quo. Lack of imagination for the future is the general rule. It is all too easy to bring up reasons why a novel procedure or idea is not worthwhile or would bring dire results. The inventor is usually quite alone with his vision.

On the other hand, those who propose radical ventures are often blinded by their enthusiasm to the risks involved. Or if they foresee a dark side to technology, they are loath to point it out, knowing too well how precarious acceptance of their scheme may be; and having a confidence that somehow the hazards will be minimized and the benefits realized.

A characteristic of America in the past century has been the love of the new, a boldness to try something different, the courage to take risks in applying the fruits of science. This attitude has been responsible for a great portion of our material welfare and strength among nations.

But now, with the immensity of consequences and the irreversible nature of many technological changes, the propensity for risk taking must be coupled with a deeper assessment of both deficits and benefits. We must continue to advance, but *mere change is not equivalent to progress.* We must not discourage the entrepreneur, the idea man, or the engineer. Indeed we must encourage the greatest degree of imagination in order to meet the problems of life and political existence. This imagination must be extended to include the full assessment of all consequences without the fear that a reactionary society will seize on the risks and deficits as an excuse for stagnation.

Science and technology have become so much a part of everything that we do as individuals, businesses, or nations that old attitudes are gone forever. No more is science taken on faith, and technology accepted in awe. A major reason for the demise of these attitudes is the enormous financial investment in research and development. It is not difficult to engender interest and stimulate technical literacy in citizens, stockholders, and the electorate when the funding of science and engineering reaches the present level of $24 billion annually. In just the last decade, public and private funds for R. & D. have totaled $157 billion.

Thus, technology costs a lot of money, brings up perplexing problems of hazard and benefit, and beckons to an ever more complex future. This is the substance of the need for Technology Assessment in the Congress.

There is, of course, an alternative new attitude: the call for a moratorium on science until society gains the wisdom to use technology safely. We are warned that mankind can know too much for his own good. A catchup period is proposed—so that mores and rational conduct can develop which are equal to the choices forced by science. In the meantime, so goes the familiar argument, a renaissance of art, literature, and the humanities should be force fed to redress the imbalance in our culture which has been brought about by 20 years of unprecedented support for research and development. I do not believe this line of reasoning appeals to many of us. Certainly not to those who have observed the pain of disease, the tragedy of starvation abroad, or the raw force of Communist subversion. Surely, what is needed is more science, more knowledge of natural laws, and more prescience of what can and should result from the wise use of our resources. Science is concerned with truth, and, regardless of the shortcomings of our civilization, we cannot be hurt by knowing more, much more, of what we are about.

Progress is being redefined as something much more sophisticated and intricate than mere change. There is a strong element of renewal present in today's planning. Lessons of the past have shown what is to be discarded and what is to be restored, retained, and enhanced in individual lives, in corporations, in cities, in transportation systems, in agriculture, and in environments. Personal renewal is evidenced in the continuous reeducation which all of us undergo here in the legislative branch of Government.

CONGRESS EQUIPS ITSELF FOR SCIENCE POLICY

The renewal of our institutions is part and parcel of the democratic process. A capability for Technology Assessment is a keystone for improved institutions and, most importantly, for the Congress. In the past [several] years we have taken [a number of] important steps to raise the level of understanding of science and technology within the Congress. The Science Policy Research Division of the Legislative Reference Service in the Library of Congress has been established. Incidentally, the dependence which the Congress is beginning to place on this skilled organization makes its expansion in the near future a virtual necessity.

The staffs of certain committees which deal substantially in technical matters have been strengthened. The National Academy of Sciences has worked through a direct contract with the Science and Astronautics Committee for a series of significant reports on basic and applied research. The sources of advice and testimony have been broadened from the traditional Federal agencies and special-interest groups to include advisory panels, professional society representatives, and men of stature from universities, independent research institutes, and industry. Technical issues which might be fragmented by our committee structure have been discussed and informally coordinated by meetings of key committee chairmen and senior members. [Various proposals for Congressional reorganization] could carry these valuable tools for legislative understanding of science even further.

But it does appear that a special effort may be necessary to bring Technology Assessment to a useful and timely status. Existing mechanisms may be modified or extended. New special arrangements for the Congress may be necessary. Our investigation has no preconceptions as to the final result. I would point out that Technology Assessment has been the concern of our Government for many years. But we have not yet felt the urgency to perfect and employ methods of appraisal, arbitration, planning, forecasting, and extrapolition to their fullest degree.

Let me quote a most pertinent viewpoint of the need for Technology Assessment. I believe its origin may surprise you:

The most important general conclusion to be drawn from these studies is the continuing growth of the already high and rapidly developing technology in the social structure of the Nation, and hence the hazard of any planning that does not take this fact into consideration. . . . In view of the findings regarding the importance of technology and applied science, it is recommended that the Federal government develop appropriate agencies for continuous study of them; and more specifically that there be set up in the respective departments science committees with the definite function of investigating and reporting at regular periods on the progress and trends of science and invention and the possible and economic effects flowing therefrom as they affect the work of the departments and of the agencies to whom they render service.[5]

The sentences just quoted came from House Document 360, "Technological Trends and National Policy", a report of the Subcommittee on Technology to the National Resources Committee, which was submitted in the first session of the 75th Congress, in June 1937. So we see that [more than] 30 years ago, the need for systematic Government-wide Technology Assessment

5. U.S. Congress, House Document 360 "Technological Trends and National Policy." Report of the Subcommittee on Technology to the National Resources Commission, 75th Cong., 1st sess., June 1937.

was recognized. Unfortunately the recommendations went largely unheeded.

But assessment has been carried out from time to time and is being carried out today on an ad hoc basis. Historically, assessment has usually occurred well after the technology was introduced and when undesirable consequences had reached serious proportions. For example, the intensive cultivation of grasslands in the Great Plains precipitated the duststorms and erosion during the drought of the 1930's. As a result, studies showed the way to corrective action of windbreaks and other soil conservation measures—too late to prevent hardships to the farmers involved.

Frequently, the call for assessment has come from inspired social critics and writers. Such was the case in environmental and human health hazards from pesticides. Rachel Carson's "Silent Spring" brought the realization of how quickly we had accepted the pest control properties of certain chemicals without questioning what the consequences of their widespread dissemination might do to valuable insects, fish, and wildlife.

Countless times a radical change was made to a locality or region prior to any assessment of all potential consequences. Invariably, some adverse condition arose which took time and effort to combat. The opening of the St. Lawrence Seaway allowed certain predatory oceanic eels to enter into the Great Lakes, much to the detriment of commercial and sport fishing. The rabbit in Australia and the giant African snail in the Pacific Islands are other poignant reminders of what happens when biological control mechanisms are bypassed or upended. On the positive side, sufficient knowledge of local conditions has and will continue to open the way for more fruitful changes. Deliberate transfer of a plant or animal can be rewarding. The thought of a flowering plain where desert once stood is not a utopian hope. Imported plants have flourished in new homes when prior research and assessment were adequate. For example, mesquite trees of Southwest United States are growing naturally in the Egyptian desert.

The most dramatic example of drastic changes is the extinction of a species. The Great Auk and the nearly extinct blue whale and the whooping crane have served to focus attention on a deadly trend—man's sacrifice of long range objectives for short term gains. Many animals which have survived as fitting in the environment are near extinction because of man-induced changes today. Their annihilation would be more than an esthetic and scientific loss. Life cycles could be disrupted and adverse side effects within the natural environment would carry over into the social and economic spheres of human beings.

Our current fight for air quality is an after-the-fact realization that the atmosphere could not be used as a convenient and inexpensive dumping place for gaseous and particulate wastes.

Many unwanted consequences have been labeled as the price of progress. But even in a nation as affluent as ours, these prices all at once seem too high. And at the same time, mature reflection suggests that the price need not have been paid at all if a thorough understanding had been gained of what was happening in the ecological system at an earlier date.

RESPONSIBILITY FOR THE RESULTS OF TECHNOLOGY

Technology Assessment has been haphazard in the United States because we have never fixed the responsibility for the total results of technology. The market place is an institution for assessing technology. Beyond mere competitive performance of goods and services, there is a realization by commercial interests that "caveat emptor" is an unworkable doctrine. Legal recourse and public opinion as well as enlightened self-interest underlie the large amount of safety testing and prevention of hazards in normal usage which goes on in every manufacturing concern.

In some cases, such as acceptability of drugs, food additives, and agricultural chemicals, or the safe design and construction of automobiles, the Government is assigning assessment functions to its agencies. For example, the Federal responsibility for assessment of nuclear technology is well established. A recent event illuminates the need for full recognition of this responsibility. Again, a Middle East crisis has demonstrated vividly that the supply of oil to the industrialized world sometimes flows at an uneven rate. Political and military conflict can even sever supply lines, producing economic and political repercussions throughout the Western World. Indirectly these confrontations add to the possibilities of abating air pollution from fossil fuel combustion to propel us faster into the age of nuclear power production. We are aware that atomic energy could be available as an endless source of efficient power. We are taking great strides to bring this about. But at the same time programs lag in devising a long term satisfactory disposal of reactor wastes. And the safety of central city location for nuclear electric power stations has yet to be confidently demonstrated.

These complex pros and cons are not sorted out by conventional appraisal processes. The marketplace does not take into account all the important values to a society as a whole. There is a tendency to accept short term gains for both the supplier and purchaser. And a Federal agency may have too narrow a mission assignment to provide adequate assessment of an entire technological system. For example, the environmental pollution problem is fragmented among many agencies with the result that abatement of a contamination of one type may simply shift the pollutant load to another part of the ecosystem.

In the case of automation, we have been aware for at least a century that technology was bent on displacing man from labor. As long as there was more work to be done than skills were available to do it, then machines and automation caused only temporary dislocations. But today cybernation promises to eliminate all repetitive physical and mental tasks performed by human beings. No existing market or government function is able to assess the impact of this revolutionary application of technology.

These deficiencies in current institutions and procedures are becoming the subject of discussion in the Congress, in universities, in professional technical societies, and in public policy foundations.

[In 1967] Senator Muskie held hearings on Senate Resolution 68 to establish a Select Committee on Technology and the Human Environment. The testimony received [was] an eloquent statement of why an enhanced assessment function is needed by the Congress.[6]

Senator Harris, through his Subcommittee on Government Research of the Senate Government Operations Committee, held seminars and hearings on a variety of science and public policy issues. In particular the impact of technology on the regional economic development and the opportunities for biomedical research [were] emphasized.[7]

Senator Allott introduced a bill [in 1967] to establish a joint congressional committee on science and technology.[8] The bill stated a policy to assure that the benefits of science and technology [would be] used most effectively in the interests of national security and the general welfare, [and called for an] annual report on science and technology from the President to the Congress . . . . Among other things, the report would [have] set forth "the impact of recent major scientific and technical developments and programs, whether developed by the Federal Government or non-Federal agencies, organizations, or institutions, and the anticipated impact of foreseeable, future developments and programs on national policy and the general welfare."

6. S. Res. 68, 90th Cong., 1st sess., Jan. 25, 1967, Mr. Muskie and others.
7. U.S. Congress, Senate Hearings before the Subcommittee on Government Research of the Committee on Government Operations, 1966.
8. S. 1305, 90th Cong., first sess., Mar. 15, 1967, Mr. Allott and others.

In addition to my bill for a Technology Assessment Board, the House [had] before it [in 1967] the Environmental Quality Act of 1967, introduced by Mr. Dingell.[9] The act call[ed] for the establishment of a Council on Environmental Quality and an annual environmental quality report—and I quote—"which shall set forth (1) the status and condition of the major natural, manmade, or altered environmental classes of the Nation, including, but not limited to, the air, the aquatic, including marine, estuarine, and fresh water, and the terrestrial environment, including, but not limited to, the forest, dry-land, wetland, range, urban, suburban, and rural environment; and (2) current and foreseeable trends in management and utilization of such environments and the effects of those trends on the social, economic, and other requirements of the Nation." [A modified version of this bill was passed by Congress in 1969 and signed into law by President Nixon in January, 1970—ed.]

[In 1967] the National Academy of Sciences prepared a report for the Science and Astronautics Committee entitled "Applied Science and Technological Progress."[10] In discussing the ways in which nontechnical legislators and decision-makers can become informed about the consequences of technology, the report stated:

Congress should not attempt to second-guess the experts on technical appraisals, but it does have the responsibility to convince itself that the experts have asked themselves the right questions, especially concerning bottleneck problems. It is also important to be aware of certain common biases. For example, technologists already committed to a particular line of effort tend to be oversanguine, to minimize difficulties and underestimate costs. On the other hand, scientists often tend to be overconservative about technological developments and to call for more research. Often they underestimate the applicability of the science that they themselves have developed. There is a universal tendency to be overoptimistic about technical progress in the short run, but too conservative about the long range future.

In appraising the situation, it is important for Congress to listen to the skeptics as well as the enthusiasts, and to ask the enthusiasts to answer the arguments of the skeptics. Laymen can learn a great deal from the confrontation of experts even when they do not understand the details. Especially in applied science and technology, priorities and goals can be established only through a multidimensional interaction between scientists, technologists, public servants, and the general public.

Representative Reuss, and the Government Operations Subcommittee on Research and Technical Programs, have provided several interesting insights

9. H.R. 7796, 90th Cong., first sess., Mar. 23, 1967, Mr. Dingell.
10. Applied Science and Technological Progress, a report to the Committee on Science and Astronautics, U.S. House of Representatives, National Academy of Sciences, Washington, D.C., 1967.

to the Federal agency technology management problems. In particular, their study of the decision-making process revealed the difficulty of allocating science and engineering resources to match national goals.[11]

These activities and legislative proposals are only a partial list of congressional approaches to the assessment of technology.

In the academic community, a growing number of research and study programs are being undertaken on the impacts of technology. At Harvard University, the Program on Technology and Society is [engaged in] an inquiry in depth into the effects of technological change on the economy, on public policies, and on the character of society.

At Columbia University, the Institute for the Study of Science in Human Affairs has been organized. The George Washington University [is] illuminating several aspects of the assessment concept in its Program of Policy Studies in Science and Technology.

Among a growing number of other projects in assessment and forecasting are the Commission on the Year 2000 of the American Academy of Arts and Sciences, and the American Association for the Advancement of Science with its study of the impacts of chemical and biological agents in the environment.

It is in this setting of increasing concern in many sectors of society that the subcommittee is beginning its own careful investigation of how to bring technology assessment to the Congress. We plan to take full advantage of the valuable and timely work of all others in the field. It appears certain that the methods which we evolve will be more useful because of the broad interest of so many keen minds.

THE LESSONS OF HISTORY

As early as 1830 our Federal Government began to assess technology. A series of boiler explosions on steamboats brought pressure on the Congress to take corrective action. Lack of information on why boilers burst prompted the Congress to direct the Secretary of the Treasury to act. In turn, the executive branch, unable to make much headway, granted research funds to the Franklin Institute of Philadelphia to conduct experiments to produce the body of data necessary to locate flaws in design, construction, and theory of steam boilers. Regulatory legislation eventually resulted.

From this early episode come two pertinent points. First, again and again

11. U.S. Congress, House Hearings before a Subcommittee of the Committee on Government Operations, Jan. 7, 10, and 11, 1966, 89th Cong., Second Session.

this country has moved to assess technology after some major crisis or catastrophe. We have only to mention recent disasters to underscore this statement. The tragic sinking of the submarine U.S.S. *Thresher,* the disastrous fire in the Apollo spacecraft, and the grounding of the *Torrey Canyon* oil tanker, triggered a series of investigations, assessments, and policy changes. The power grid failure of June 5, [1967] affecting a four-state area and 13 million people, fortunately was not as disruptive as the earlier one. But in both cases we have seen how huge electrical power systems have grown so as to achieve greater and greater efficiencies. Also we can see a society made increasingly interdependent by advancing technology. Efficiency gains have been closely followed by a higher risk of regional darkness. These disasters, in each case, may have begun or strengthened a process that I call continuous assessment.

The second lesson illustrated by history is that technical information needed by policymakers is frequently not available, or not in the right form. A policymaker cannot judge the merits or consequences of a technological program within a strictly technical context. He has to consider social, economic, and legal implications of any course of action.

While the data on bursting boilers were not available in 1830, I feel that the technical data relevant to our multifarious technical programs of today are often available and accessible. However, they are not always presented to the decision-maker in the proper form. Continually, the Congress has to make judgments on programs with far-reaching consequences. Frequently we are forced to decide without the advantage of a balanced, systematic risk/benefit appraisal. Unwanted, undesirable or uncertain effects are not pointed out and carefully assessed. They are often actually underplayed.

In some cases, where there is an unknown, an uncertain consequence, experimentation is necessary. If data are not available, then additional research may be able to predict the consequences. For example, the effect of the sonic boom created by overflights of the supersonic transport is unknown. Just how detrimental and disruptive will this frequent startling noise be? If the consequences are potentially great, but uncertain—and this is apparently the case with the SST—then one logical alternative mode of operation is to fly only over uninhabited areas or water until research on the psychological impact of the sonic boom gives rise to some confident answers.

Another example is found in the complex question of human experimentation in medical research. In order to gain the benefits to all society of advanced surgical techniques, prosthetic devices, and drugs, it may be necessary to risk the health and longevity of other citizens. Ethical and legal problems are inextricable from the scientific quandaries of such a situation.

ASSESSMENT FOR CONGRESSIONAL PURPOSES

Major technological inventions—airplane, motion pictures, radio, atomic energy—have changed the face of our society and prompted many social inventions as we adjusted to their impact. Granted, we will have to create new institutions as technology expands and surges ahead. De Tocqueville wisely pointed out that we are a nation that loves to create new organizations. At the same time, and this is particularly pertinent to the Congress, we have to devise ways to strengthen existing institutions. One of the qualities contributing to the Congress's effectiveness is flexibility. We have been able to adjust to changing needs of society and new capabilities of science and technology remarkably well.

DEFINITION OF TECHNOLOGY ASSESSMENT

On the whole, the Congress can strengthen its ability to assess and judge technological programs without radical change. I take this view because, simply stated, Technology Assessment is a form of policy research which provides a balanced appraisal to the policymaker. Ideally, it is a system to ask the right questions and obtain correct and timely answers. It identifies policy issues, assesses the impact of alternative courses of action and presents findings. It is a method of analysis that systematically appraises the nature, significance, status, and merit of a technological program. The method may well vary from case to case. For example, assessment of birth control devices undoubtedly will proceed somewhat differently from that of pollution abatement.

Technology Assessment is designed to uncover three types of consequences—desirable, undesirable, and uncertain. The benefits that accrue from technology are naturally the driving force for its application. Economic growth is fostered by more convenient and efficient services or by new and less expensive goods. Society benefits when technology is fashioned around some value or goal, consistent with democracy. Promotion of the general welfare, through medical research and services, or the use of technology in education, are institutionalized social goals.

Undesirable consequences, sometimes played down by calling them harmful side effects, can be expected with most innovations. Technology means change—change to the natural environment, change in personal habits and behavior, change in social and economic patterns, and not infrequently change in the legal and political processes. While many of these changes are beneficial, many are disruptive and dislocative. They change situations more rapidly than the pace at which individuals can adjust. The well-known cultural lag finds its logical beginnings in this phenomenon. Assessment of the risks is a necessary concomitant to assessment of the benefits.

Uncertain consequences are the third type to be identified and assessed. Available information may point out only that an effect will occur and can give no idea of the degree of impact. When the severity of impact is not known further research is often warranted. For example, new discoveries in disease control and prevention have to go through a prolonged trial period so that harmful effects are discovered before widespread use is sanctioned. In general, experimentation and pilot projects are required to determine what proscriptions might be necessary before the technology is able to safely diffuse through society.

THE SCOPE OF TECHNOLOGY ASSESSMENT

If assessment is a method of policy research that identifies the amount and type of change for alternative courses of action and provides a balanced appraisal of each alternative, then what is the scope of technology assessment? What will it try to measure? What time frame will it consider? What yardsticks will be used? How does assessment differ from other methods of analysis?

Answers to these questions will more concisely define Technology Assessment and more clearly show its relationship to the policymaking process.

Technology Assessment for the Congress will deal for the most part with applications in the United States. It is worth noting, though, that the entire world, and even outer space, is the system with which we are concerned. Some of the technologies which must be assessed in a broader sense are nuclear blast effects, climate and weather modification, famine and disease epidemics, and oceanography. The international aspects of Technology Assessment will become more important as the power and ubiquity of man-made forces continue to increase.

Another division of viewpoint for assessment efforts is the difference between technology for the rich nations as opposed to that for the emerging countries. A risk which the Western world might avoid would perhaps be acceptable to a nation struggling with starvation. For example, the ecological hazards of chemical pesticides might be sufficient to restrict their use in the United States. But in India or Southeast Asia with the threat of malaria coupled to a severe nutritional problem, the use of a broad gage insecticide would be justified. On the other hand, the mistakes in applying transportation technology which have knotted many American and European cities can be avoided by better planning as new population centers are built elsewhere in the world. In either case, the full knowledge of good and bad consequences can be of great value to either the "have" or "have-not" cultures.

To assess technology one has to establish cause and effect relationships from the action or project source to the locale of consequences.

A direct or immediate effect is easy to spot and assess. The direct effects in turn will cause other consequences—indirect or derivative effects. As the scope of assessment moves outward in time the derivative effects become the result of many causes and not of one specific technological change.

Looking into the future we know birth control devices will have a profound impact on the world. There will be a change in the birth rate (a downward trend in the United States is already apparent). Following this will be a consequent shift in hospital facilities, various economic changes and, ultimately, changes in sexual behavior, morals, and perhaps even religious beliefs. The function of technology assessment is to identify all of these—both short-term and long range. The emphasis, though, will be on the short-term impacts that can be measured by natural science parameters. That is, the focus of Technology Assessment will be on those consequences that can be predicted with a useful degree of probability.

Possible changes in values, attitudes or institutions are important but not easily predicted. These changes are usually long term and fall beyond the primary focus of Technology Assessment. Therefore, because of their slow evolution, present human values and political institutions will serve as the frame of reference for purposes of measurement and appraisal.

Assessment is a form of policy research and is not technological forecasting or program planning. It is a balanced analysis of how a technological program could proceed with the benefits and risks of each policy alternative carefully described. It incorporates prediction and planning but only to expose the potential consequences of the program.

Assessment is an aid to, and not a substitute for, judgment. Technology Assessment provides the decisionmaker with a list of future courses of action backed up by systematic analysis of the consequences. In this sense it is an analytical study that could be prepared by anyone. Its utility would be enhanced if it was undertaken for a policymaking group that could sketch in the nature of the problem for the study team beforehand. In a broader sense assessment is part of the legislative process. Our subcommittee will gather and assess information before we can make any judgments. Part of this information will be actual assessment studies prepared for the subcommittee by the scientific community and the Science Policy Research Division. When viewed as either a method of research or a part of the legislative process, Technology Assessment serves to provide information tailored to the constraints and needs of the policymaking process.

SEQUENCE OF STEPS IN TECHNOLOGY ASSESSMENT

What might this method involve? Seven steps are suggested as one approach to Technology Assessment. Briefly stated, the assessor would identify all impacts of a program; establish cause and effect relationships where possible; determine alternative methods to implement the program; identify alternative programs to achieve the same goal and point out the impacts; measure and compare sums of good and bad impacts; and present findings from the analysis. In the initial step one would place the technology within the total societal framework and identify all impacts in the natural, social, economic, legal and political sectors. Direct effects would be separated from derivative effects.

Then, causal chains emanating outward in time from the impacting technology would be established. Short-term effects on each sector directly attributable to the program, could be separated from long-term effects, that are the result of many forces.

Next, the question is asked: In what alternative directions could the program be guided? Or, what freedoms of choice does the situation allow? Each course of action would have a slightly different set of consequences.

A second search for alternatives is then begun. The given goal is reformulated in order to identify other programs or policies in addition to the technology program in question that could achieve the same objective. Identification of new consequences is necessary at this point.

The three types of consequences—desirable, undesirable, and uncertain—would then be separated for each alternative.

Ideally, the assessor would measure and compare the effects where possible and finally make findings from the analysis. The conclusions would point out policy issues arising from the benefit/risk ratios of alternative courses of action, and from uncertain consequences where further experimentation is feasible and desirable.

THE SUBCOMMITTEE PROGRAM

The preceding description of Technology Assessment is a tentative one but suitable as a basis of the subcommittee program. A three-phase approach is intended to lead to the selection and recommendation of the ultimate answer to congressional needs. Our objective is to involve many diverse interests in the program and I particularly wish to receive suggestions and advice from my colleagues in the House.

Our goal is a legislative capability for policy determination in applied science and technology which will be anticipatory and adaptive rather than reactionary and symptomatic.

HEARINGS AND SEMINARS

The first phase is the scheduling of hearings and seminars to refine our ideas about Technology Assessment. The question for discussion is not why assessment is necessary. The requirement has been amply demonstrated by . . . hearings in both Houses of Congress, by commentary in literature and magazines of opinion, and by our own experience in dealing with lesiglation on such subjects as pollution, conservation, aircraft noise and sonic boom, and agricultural chemicals. The question on which we seek testimony and discussion is how to assess technology for congressional purposes.

The scientific and engineering community will have much to offer, for science by its very nature exposes its activities to trial and criticism. Technology Assessment often requires experimentation for its own purposes. The analysis and interpretation of data in impacts and consequences is an extension of the scientific method. Although Technology Assessment must include many nontechnological factors, the bulk of the information must come from technical sources. Therefore, government and private sector technologists will be called on for opinions and suggested operational assessment procedures.

Other voices of society are also necessary for we are interested in assessment in terms of human values as well as natural science statistics. The important role of social and economic indicators will be sought out by the subcommittee. These and esthetic values which cannot be quantified are nevertheless part of the ultimate judgment of technological progress. The legislative process integrates the five value realms of science, economics, politics, society, and law. Our study will also elicit viewpoints from all of these sources. . . .

THE NATIONAL ACADEMIES
OF SCIENCE AND ENGINEERING

In addition to public hearings and seminars, the subcommittee has arranged with the National Academies of Science and Engineering a substantial and concerted effort in developing the Technology Assessment concept. The

Academies, in their chartered role as an advisory group to the Congress, have formed working groups from their membership with the following objectives:

1. Arrange for pilot assessment projects. There are a number of contemporary issues in applied science and technology which call for assessment now. While gaining the immediate benefit of the results of a current appraisal we can also evaluate alternative methods of assessment. Further, different organizational arrangements can be compared. For example, the assessment task may be given to a specially formed committee, to a contract research organization, to a Government agency, or to a professional technical society.

The NAS-NAE working groups will select a limited number of pilot assessment projects which would yield a maximum of experiences on the assessment concept.

2. The results of these assessments will be reported to the Congress for immediate incorporation into the decision-making process. But more importantly, the working group would evaluate the various approaches and performers; and report to the Congress the most efficient and useful techniques for an eventual permanent Technology Assessment apparatus. It is intended that the Academies' working groups would be asked to participate in the concluding phases of the subcommittee study as recommendations and formulations are made to meet the congressional need.

COMMITTEE STAFF AND LRS SUPPORT

The subcommittee has arranged for several other compilations and analyses in support of its investigation. The Science Policy Research Division in the Legislative Reference Service is gathering an inventory of other current Technology Assessment projects throughout the world. Correspondence indicates that relatively few of these programs exist but that the data will be of continuing interest and value to the Congress.

A summary and analysis of historical attempts at assessment will be made. Such questions will be examined as: What part of society sounded the alarm?; how obvious were the consequences before counteraction could be obtained; and what political processes and institutions were involved in restoring the balance of benefit and deficit?

A listing of previous congressional involvement in Technology Assessment will be valuable. Often this has occurred in the oversight of agency programs. In some cases, the Congress has built in an assessment function when authorizing new technological projects.

Finally, the subcommittee will seek the counsel of other committees and

Members of the Congress to gain the experience which does reside in the long history of responsible legislative attention to science and technology.

From all of these activities we anticipate the selection and recommendation of a system for Technology Assessment which will demonstrate to the electorate a confident and competent capability to create policies for the wise usage of technical knowledge.

Technology: Processes of Assessment and Choice

HARVEY BROOKS AND RAYMOND BOWERS

In recent years concern has mounted over society's apparent inability to channel the application of technology in directions that sufficiently respect the broad range of human needs. Rightly or wrongly, the belief is now widely held that the continuation of certain technological trends poses great danger for the future of man. The unwise or incomplete application of technology has already contributed to some of the most urgent of our contemporary problems: the threat of thermonuclear destruction, the social crisis of our cities, the deterioration of the natural environment, the displacement of workers, and the potential invasion of privacy. There is a growing skepticism toward proposals and projects (for example, the SST) that in an earlier day might have been hailed as symbols of human progress. Influential and thoughtful segments of the public have begun to ask whether technological progress is always for the best—whether we can afford to wait until unforeseen side-effects of technological application reach crisis proportions before we seek means to alleviate them on a piecemeal basis.

There are even some who wish to make modern technology the scapegoat of all our social ills. They perceive technology as having become the master of man and not his servant. This wholly pessimistic attitude rests upon a vast oversimplification, as does the converse notion that technology is the universal solvent of man's problems and needs only to be applied more vigorously to assure an increasing measure of the good life. Between the two extreme positions lies the view that benefit and injury may both result from technology. For those holding this view, it is important and urgent to ask how technological change can be guided by a deeper concern for the interaction between man's tools and the human condition that they modify. This is the concern of "technology assessment." This term is used to describe the examination and evaluation of the likely consequences of technological development and application in order to foster a more constructive evolution for technology. The concept is an extremely broad one embracing the preservation and enhancement of environmental quality, the improvement of the measurement and understanding of social change, and the development of a longer planning horizon in technological development. All these factors also bear on the allocation of public resources.

The growing concern with such problems has brought forth a number of suggestions on how our governmental apparatus should be modified to deal more effectively with them. Proposals have been made for a council of ecological or environmental advisors, an interagency council on environmental quality, a select Senate committee on technology and human environment, and a council of social advisors. Proposals exist for amendments to the Constitution asserting the right to a pure environment and for the creation of a fourth branch of government, an "evaluation branch."

This article describes an examination of the problem of technology assessment by a group convened by the Committee on Science and Public Policy of the National Academy of Sciences; the study was carried out at the request of the Subcommittee on Science, Research and Development of the House Committee on Science and Astronautics.[1]

The origin of the study can be traced to Representative Emilio Q. Daddario's bill to establish a technology assessment board, "to provide a method

1. This is a summary of *Technology: Process of Assessment and Choice*, Report of the National Academy of Sciences, Committee on Science and Astronautics, U.S. House of Representatives, and is available from the Superintendent of Documents. The members of this panel were, apart from the two authors of this article, Laurence H. Tribe, Hendrik W. Bode, Gordon McKay, Harvard University; Edward C. Creutz, Gulf General Atomic, Inc.; A. Hunter Dupree, Brown University; Ralph W. Gerard, University of California, Irvine; Norman Kaplan, George Washington University; Milton Katz, Harvard University; Melvin Kranzberg, Case Western Reserve University; Hans H. Landsberg, Resources for the Future, Inc.; Gene M. Lyons, Dartmouth College; Louis H. Mayo, George Washington University; Gerard Piel, Scientific American; Herbert A. Simon, Carnegie-Mellon University; Cyril S. Smith, Massachusetts Institute of Technology; Morris Tanenbaum, Western Electric; Dael Wolfle, American Association for the Advancement of Science.

for identifying, assessing, publicizing and dealing with the implications and effects of applied research and technology." The original bill was introduced not as a piece of perfected legislation but rather as a stimulant to discussion. Representative Daddario and his subcommittee sponsored not only the study described in this article but also a parallel study, carried out quite independently, by the National Academy of Engineering.

To make our task manageable, the study group was forced to delineate boundaries. We set aside as beyond our scope the ultimate philosophical issues posed by technical civilization. Nor did we discuss the value implications of theoretical discoveries in the sciences. Our focus was on technology—what man can do and what he chooses to do with what he knows. We did not attempt to assess in detail the specific consequences or implications of any particular technological development. (In this sense our study is complementary to that carried out by the National Academy of Engineering, which did consider some specific cases in detail.) We recognized at the outset that the assessment of technological prospects and hazards is already a pervasive activity in both industry and government, as well as among many private associations such as conservation groups. Thus we undertook to identify what seem to be the most serious deficiencies in existing processes of assessment and decision making. The critical question is how broad are the criteria on which these assessments are made. Do present assessment processes deal with a wide enough sphere of effects, both social and environmental? Since we concluded that they do not, we then asked how we could begin the extremely difficult task of altering present evaluative and decision-making processes so that private and public choices would reflect a greater sensitivity of the total effects of technology on the human environment. We sought mechanisms for achieving this without denying ourselves the benefits of continuing technological progress.

It was necessary to concentrate frequently on the detrimental effects of technology. This was an almost inevitable consequence of our assignment to identify the deficiencies in present procedures; it is not to be construed as an antitechnology bias. Indeed, it was not our function to set up a net balance sheet on technology, but rather to deal with the institutions that govern the rate and direction of technological change.

It was the belief of our panel that, although current political attention appears to be focused on the negative effects of technology, an effective system of technology assessment would as often stimulate the development and application of under-utilized technologies and identify new opportunities for beneficial use of technology as it would alert us to possible deleterious side effects. Many of the problems currently identified as products of technological development—overpopulation, congested cities, deteriorated housing, crowded airways, polluted air—can also be seen as having resulted from the failure to develop and disseminate parallel technologies which would have mitigated the undesired effects—methods of fertility control, cheaper industrially produced housing, air traffic control systems, better design of fixed and mobile power plants. Thus, it is not technology itself but the unequal and unplanned relative speeds of development and application of different technologies that has partly created our problems.

In the 1930's the Great Depression showed us that we could no longer afford the waste of productive resources involved in permitting individual economic decisions to proceed without social control. Yet, in many ways the controls that were instituted strengthened the market system and increased the options of the entrepreneur and the consumer, while protecting them from some of the risks of economic disaster. We believe that the current years are presenting an environmental and social crisis, resulting from unguided technology, that bears a close resemblance to the economic crisis of forty years ago. We also believe that the control measures that are necessary can strengthen rather than weaken technological innovation, and can shield it from the unreasoning and capricious political reaction that will surely result as we move from one environmental and social crisis to another in the absence of adequate foresight and planning. Already we see that much of our technological planning—in highways, airports, power plant location, aircraft development, for example—is being increasingly disrupted by unanticipated public resistance, at great costs not only to technology itself, but also in postponement of benefits to the public. Furthermore, the progress of science in recent years has greatly increased the menu of technological options available to us. We are in a position to choose among many feasible technological paths to the same objective, sometimes at an increased economic cost, which, however, society will be increasingly willing to pay if an equitable way of assessing it can be found. Thus an important aspect of technology assessment is the evaluation of alternate means to the same end and a comparison of their social and economic costs. Choices between alternative technologies are partly economic and political decisions. In our opinion, it is neither feasible nor desirable to develop an assessment mechanism that would circumvent market and political modes of accommodating the conflicts of interests and values that must arise; rather, we view assessment as one of many inputs into the complex network of public and private decision-making processes that together mold the growth of technology and its integration into society.

The earliest form of technology assessment in the U.S., and the one which is still dominant, emerged with the development of capitalism and the system of markets and prices to assess needs and priorities. In this country, the federal government has also long played a significant role in affecting the direction of technological development. Federal involvement through interstate commerce regulation, the patent system, and participation in technological ventures has roots that go back to the early days of the republic. However, the involvement of the federal government on a massive scale did not occur until World War II. Today the government finances nearly 50 percent of industrial research and development, and virtually every government agency is deeply involved in technological programs. The influence of the federal government is now critical in highway planning and construction, water resource development, housing, the development of nuclear power, agriculture, the extraction of natural resources, aviation, the exploitation of the oceans, and many other areas. Numerous agencies have been created either to regulate technological activities or to perform specialized functions related to the impact of technology on particular facets of the environment or on the consumer. These include the Federal Communications Commission, the Federal Power Commission, the Food and Drug Administration, the Atomic Energy Commission, and many others. Government involvement in technology development is now pervasive and has in many cases significantly modified and even replaced the forces of the market in determining the rates and directions of technological change.

Within this set of governmental and market processes, the initial assessment of the costs and benefits of alternative technologies is normally undertaken by those who seek to exploit them. Thus, the frame of reference for the assessment is often quite limited. While diverse groups such as professional societies and conservation organizations may have inputs to the evaluation, the assessment is usually based on the contending interests of those who already recognize their stake in the technology and are prepared to enter the public arena to defend their position. In all but a few special situations, usually when Congress takes a special interest, no other assessment occurs. The regulatory agencies when involved are often restricted to narrow assessments because of specified limits in their jurisdictions and mandates; these limits are sometimes arbitrary and sometimes appropriate. While technological decisions are made within a framework of social and legal restraints, the central question asked in contemporary technology assessment is what the technology will do to the economic and institutional interests of those who wish to exploit it or what it will do to the interests of those having a stake in competing technologies. The recognition and analysis of broader impacts usually occurs only later in ad hoc assessments of the problems after they have reached serious proportions and have generated acute public concern. No mechanism exists to trigger such studies in a systematic way at the early stages of the process of technology development and diffusion. The vacuum that is left is partially filled by the activities of articulate individuals such as Ralph Nader and Rachel Carson as well as by conservation organizations which attempt to represent the "public interest." Their efforts, which excite both admiration and criticism, are a consequence of a deficiency in our present evaluation and decision system.

The important problems of technology assessment must inevitably involve conflicts of interests, values, and goals. Technological development will necessarily affect some people adversely and others beneficially. There is no agreed quantitative method by which the costs and benefits may be evaluated. We seriously doubt that concepts such as the "general welfare" or "the public interest" can be aggregated like the final figure on the balance sheet showing net profit or net loss. The assigning of costs and benefits to different groups is fundamentally political, and the purpose of technology assessment is to clarify the political choices rather than to come up with a final answer.

The difficulties of computing all costs and benefits should not prevent us from formulating general principles. For example, the preservation of future options must be a key factor. Other things being equal, those alternatives that leave maximum room for maneuver in the future should be favored. For example, policy should reflect the fact that the pollution of a lake is more difficult to reverse than the pollution of a river. The reduction of future options ought to be counted as a cost incurred in a particular undertaking; yet this is rarely done in current assessments. In less affluent societies than ours, it may be necessary to discount the future for short-term gains, but in the United States this policy becomes harder and harder to justify.

Technology assessment by its very nature deals with uncertainties. In the past, the benefit of the doubt was most frequently given to the developer. The working assumption was that a technological trend should be permitted to continue so long as it yielded a profit to those who exploit it. However, our experience in the last few years with such events as the Santa Barbara incident and the accumulation of pesticide residues suggests a reconsideration of this assumption.

It is clear that some of our present difficulties can be attributed to the lack of effective constituencies informed and influential enough to inject diffuse and poorly articulated interests into the decision-making process. There is often an absence of influential spokesman within this process whose task it is to see the impact on segments of society beyond those that perceive themselves to be directly and immediately affected. This certainly does not mean that the advantages lie always with those who are proposing technological innovations; often the antitechnological forces are very strong. New technology that promises to upset power relations, employment patterns, or traditional procedures in an industry usually excites vigorous and sometimes successful opposition; think, for example, of the building industry, shipping, and even education. The difficulty lies not with the representation of those groups that directly perceive their interests to be affected either positively or negatively, but in the fact that those groups for which the consequences are less obvious or more remote in time have little voice in the decision-making process. Slight effects on many people over long periods of time are likely to be neglected in comparison with more dramatic damages or benefits.

Another problem is the lack of consistency in the criteria of assessment or regulation of alternate technologies that serve the same social purpose. For example, are safety standards or environmental pollution standards with respect to the extraction and transportation of oil more or less stringent than the safety standards for the location and construction of nuclear power plants? To the extent that these standards are not treated consistently, an arbitrary bias may be generated with respect to one type of power plant over the other.

The achievement of a more rational and effective system of technology assessment faces some major obstacles; a satisfactory methodology of assessment is far away. We do not know how to balance conflicting interests. We do not know how to value in a quantitative manner goals such as clean environment or preservation of future choice. There is an absence of analytical tools. Projections of the impact of technology are limited by failure of imagination, especially when it comes to foreseeing the cumulative effects of scale. For example, in 1948 there were 100,000 television sets in use; one year later there were a million; a decade later there were fifty million. The social and psychological consequences of such phenomenal growth are hard to contemplate, let alone predict. Our failures to imagine all the possible uses of new technologies can often preclude adequate perception of social and environmental consequences. As late as 1958, an authoritative report on the consequences of the automobile failed to mention atmospheric pollution. Nor can we imagine all the consequences for the supporting system that a new technology will require. For example, the current crisis in air transport arises in part from failure to develop an air traffic control system adequate for the technology of modern aircraft, and also from failure to develop airports and ground transportation adequate for the volume of traffic. Perhaps the greatest difficulty is that of forecasting changes in technology itself that can both ameliorate and aggravate consequences perceived at the beginning of the development period. Our understanding of the interaction of technology with society is not well founded; much remains to be learned about how pollutants disperse in the environment and how children react to various kinds of television programs. Nor is the data base on which general theories might be constructed at all adequate. Our monitoring of secondary effects of technology is in a primitive state. And the obstacles go beyond inadequate analytical methods and insufficient theoretical understanding. In large measure, the problems are institutional: economic, legal, or political constraints upon the interests and authority of the decision makers. These necessarily result in distortion. Institutional constraints must affect technological decisions when an institution feels that it only has the mandate to consider those consequences directly affecting its own constituents or clients. For example, public utility commissions have no authority to consider investments that improve the environment in establishing the rate base for power plants. Moreover, some institutional structures result in a very strong vested interest in the stimulation or prevention of a particular technology. In government, there are jurisdictional boundaries which frequently bear no relationship to the technological problem under examination. This problem is probably most acute in environmental questions.

Technology assessment is so complex, that it is not surprising that during our study we frequently had doubts that anything significant could come from viewing it on the all-inclusive basis that seemed to be required. The processes we seek to improve are too bound up with the very fabric of our society to admit of sudden and sweeping alteration. But the rejection of instant solutions does not mean that we cannot begin in an evolutionary manner the extremely difficult task of altering present evaluative and decision-making processes in a way that would remove some of the obvious defects of our present procedures. Our study concluded that improvements are feasible. We believe there is a need for additional mechanisms of technology assessment beyond those currently operating because these are inadequate to deal with the scale of application of technology expected in the future. New mechanisms are necessary to supplement and coordinate existing mechanisms rather than to supersede them. Existing procedures, whether they involve government agencies, private industries, or professional groups have intrinsic limitations both by design and because of unconscious biases. There is a need for a program of technology assessment that is broader in fundamental conception and scope and better designed to take into account the interests of groups which, at the inception of a technological development, are unorganized or do not yet perceive their interests potentially affected. We need evaluations that are more responsive to changes in the values, sensitivities, and priorities of society. Neither the evaluation nor the original formulation of relevant questions should be too limited by the interests and biases of direct interest groups. While one will never be able to devise procedures that totally avoid such distortions, much can be done to improve the current situation.

Technology assessments are carried on at many locations in our society, but they are too fragmented and uncoordinated to provide an institutional basis for the support of research, analysis, education, and monitoring that is necessary for a national technology assessment capability. No group at present has the responsibility for standards and criteria and for the development of coherent principles of assessment that can be applied consistently in many different situations. There is no system of precedents, analogous to case law, which can be transferred from one assessment problem to another.

While we see a need for new procedures and institutions to strengthen the quality of technology assessment, we also acknowledge that the present multiplicity of processes is essential because technology pervades almost every aspect of our social organization. Our study did not contemplate a highly centralized process of technology assessment as a solution. Even if practical, centralization would be unwise, politically unacceptable, and even dangerous. Pluralism in this matter is essential in the context of our society, not only because it is the only principle consistent with our political values, but also because it insures a healthy competition of ideas and avoids at least some of the negative impact of innovation which could be as dangerous as the side effects of technology.

We thus envision a constellation of organizations, with components located strategically within both political branches, that can provide a focus and a forum for technology assessment activities throughout the government and the private sector. We see the following functions for the new technology assessment mechanisms: (1) examine particular areas of technology using both in-house personnel and contracts with outside organizations to undertake comprehensive assessments of social and environmental effects of technology; (2) sponsor basic research on theoretical problems and issues related to technology assessment by extending grants for studies to be conducted by government agencies, universities, and not-for-profit organizations; (3) review specific assessments performed by other agencies, confining this review to an evaluation of the criteria and procedures employed in the assessment processes, the nature and reliability of the evidence relied upon, and the adequacy of the representation of potentially affected interests; (4) develop an information center on technology assessment and carry out research to identify gaps in the existing body of data; (5) issue an annual technology assessment report reviewing governmental work in this area, describing new methods and new problems that have emerged, and suggesting future priorities; (6) provide an effective forum for responsible assessment activities of individuals and groups currently operating outside the present governmental and industrial technology assessment institutions. We include in this last activity the sponsorship of conferences, symposia, and the holding of public hearings; (7) prepare policy papers recommending specific actions to Congress, the President, and executive or administrative bodies bearing on the sponsorship or regulation of technology.

An important goal is to achieve greater consistency in assessment principles; these could be used to improve the quality of assessments carried out by private organizations and specialized government agencies. Such principles could result from a conscious attempt to formulate general policy, but they could also evolve from the experience gained from dealing with individual cases selected in part for their potential in setting precedents.

Before discussing specific organizational arrangements, we wish to make some general comments concerning the limitations of the scope and powers of the new institutions we shall propose. Any new technology assessment mechanism must maintain as detached and neutral a stance as possible toward each issue that comes before it. For this reason, it should be insulated from direct policy-making authority. It should have neither the responsibility for promotion of any particular technology nor regulatory powers. Above all, it must be given no authority to screen or clear new technological undertakings, though obviously its evaluations and recommendations should carry weight with those agencies which have such authority. Unlike the Federal Aviation Agency it must not itself be entrusted with the realization of a supersonic transport or even an operational air traffic control system. Unlike the Atomic Energy Commission it should not be held accountable for the avoidance of excessive radiation. To give it responsibilities of this kind would deprive it of its unique perspective as an entity with no ax to grind. Given the current popularity of proposals to entrust some environmental agency with the power to censor all technological developments and forbid the introduction of those deemed excessively injurious, a further word on this subject seems in order. Our study concluded that one could not vest such authority in any agency without subjecting it to external political pressures that it could not resist. That is, the allocation of such sweeping powers to a new assessment entity would rob it of any special claim to objectivity and render its judgments at least as suspect as those of any other regulatory or technology-promoting agency.

At the outset of the creation of this technology assessment mechanism, its activities should be restricted to those areas of technology that are strongly and directly influenced by federal policy. We believe that the federal government ought to put its own house in order before it seeks to impose new requirements for state or local action or new standards for the private sector. The involvement of the federal government in technology is so broad that this restriction still leaves an enormous sphere of activity.

In the design of a new governmental institution, it is important to be sensitive to the dangers of technology assessment, especially its possible secondary consequences. The most serious problem lies in its effect on the delicate process of industrial and technological innovation. There is a very real risk that new assessment institutions could stultify progress by magnifying risks or difficulties and ignoring the possibility of finding solutions as problems arise. New assessment mechanisms could create sufficient new uncertainties in the prospects for innovation that private and public investment in new areas of technology would be discouraged. If the technology assessment mechanism is not sensitive to the need to encourage innovation, the cure may be worse than the disease. It must be recognized that new technology has unanticipated or secondary benefits as well as undesirable side effects. When the development of nuclear power was started, it was not anticipated that this power might alleviate the problem of atmospheric pollution.

Another danger is one that is inherent in every attempt to improve rationality in politically charged areas of discourse. Just as systems analysis has occasionally been used to provide a spurious mantle of objectivity for essentially predetermined value preferences, so, too, there is a risk that technology assessment, without independent criticism, may become a weapon of individuals and groups in defense of their own interests or narrow ideological aims.

In trying to design a governmental organization that is likely to be effective in this area, one can specify a number of desirable characteristics. However, these characteristics are likely to be mutually contradictory, at least to some degree. For example, any effective assessment organization needs to be close to the center of important political decisions in order that it may be influential; yet it needs to maintain a degree of political neutrality in order to ensure the integrity, objectivity, and credibility of its evaluations and assessments. It needs to address politically pressing and urgent issues; yet its time perspective should be longer than that of most political decisions. It must provide critical analysis of private sector plans affected by federal policies and programs; yet it must be an organization that will obtain the confidence and cooperation of industry. It must provide a forum for public representation and open hearings; yet it must be able to respect the privacy of individuals and the legitimate proprietary interests of industrial organizations. Clearly compromises will have to be made in designing new mechanisms. Any new system should be able to modify its procedures, assumptions, and even its location within government as it learns from experience. Perhaps, if new mechanisms and institutions are created by statute, their organization, procedures, and accomplishments should be subject to formal review after a specified term of existence.

Our study group concluded that it was necessary to have important components of the new technology assessment mechanism associated with both the executive and congressional branches of government. The executive component should be closely linked to the President. Having considered many alternative means of achieving this, we concluded that the best location would be within an expanded Office of Science and Technology (OST), possibly under a deputy director, since it is difficult to separate technology assessment from many of the functions currently performed by OST. Furthermore, a wholly separate office would be likely to lead to a situation in which the new office became the rallying point for antitechnology forces while OST took on an increasingly protechnology bias. The responsibilities of this part of the mechanism would include the direction of an information management system for technology assessment, the preparation of an annual report, the initiation of conferences and symposia, and the preparation of in-house policy papers. We hope that such activities would strongly influence the political and budgetary decisions carried out in the office of the President. Since we cannot foresee the expansion of the OST component to the scale necessary to support related extramural activities, we believe that there should be a new Technology Assessment Division within the National Science Foundation to complement the activities of the Office of Science and Technology. This division would administer the substantial program involving work to be performed outside of the executive office on contracts and grants, especially in universities and other private organizations. The executive component could be expected to review specific assessments performed by other government agencies or departments either on its own initiative or by requests from other agencies. Such a review would be limited to an evaluation of the criteria and procedures employed in the assessment process, the nature and scientific adequacy of the evidence relied upon, and the representation of potentially affected interests. We would guess that the total annual budget of the new operation in the executive branch might ultimately reach the order of $50 million with about 20 percent being spent "in-house" and 80 percent in the contract or grant program with external organizations. Some idea of the scale of this operation can be given by noting that the following government organizations had budgets of approximately this magnitude in fiscal 1969:

General Accounting Office	$58 million
Library of Congress	$50 million
Civil Aeronautics Board	$63 million
Food and Drug Administration	$70 million

We do not believe that a viable technology assessment mechanism can be built if it is restricted to the executive branch. There are many arguments for this point of view, but most of them ultimately center on undue influence of the President and his executive agencies on the course of the assessment process. Complementary organizations more directly accessible to the Congress are needed. We need to provide within Congress or close to Congress an effective public forum for responsible assessment activities of individuals or groups operating outside present governmental and industrial institutions. Congress needs direct access to more sophisticated and professional judgments relating to the technology assessments it considers. Such judgments cannot be obtained entirely from existing substantive and appropriations committees, though they will surely play a role. They do not provide adequate focus because of internal rivalries and fragmentation by jurisdictional divisions. We have considered two possibilities. One is a joint congressional committee on technology assessment. This committee's relationship to the proposed executive technology assessment entities would be analogous to the relationship of the joint committee on internal revenue and taxation to the Department of the Treasury or the joint economic committee to the Council of Economic Advisors. Using these as a model, we believe that the high standard of professional competence required in the staff of the committee can be achieved. We do not propose that this joint committee have any jurisdiction over specific legislation or appropriations. While it will obviously wish to develop its own independent sources of information, we assume that it would have access with appropriate safeguards to the information system developed in the executive branch.

An alternative congressional component could be centered in a separate technology assessment office serving the Congress as a whole. Such an office would carry out assignments given to it by the Vice-President, the Speaker or the chairman of any interested committee of Congress. Unlike the Legislative Reference Service and the Legislative Drafting Service, it would not be expected to accept assignments from individual members of Congress. Its functions would be similar to those suggested for the joint committee. The director of such an office might be appointed by the President with the advice and consent of the Senate, but his term of office should be sufficiently long to provide a measure of insulation from presidential politics, perhaps analogous to the comptroller general, who is removable only by a concurrent resolution of both houses of Congress.

While developing these recommendations we did consider a quasi-independent commission separated from both of the political branches. While this kind of separation has obvious advantages in terms of freedom from political interference, the separation of the assessment process from the center of political decisions seems a very heavy price to pay. In any case we believe that a totally apolitical assessment mechanism is a myth. It cannot be totally apolitical and relevant simultaneously.

One question of great importance that did not receive much attention in the panel's deliberations was the assessment of military technology. While many will think it is absurd in a discussion of the impact of technology on our society to exclude consideration of the military, there are features of military technology that made it difficult to include in our evaluation. Military technology is frequently not visible to the public and a considerable proportion of the technological data is either classified or proprietary. The control over the flow of this information is effectively in the hands of the proponents of technological innovation who assess technology only in terms of national security conceived in the narrowest sense. Furthermore, military technology is strongly conditioned by the interpretation of intelligence and information which can be of a highly sensitive character. While our discussions did not encompass military technology, we nevertheless were convinced of the importance of having some mechanism for independent assessment of proposed military technology by a group of fully cleared experts not directly responsible for national security and sensitive to broader social, political, and environmental implications.

Our study concluded with the conviction that however our specific recommendations be viewed, *some* form of constructive action is imperative and cannot be long delayed without increasing the difficulty of implementation and diminishing the prospects of success. The future of technology holds great promise for mankind. However, if society persists in its present course, the future holds great peril whether from the uncontrolled effects of technology itself or from an unreasoned political reaction against all technological innovation, which could condemn man to poverty, frustration, and the loss of freedom.

A Study
of Technology Assessment

COMMITTEE ON PUBLIC ENGINEERING POLICY
OF THE NATIONAL ACADEMY OF ENGINEERING

In response to a request from the Committee on Science and Astronautics, U.S. House of Representatives, the National Academy of Engineering has undertaken a study of technology assessment. The phrase "technology assessment" was first introduced by Congressman Emilio Q. Daddario, Chairman of the Subcommittee on Science, Research, and Development, to characterize the sociotechnical research that discloses the benefits and risks to society emanating from alternative courses in the development of scientific and technological opportunities.

The conduct of this study has been the responsibility of the Committee on Public Engineering Policy (COPEP) of the Academy. To assist it in this study, a Committee on Technology Assessment was appointed to analyze and observe the experience of three separate experiments in technology assessment. These were conducted by task forces ancillary to existing NAE committees dealing with issues in mature, developing, and embryonic technologies. The experiments were investigations of methodology, feasibility, and the potential value of technology assessment by groups with varying backgrounds. The results do not represent, nor were they anticipated to be, complete technology assessments. . . .

SUMMARY OF FINDINGS

The social impact of technological development has become so great that it affects many fundamental aspects of national policy and national life. Unless dependable means are developed to identify, study, and forecast the varying impacts that these technological developments might have on sectors of our society, the nation will be subjected to increasing stress in a time of social turbulence and will not benefit fully from technological opportunities.

As a result of studies conducted by committees of the National Academy of Engineering, the Committee on Public Engineering Policy believes that technology assessment can help Congress to perceive, appraise, and initiate actions required to secure the greatest values from technology. Technology assessment can be expected to perform important roles by:

(1) *Clarifying* the nature of existing social problems as they are influenced by technology, possibly with indications of legislation needed to achieve satisfactory control.

(2) *Providing* insights into future problems, to make possible the establishment of long-term priorities and to provide guidance for the allocation of national resources.

(3) *Stimulating* the private and public sectors of our society to take those courses of action for the development of new technology that are most socially desirable. Such actions may be creative or defensive. Creative actions would be those that follow from the awareness of new opportunities for social development; defensive actions would be those involving restrictions on the use of technological developments.

(4) *Educating* the public and the government about the short-term and long-term effects of the range of alternative solutions to current problems.

. . . The Committee on Public Engineering Policy considers that the following are the principal findings of this study.

(1) Technology assessments on a broad range of subjects are feasible and can be expected to be useful to the decision-making processes of the Congress, when prepared by properly constituted, independent, ad hoc task forces with adequate staff support and time.

(2) Technology assessments should be produced in an environment free from political influence or predetermined bias. Especially when political factors are involved, it can be inferred from the pilot studies that the selection of a preferred course of action, among alternative strategies derived from the assessment, is not a suitable task for the technology assessment group. This

function should remain the prerogative of the legislator after he has been provided with bases for the application of his judgment.

(3) Members of a technology assessment task force should be chosen for their expertise but not as representatives of affected parties or special interests. The viewpoints of affected parties should be brought to the task force by volunteered or solicited presentations, and with special concern to elicit views from those affected parties who are not normally organized in their own interests.

(4) Task force members will necessarily come from public and private organizations that have knowledge about the subject under assessment. Experience shows that task forces composed of members possessing a wide range of personal interests have been able to focus on the public interest and to neutralize the biases of the organizations with which they are associated.

(5) The necessary, thorough investigation of the sociological and political impacts of technologies under assessment requires extensive participation by behavioral and political scientists. The NAE experiments in technology assessment indicated that engineers and economists were able to work in harmony with these other professionals.

(6) To be of most use, a technology assessment should be completed in about one year; the conduct of the assessment should be the sole mission of the performing group.

(7) A management organization, controlled by and answering to the Congress, should arrange for the preparation of technology assessments for congressional purposes. No single, permanent organization can be envisioned that could provide adequate in-house expertise to execute assessments in all of the fields that may be required by Congress. Therefore it would be useful to establish such a small management organization to contract for or to administer and organize the assessment task forces.

(8) In order to give full consideration to social as well as technical issues, technology assessments should include analyses of the cause-effect relationship between different government strategies and their social impacts and should be supplemented by the intuitive judgments of knowledgeable individuals.

(9) It is useful to classify technology assessments as initiated (a) by an existing social problem or (b) by the potential of a new technology. The methodology of assessment should proceed differently for each; more fully tested methodologies of system analysis are available for the first class, but the Congress is probably more concerned about the second.

(10) The goal of a problem-initiated assessment is obviously to arrive at the best possible solution using the technologies at hand. The inherent proliferating set of impacts in the technology-initiated case requires a choice between diffuse searches seeking some early warning signals and conversion to a problem-oriented study by selecting a few applications of the technology that might reveal the most significant impacts. The uncertainty in this approach is that in making the selection of problems to be addressed by the technology under assessment, important social and political impacts could be overlooked.

(11) As elements in technology assessment, forecasts covering more than five years are likely to be unreliable because of unforeseen events and scientific discoveries. The longer-term forecast is nevertheless valuable for planning and for "setting the stage" to evaluate the impact of unforeseen events when they do occur.

(12) Criteria for establishing the priority of topics for assessment include the breadth and depth of the expected social impact, the visibility of the problems to legislators and to the people, and the current and expected rates of development of the technologies.

(13) The appraisal of the accumulated spectrum of consequences of technological developments must include the derivation and use of measures of social value pertinent to "the quality of life," in addition to the conventional economic and technical risk-benefit criteria.

(14) Technology assessments can help alert the nation to future benefits and to future problems and can thus provide the public support necessary for national programs designed to secure the benefits and to avoid those problems.

EXAMINATION OF THE THREE NAE EXPERIMENTS IN TECHNOLOGY ASSESSMENT

[The NAE performed three experimental technology assessments. In one, the problem of subsonic aircraft noise was examined with respect to social considerations (e.g., individual rights), economic factors (including effect on GNP), technological considerations (e.g., technologically achievable noise reduction), and political considerations. The second dealt with the technology of teaching aids, focusing on instructional television and computer-assisted instruction. In the third, technological aspects, potential social benefits, and potential impacts on society of multiphasic health screening centers (in which large numbers of individuals are given a sequence of health tests) were explored. The details of each of these assessments are contained in the full report. Here, the three experiments are examined together in order to see what might be learned from them—ed.]

Section 1: Methodology Used in the NAE Experiments

The NAE experiments in technology assessment used primarily a methodology that is closely congruent with steps outlined by Congressman Daddario, although not necessarily in the same order. The steps used by the NAE Task Forces were as follows:

(1) Identify and refine the subject to be assessed.

(2) Delineate the scope of the assessment and develop a data base.

(3) Identify alternative strategies to solve the selected problems with the technology under assessment.

(4) Identify parties affected by the selected problems and the technology.

(5) Identify the impacts on the affected parties.

(6) Valuate or measure the impacts.

(7) Compare the pros and cons of alternative strategies.

The differing formats and emphases of the three reports may submerge some of the common elements, but examination will disclose some or all of these seven steps in varying degrees in the three pilot assessments.

Identifying and Refining the Subject to be Assessed. The first step of the assessment process as practiced by the NAE Task Forces was to identify and refine the subject area under assessment in each study.

The character of each of the pilot assessment studies undertaken, whether problem-initiated or technology-initiated, had to be recognized. The goal of a problem-initiated assessment is obviously to arrive at the best possible solution to some problem using technologies at hand. In technology-initiated assessments, the goal is either to identify possible impacts, both good and bad, of some new developing technology or to convert the effort to a problem-initiated study by selecting applications that match the technology to several actual or potential problems.

The assessment experiment in the field of teaching aids began as a technology-initiated study when that Task Force first defined its assignment as:

Given the existence of a range of technology-based teaching aids, where can they make a major impact on education, what will this impact be, will the overall consequences be favorable, and what will be the trade-offs among favorable as well as unfavorable impacts?

After an initial period of data base accumulation, the limitations of time and effort and the apparently ever-expanding series of necessary considerations led the members to focus the study on the application of two specific technological teaching aids, namely instructional television and computer-assisted instruction, to two significant problems in *higher* education. The goal of the study then became:

> To assess the promise of various alternative strategies for the development and use of systems of instructional television and computer-assisted instruction at institutions of higher education in the United States, as a means for alleviating rising costs without sacrificing quality of instruction and as a means for reducing or eliminating incidents of student unrest.

The assessment experiment in the field of multiphasic health screening was also a technology-initiated study, originally being concerned with all the impacts and applications of that medical technology. It was also converted to a study of a specific application of the new technology, namely, the application of an automated health screening system to cope with increasing *public* health problems in the United States.

The assessment experiment on subsonic aircraft noise was problem-initiated, and its goal was recognized to be the identification of means to reduce the undesirable effects of aircraft noise near airports, without introducing equally or more undesirable effects on the growth of civilian aviation services.

Delineating the Scope of the Assessment and Developing the Data Base. The second step was to set appropriate limits on the scope of the studies and to develop the best possible data base once this delineation of the scope had been made.

In these studies, the Task Forces needed and were given wide latitude in the definition of the scope and goal of the assessment exercise. However, it was also understood that in an actual assessment effort, a management group would initially provide the task forces with a detailed definition of the assessment area and goals and the membership of the task force would be chosen and modified as necessary during the conduct of the assessment so as to be able to carry out the assigned task.

Each experimental assessment effort led its Task Force members to the realization that a complete assessment would require a very substantial investment in time and effort. These feasibility studies showed that it is necessary for task force members to meet and react with each other sufficiently to develop respect for all opinions, viewpoints, and judgments. This interaction requires a number of meetings, and suitable time and circumstances should be provided for repeated exchanges during full-scale technology assessments.

Identifying Alternative Strategies to Solve the Selected Problems with the Technology Under Assessment. In the third step in the experimental assessment studies, alternative strategies were identified as the means to solve the selected problems with the technology under assessment.

In these experiments, each group considered the consequences of a limited number of strategies for utilizing the technology under assessment. An actual technology assessment must consider all the probable strategies that become known to it.

In the teaching aids study, four strategies were identified. Three were based on different funding levels, and one was based on a change in emphasis in the existing programs of the developing technology. Only one of these strategies was pursued in some depth. In the subsonic aircraft noise study, ten strategies were identified and five of these were examined in some detail. In the multiphasic health screening study, the available data base was not sufficiently developed to permit meaningful definition of alternative strategies.

Insight about possible strategies for implementation seemed to develop early in the Task Force deliberations. Attempts were made to identify as many strategic options as possible and to record them as they arose. It was important for the Task Forces to make concerted searches for these options from the very beginning, since they were central to later activities and deliberations.

Identifying the Parties Affected by the Selected Problems and the Technology Under Assessment. The fourth step in the assessment process was the identification of the parties affected by the technology under assessment. Professionals from the social and behavioral sciences were most helpful in identifying potentially affected groups.

The initial identification consisted of listing groups that have expressed interest in the subject under assessment, groups that the Task Force believed were likely to be affected or that may be known to have special interests. Considerable care was required because parties may be affected that initially may not themselves be aware of any involvement. As the analysis proceeded, new groups were identified and these were added to the list. In more complete assessments, some groups initially identified may later need to be differentiated more finely. For example, within a group of educational institutions, distinctions may need to be made between large institutions and small institutions, or between state-supported institutions and privately supported institutions.

All alternative strategies considered may affect the same parties, as in the teaching aids study; or different groups may be affected by the various alternative strategies, as in the subsonic aircraft noise study.

Identifying the Impacts on the Affected Parties. The fifth step was the expression of the impacts on the affected parties.

This step was attempted most extensively in the teaching aids study and to a lesser degree in the aircraft noise study. There was a natural inclination among members of the Task Force to relate the expected consequences to technical developments. However, they recognized this tendency and made serious efforts to appreciate economic, social, and political impacts as well. Impact identification tended to focus on near-term consequences, even though efforts were made to extend the time range of the analysis. The portions of the experimental studies dealing with impact identification are presented as illustrations of procedure rather than of completeness.

Valuating or Measuring the Impacts. The succeeding step was to valuate and cumulate the impacts on all the affected parties according to criteria and/or scales of values. This appears to be the most difficult step in the technology assessment process. Since impacts or consequences are often not quantifiable in readily appreciated terms, such as cost, sophisticated and comprehensive judgments about societal values must be made.

The limited merit of assigning only dollar costs to impacts on society can be quickly illustrated if an attempt is made to evaluate the impact of aircraft noise in monetary terms. A resident near an airport who is disturbed by the noise of an airplane during its approach or landing is probably not nearly so concerned with the effect of the noise on the value of his property as he is with irritation and disturbance of his peace of mind. Groups of residents aroused by noise may take legal or political action to have it abated. Evaluation of the probability of such action is neither primarily a technical question nor a matter that can be resolved by simple cost-benefit studies. In some fields that are likely to come under assessment, such as transportation policy, societal value determinations are currently the subject of intensive research and development; in other fields, few guidelines for valuation schemes are available. In the absence of rational methodology, the synthesis of the intuitive judgments of a suitable task force may be most helpful. Valuation of the impacts is a crucial step in the assessment process and will require a substantial commitment of effort from task force members preparing full-scale assessments. Social scientists can be of great assistance in the evaluation of impacts. The identification and accurate forecasting of public reactions is particularly vital information to the legislator for his further deliberations.

It must be emphasized that the impact valuations contained in the assessment experiments discussed here were made principally to serve as examples for the development of assessment methodology.

Comparing the Pros and Cons of Alternative Strategies. Once the impact valuations have been made, one further additional step should be attempted: a synthesis of these impact valuations in order to indicate the most attractive strategy or strategies for matching the promise of the technology under assessment to the problems selected for application.

In its exploration of one strategy in some detail, the Task Force on Teaching Aids conducted the impact valuation for that strategy and commented on possible courses of action that might be followed in the cases where unfavorable consequences were predicted. A much greater effort would be required to accomplish that analysis for the number of alternatives that would be considered in a full-scale technology assessment. In fact, some individuals who were involved in the experiments felt that the selection of an optimum or preferred course of action is not a suitable task for a technology assessment group and that this function should remain the prerogative of the legislator after he has been provided with bases for the application of his judgment. This may be an area of continuing controversy during the conduct of future technology assessments.

Section 2: Characteristics of ad hoc Task Forces
for Technology Assessments

Since all three NAE experimental assessment studies were produced by Task Forces, the results obtained may be used to measure and to characterize the task force mechanism for the preparation of technology assessments. A review of the activities of the three Task Forces led to the identification of several important considerations for the conduct of future full-scale assessments by this mechanism.

Selection of Assessment Task Force Members. The selection of a task force chairman, and with his assistance, the selection of task force members, is probably the most sensitive step in assuring an effective technology assessment.

Members of a technology assessment task force should be chosen for their expertise in one or more phases of the subject under assessment. They should not be chosen as vehicles for the presentation of the coordinated viewpoints of affected parties; as a matter of fact, the coordinated viewpoints of affected parties should be brought to the task force by means of special and separate presentations rather than directly through its membership.

Composition of the Task Force. The Task Force chairmen felt that in going beyond their initial experimental studies, the in-depth investigation of sociological, political, and economic impacts would require, in addition to extensive further contributions from the Task Force members, supplementary personnel, including economists and sociologists.

The engineering profession is skilled in the application of technical and scientific knowledge to the solution of well-defined problems that are usually stated in relation to economic goals. Economists and other social scientists are skilled in studying the interaction of external and internal forces with the welfare of the population. Experience in the assessment studies indicated that engineers were able to work in harmony with the economists and the social scientists who participated in these exercises.

Assignment of Responsibilities to the Task Force. By requesting existing committees of the NAE to undertake, as an additional task, the management of experimental assessment studies in subject areas related to their respective principal activities, it was hoped that there would be indications that this might be a way to speed up the assessment process and reduce its cost. The assumption was that the ready availability of a reservoir of expertise, assembled for a related purpose, would [permit] some increased efficiency. The limited experience indicates that little appears to be gained by this approach. An assessment effort seems to require that its conduct be the sole mission of the performing group for the following reasons:

(1) The conduct of the assessment will usually require additions to the membership of the managing or the executing group to take actions or to meet schedules that might be incompatible with the nature of other current assignments to a group established for other purposes.

(2) The time available from qualified task force members is always likely to be limited by their other occupations. Extracurricular demands, in addition to those of the assessment, might exceed that limit.

(3) To be most useful, an assessment should be completed in about one year. Such time pressure requires the most direct application of the energies of the task force carrying out the assignment.

Biases of Task Forces. Task force members will come from public and private organizations that have vital interests and knowledge about the subject under assessment. It is such individuals, of course, who possess the most intimate expertise about the subjects involved. Inevitably the question arises: Can a task force composed of such members eliminate special-interest considerations from its findings? A properly chosen task force will be able, we believe, to produce a report that is free from any strong bias. In other circumstances in the past, task forces with members possessing a wide range of interests have been able to focus their attention on the public interest and to submerge the biases of the organizations with which they are associated directly or indirectly. Such task forces have been able to seek out the full range of available viewpoints and to keep any one viewpoint from dominating the deliberations. The repeated demonstration of success in avoiding bias in the conduct of technology assessment will build public acceptance for this procedure.

Ability To Assemble a Data Base. The existence and availability of background information is essential for any assessment effort.

It is apparent that every technology assessment task force will identify information that it would like to have and that it thinks is possible to produce, but that will not become available within the time allotted to the study. Obviously, if one had to wait for the development of the complete data base before concluding any technology assessment, the identification of some courses of actions for avoiding some of the readily uncovered unfavorable impacts of a technology may be delayed to the detriment of the general public. Incomplete data bases may be a problem for some technology assessment task forces, but it also appears, from these experiments, that task forces can produce useful reports within the limitations of the readily available data bases.

The experience of the NAE Task Forces indicated that since most of the members were professionals working in the technologies involved, the *technical* state of the art was well known to them. Forecasts about the future development of technologies could also be made with reasonable confidence in most cases. However, data were incomplete, in general, with respect to potential *political* and *social* impacts of the technologies. The inability to distinguish the most strongly causative factors from the many that might be involved pointed to the areas in which better data were needed.

Also, in the experimental assessment of the utility of instructional television and computer-assisted instruction, sociological data were not available concerning the consequences of the possible realignment of the relative roles of education of the home, the school, and industry. Broad social and economic repercussions could result from such changes in the higher education system of the country. To go beyond the speculation of informed individuals would require some broad sociopolitical studies that have not been undertaken to date.

Section 3: Observations on the Methodology
and the Organizational Mode Used in the NAE Experiments

Each Task Force chairman confirmed that his first undertaking was to work with the members he had selected toward a clear identification of the technology or of the problem that was to come under assessment.

Based on discussions with the Task Force chairmen, COPEP notes that the following observations can be made:

(1) The Task Force members were able to identify significant alternative strategies for matching the technology under assessment to the selected problems, although by no means were all the possible strategies identified. In the study of instructional television and computer-assisted instruction, an attempt was made to follow the process through to the evaluation of a particular strategy. A comparison of alternative strategies was beyond the scope of that experiment.

(2) Although identification was readily made of particular groups affected by the technologies under assessment, data were often limited or unavailable concerning the viewpoints and the scale of values of the public at large when its interests were identified as being affected. For example, in the instructional television and computer-assisted instruction study, there was considerable speculation and discussion about the causes of student dissatisfaction. Since that problem is still being articulated and since it is difficult to obtain meaningful information about its origins and status, it is certainly hard to make judgments about the impacts that instructional television and computer-assisted instruction might have on the public at large.

(3) Even though the study efforts are fragmentary, both with regard to the identification of alternative courses of action and to the identification of affected parties, there appears to be adequate evidence that task forces, given sufficient time and resources, would be able to carry out these critical steps in technology assessments.

(4) The classification of impacts into categories of favorable/unfavorable, likely/unlikely, and controllable/uncontrollable was the principal valuation scheme used in the Task Force reports. The "controllable" impacts are considered especially meaningful for the process of technology assessment because these were defined as those impacts that could be modulated by governmental action, either by legislation or by regulation. The use of this class permitted, for example, the identification of certain needs that were not obvious prior to the conduct of the study of technological teaching aids, such as the need for revised legislation on copyrights to allow the fullest development

of ITV/CAI. The merit of including a category for reversible or irreversible impacts was also considered.

(5) Since the experimental assessments were intended only to develop and test methodology, any discussion of the ability of task forces to reach conclusions from technology assessment must be prefaced with cautions about attributing full validity to the conclusions cited in the present studies. Neither the time nor the resources were available to give study conclusions the intensive review and evaluation that would be essential in the case of full-scale assessment. Keeping in mind, therefore, that the conclusions cited are basically illustrative of method, the Task Forces did reach conclusions that had not been appreciated from related studies not focused by the methodology of technology assessment. For instance, in the teaching aids study, the following conclusions were reached: . . .

(a) The net effect of using the two technologies under assessment, as presently used, will be to *increase* the cost of instruction.

(b) With federal support at the level now envisioned for the next five to ten years, the two technological teaching aids examined will not be significant in helping to solve two of the major current problems of institutions of higher education (the incidence of student unrest and the increasing costs of higher education).

(c) Improved understanding of the processes of learning is necessary to enable ITV and CAI to have a more beneficial impact on the operations managed by the institutions of higher education.

(d) An improved time-sharing computer is needed to permit major reductions in the complexity and cost of the computer programming task.

(6) The identification of data base gaps and needed research and development to fill those gaps represents one of the important kinds of conclusions that arose from the NAE assessment efforts. Based on the examples given above, it seems likely that task forces can reach important, pertinent, and dependable conclusions in future assessment efforts.

The Role
of Technology Assessment
in Public Policy

HUGH FOLK

Recent discussions of technology assessment suggest that additional information will improve policy making in technology and science. It is premised that the government wants to make good technological policy, has the power to make good policy, and would recognize a good policy if one were proposed. These premises are at least questionable, if we interpret "good" as meaning in the interest of the survival, prosperity, and liberty of the mass of the population. Many powerful politicians (such as appropriations subcommittee chairmen) have no concern for the national interest at all, but serve the parochial interests that permit their political survival. The government is often powerless to deal with significant problems because of the domination of significant parts of the regulatory apparatus by those who are subject to regulation and because authority is fragmented. Few politicians either possess the scientific sophistication necessary to make good judgments on technological questions or trust persons with the capacity of judgment. If viewed as a part of the policy making process, and not merely another sterile academic exercise, technology assessment must be adapted to the existing political process in which special interests, restricted and fragmented governmental jurisdiction, and untrustworthy advice flourish.

Technology assessment may be viewed as part of a rational process of policy making with four steps: (1) identifying possible outcomes of policy alternatives; (2) estimating the valency or probability of each of the possible outcomes; (3) estimating the utility or disutility of each of the outcomes to the interested parties; and (4) weighing the utilities and disutilities to the interested parties and deciding if the policy alternative is better than other alternatives.

Policy for technology may be treated in this framework and differs in no interesting formal way from any other kind of policy. Technology assessment is merely a special type of policy assessment. Policy assessment encompasses the first three steps of the policy-making process. It generates data for the decision maker, who carries out the fourth step.

WHY POLICY MAKING IS NOT RATIONAL

As a consequence of the technical complexity of the decisions, the vast number of decisions they must make, and the shortage of time, neither the Administration nor the Congress is capable of developing sound policy assessments on which decisions could be based. At the same time, they do not often identify and employ trustworthy experts to perform policy assessments for them. Even worse, they do not always believe technology assessments if they are made.

This lack of procedure for utilizing trustworthy experts has created the debate over technology assessment which has led the Science Policy Research Division, Legislative Reference Service, Library of Congress,[1] National Academy of Sciences,[2] and National Academy of Engineering [3] to produce reports on the subject.

Why was not such a procedure constructed years ago? The funds are at the command of the government. The NAS and NAE panels believe the desirability is obvious. I can only conclude that neither the Administration nor the Congress want a rational system of policy assessment. Politicians are elected at vast expense because they serve powerful interests not all of which are compatible with the public interest. Many of them are honest men, at least intellectually honest, and make the decisions they believe are best.[4] But they understand that sound policy assessment might limit their freedom of action and their ability to serve their masters in good conscience

1. *Technical Information for Congress,* Report to the Subcommittee on Science, Research and Development of the Committee on Science and Astronautics, U.S. House of Representatives, 91st Congress, 1st Session. Prepared by the Science Policy Research Division, Legislative Reference Service, Library of Congress. Washington, D.C.: U.S. Government Printing Office, 1969.

2. *Technology: Processes of Assessment and Choice,* Report of the National Academy of Sciences. Washington, D.C., Committee on Science and Astronautics, U.S. House of Representatives, July 1969.

3. *A Study of Technology Assessment,* Report of the Committee on Public Engineering Policy, National Academy of Engineering. Washington, D.C., Committee on Science and Astronautics, U.S. House of Representatives, July 1969.

4. Policy decisions nearly always hinge on questions of judgment, such as the probability of various outcomes. No responsible politician is willing to abdicate his power to experts, especially those whose good judgment is not beyond question. Technology assessment, as conceived of in the current model involves a division of political responsibility that few politicians are willing to accept.

and political safety. Agency bureaucrats also recognize that external assessment may make serving their clientele more difficult.

Under the present procedure for gathering "expert advice," agencies and interests produce expert testimony. Anyone with the ability to pay $300 a day can find a qualified expert who will testify to anything. Thus, expert advice conflicts if interests conflict. In this situation the politician can decide the issue the way he wishes, defending himself by selecting favorable expert testimony. By making the decision on technical grounds he can conceal his personal social welfare function by which he reduces conflicting interests to a single decision. Thus a servant of the military-industrial complex can masquerade as a moderate on war questions, a servant of domestic oil producers can masquerade as a defender of the consumer, or a servant of the American Medical Association can masquerade as a promoter of public health. If the policy assessment were distinct from the decision making, these masquerades would be impossible. Many politicians who seek to conceal their real values perceive intuitively that good advice would threaten their survival.

Not that they get much of it, for there isn't a great deal of it around. There are not enough "experts" who are very expert.[5] No one seemed capable of determining whether a battery additive was any good, or identifying the hangups in foreign aid in a fashion generally acceptable to the scientific community. The judgment of scientists on questions of war has frequently been as wrong as that of politicians or generals.

Few scientists know anything that is interesting to policy makers. They are extraordinarily unscientific when they are justifying a grant or criticizing some other specialty of which they are ignorant. Only a few possess any capacity to foretell the future, and who can say which ones they are? Politicians apparently believe that scientists are irrelevant, and scientists believe that politicians have their minds made up. I suspect both are correct more often than not. The distrust of politicians for scientists' judgment, and of scientists for politicians' honesty and intelligence is the critical political problem in technology assessment. No matter how objective an assessment might be, it will become embroiled in political controversy if the matter is important.

Neither the NAS or NAE reports want anything to do with politics or politicians. All they want is for the politicians to pay attention to the advice

---

5. The key problem is that good advice hinges on a thorough grasp of the technical background on the problem and an understanding of and tolerance for the political issues. On military and foreign policy questions, at least, this background often depends on access to official and classified information. On most policy questions much of the political information needed is not generally available or known.

they get and "to raise the level of political discourse."[6] They want to be close to the President or Congress but free of political influence. They want the impossible. Even the President's dog is political. Neither the NAS or NAE panelists face up to the fact that politicians would appoint or at least influence the composition of the assessment panels.[7] Most politicians know what kind of advice they want, and will make sure that they get it. The President knows what kind of NSF Director, Assistant Secretary of HEW for Health, or Council of Economic Advisors he wants, and he tries to get them. The Department of Defense knows what kind of advice it wants on ABM and it gets it. To scientific outsiders, at least, the kinds of technology assessment prescribed by the NAE and NAS Reports would be more of the same preselected conclusions politicians already get. The selection of outside reputable scientists who might appear to the public to have some expertise merely make foregone conclusions more difficult to attack.

There are two major problems in the use of outside experts for technology assessment. The first is that outside experts are either inexperienced in the area under study or are unlikely to be very good at technology assessment. It is at present a nonexistent art for which there are no artists. The combination of technologist and social scientist with appreciation for the relevant technology and the political considerations is rare, perhaps nonexistent. The intuitive understanding which scientists often believe they have may not stand up when subjected to sophisticated technological and methodological criticism, and this is the second problem. A technology assessment is a target and it will be shot at by those who disagree with the results. In many instances the critics will be the "scientific outsiders" not entirely ignorant of the technological and scientific questions involved, but typically ignorant of political reality, prone to oversimplify, and profoundly mistrustful of the small self-selected scientific elite.

Despite the rather unworldly air of the NAS Report, it is a sound piece of

6. The public is seldom concerned, never informed, and scientists have neither the interest nor the competence in either alerting or informing them. This makes many scientists political outsiders.

7. Most of the panelists know of the system of co-optation (having themselves been co-opted) by which expertise is brought into government, but they cling to the view that the President's Science Advisory Committee and his Special Assistant for Science and Technology are "not political." But they would not have got into those roles unless they were useful to politicians and at the same time acceptable to the scientific community. To be a politician one need not smoke cigars and kiss babies. Nevertheless, many scientists cling to the belief that scientists (sometimes "only scientists") are "objective" while politicians are not.

analysis, well thought out, intelligent, and well researched. Except for its confidence that an assessment panel can deal with the needs of diverse interests in advance, it is a useful analysis. The NAS Report discusses in considerable detail the organizational location of technology assessment activities, but it does not in fact deal with the important political problem of what happens to the assessment once it is done. But the NAS is only talking about assessment, the NAE tried to do it.

SOME BAD EXAMPLES

The NAE assessment studies are themselves subject to these criticisms. The panel believes good assessment depends on experienced assessors and narrow definition of problems, but narrowness is itself a problem.

The Aeronautics and Space Engineering Board of the National Academy of Engineering, which prepared an assessment of subsonic aircraft noise, is made up largely of experts whose experience and economic interests are related to the airline and aircraft industries. It is inevitable that experienced experts will usually be drawn from the interests involved in a problem. In many instances the experts will have created the problem. The ASEB appears to be incapable of entertaining an idea injurious to air transport. Just as automotive executives and engineers could not generate any interest in automotive safety, so these men cannot generate any interest in quiet. They perceive the problem in terms of "tolerable noise," as does the Federal Aviation Agency (which is well represented on the panel) which establishes standards at levels slightly below that at which people complain vigorously, and thus keeps the public sullen but not mutinous. Even so, the FAA has never taken any serious action to enforce its standards even after it was coerced into establishing them.

Turning to the assessment itself, we read "Abatement will be costly and will occur only when public pressure fosters regulation from federal and local authorities and when the airline and manufacturing industries work out feasible alternatives together (p. 76)." That is to say, when they are finally forced to, the industry and the FAA will serve the public welfare. They will resist as long as they can, but as long as court relief is refused they will punish the public without restraint or compensation. This is a bald admission that the public cannot expect protection from the Administration or Congress without political action.

The assessment itself is not very useful for it says nothing about the costs and benefits of the various strategies. As a result, no politician has the uncomfortable data which might influence his decision. He can continue to do what he has done. Because there are no quantitative results, there is no real policy assessment. The Board is quite casual about the inadequacy of their report. Consider (p. 95) ". . . technology assessment of subsonic aircraft noise must deal first with the question of whether the public pressures directed at airlines, airport operators, or the Congress are sufficient to force heavy economic investment needed to solve the problems by any of the strategies available. It would be a waste of time to study other alternative strategies if it is found that the problem does not warrant high-priority public action beyond the status quo strategy."

Well, there it is. Squeaky-wheel politics at its most cynical. No grease until a Ralph Nader is awakened by a low-flying jet.

But this is what you get from technology assessment as the NAE conceives it. Similarly, when one turns to the other bad example, one finds even the exiguous "assessment" of Multiphasic Health Screening is castrated in advance. "The center must be sufficiently flexible in operation to permit each physician to dictate the specific tests that are to be given his patients. . ." (p. 102). The major problem in medical technology is the individual physician, his incompetence, his technical backwardness, his unwillingness to be part of a medical system. There is no technical difficulty in MHS. The Kaiser Foundation has used it for years. They find it useful in their integrated medical care delivery system. The individual physician dominates medical politics and economics. He impedes the use of MHS, and it is his self-interest to which this whole assessment is subordinated. The panel clearly wants to retard MHS because they foresee widespread screening will produce knowledge of unknown illness which the present system cannot handle, and they subordinate their assessment to the dominant political power in medicine.

All of the NAE assessments are "politically realistic" in that they consider alternatives which the panelists view as attainable. But in doing this they prejudge the political questions. Why should a body of experts take institutional arrangements, pressures, and power as given? If they will not consider bold new technical alternatives, who will? Besides, technical experts are seldom competent to judge political feasibility, and when they examine only "realistic alternatives" they are acting as politicians. It is not for technology assessment to play at politics, but to say what all alternatives are, and whom they will affect. Politicians will provide a sufficiency of attention for political considerations.

A RESPONSIBLE PROCESS OF TECHNOLOGICAL DEBATE

Both the NAS and NAE panels admit that a single best policy is unlikely to exist, and if it exists it is unlikely to be found. Even so they believe that suitable objective panels can be selected, conduct their deliberations quickly, and provide essentially value-free advice to Congress and the Administration. If done with sufficient care, the advice will assist the decision makers in making policy. It won't be this easy. The panels will be made up of experts, and these experts will have interests that will consciously or unconsciously smuggle values and implicit policy into the technology analysis itself. Even if through divine intervention the panel produces a value-free assessment, those whose interests are adversely influenced by the tendency of the report are unlikely to accept the results as value free. The integrity, probity and intelligence of the panelists will be examined in detail. It is not inconceivable, as Ralph Nader and Judge Haynsworth discovered, that political opponents will develop a sudden interest in the sex life and investment activities of those who offer themselves to do good things for their country. We may deplore such inquisitions, but is it not foolish to deny that they are commonplaces in the political process. What aegis will protect the assessment panels from attack? Dedication to the pursuit of science is no longer a certain shield and sure protection against criticism, as anyone who has visited a university campus in recent years should be aware. Nor should we dismiss the criticism that campus activists direct against scientific research as trivial, for an increasing amount of it comes from our best students and even some of our most awe-inspiring fellow scientists.

It would seem to me wise to accept as a political fact that any assessment of an interesting problem is likely to be embroiled in controversy. Those who wish to engage in such exciting activities should look to their flanks. When they prepare assessments they should employ "no men," devil's advocates, and experts on "the intentions of the enemy." Even forearmed, they should be ready for criticism.

For criticism and debate is an essential part of the democratic political process. It is only through adversary proceedings that that part of policy assessment which is sound may be identified, and that part which is insupportable may be shown up for what it is. If we are careful, and also very fortunate, it may be possible to construct a responsible process of technological debate to which government-sponsored technology assessment will be subjected. But it takes two responsible parties to produce a responsible debate. If the government assessments are not fair and open, if they rely on information too confidential to be shown the public, if they generate only information that supports positions acceptable to the government, then who would expect the opposition to act responsibly. But let us assume, if only for the sake of argument, that the Administration and Congress tried to generate reasonably responsible technology assessments. The remaining need is for a responsible technological opposition. This would require a marked change in behavior for the opponents of government. They would have to produce respectable counter-assessments, and to do this they would need to generate experts on the questions under consideration. Those who would pursue counter-assessment as a profession cannot expect government to employ them or grants to support their studies and researches. I would expect most of the counter-assessors would have to generate their competence in social technology as a hobby or sideline to a reasonably straight scientific career. It is to be hoped that the sideline would not draw retaliation on them.

It has taken centuries for European governments to discover that oppositions are essential to stable government, and the Soviet Union has not yet made this discovery. There was often an irreversible tendency for those who opposed Louis XIV or Henry VIII to lose stature, frequently by a head's length. Since the McCarthy era opposition has been somewhat safer for American scientists, but opposition must be responsible if it is to survive for very long. Responsible opposition involves a fundamental acceptance of the legitimacy of the process, an acceptance of the rules of procedure, and a readiness to assume political responsibility if the occasion arises. Not all of the opponents of governmental technology policy meet these criteria. But if technology policy is to be forged in the fire of political controversy, then a responsible technological opposition must constitute itself. These counter assessors must separate themselves from the closed, co-opted, scientific and technological elite that pretends to be above or beyond politics and ally with those political interests and politicians whose objectives are consonant with survival, prosperity, and liberty as the counter-assessors perceive these goals. They must train themselves in the skills, the arts, and even the wiles of the assessment process.

The university can make essential contributions to the creation of responsible technological debate, just as it has to debate on social and economic policy in the past. Responding to the demands for "relevance" emanating even from places so unlikely as schools of medicine and engineering, the university can organize itself to educate both the assessors and the counter assessors in the values, goals, and aims of a human society, in the tools of social analysis, in the technological and scientific possibilities which both motivate and constrain human action. In so doing, the university will both relieve the stresses that threaten to tear it apart and instill in science the human goals that were once its impulse and its recompense.

The Adversary Process in Technology Assessment

HAROLD P. GREEN

My purpose in this paper is to show the importance of introducing an adversary process into the technology assessment mechanism in order to assure that the assessment function will properly and effectively protect the public interest.

When I speak of an adversary process I am not suggesting a formal adjudicatory process in which opposing parties contend through legal mouthpieces with a decision made on the record. Rather, I suggest only that a mechanism be developed to permit and facilitate the articulation in public of all relevant facts, pro and con. And when I speak of technology assessment, I do not encompass the assessment of the full potential range of the social consequences of a technology. Rather, I am concerned about technology assessment solely from the standpoint of identifying and controlling those attributes of a technology that adversely affect basic individual rights that have traditionally been protected by the legal system, i.e., specifically, those incidents of a technology that may threaten the health, safety, and security of the public. I believe, incidentally, that this aspect of technology on which I am focusing is its principal element and the very raison d'etre for the present public discussion of technology assessment.

Most of the discussion of technology assessment that has taken place to date has assumed the need for a new governmental assessment institution to identify and quantify the benefits, costs, and risks of technology, then strike a balance among these factors, and pass on its conclusions and recommendations in predigested form to Congress as a predicate for legislative action. This approach is reflected in Congressman Daddario's bill and was followed in a paper presented to this seminar by Richard Carpenter. Mr. Carpenter's view was that Congress as the *political assessment* body in our society must have the output of *technology assessment* bodies in order to do its job properly. . . . I believe that this approach is not adequate, would not be effective, and is in derogation of the appropriate role of Congress and the public in policy formulation.

The assessment function is properly concerned with balancing the benefits of a technology to the public against its costs (including risks) to the public and emerging with a conclusion as to what government's role with respect to that technology should be. Unfortunately the benefits and costs (including risks) do not fall upon all segments and members of the public correlatively. There is, I suppose, a high degree of correlation if we are talking about lawn mower technology; but if we are talking about detergents, pesticides, or the supersonic transport plane, it is clear that those who enjoy the benefits of these technologies will not necessarily be the same persons, or in appropriate degree, as those on whom the costs (including risks) will fall.

Since the issue is one of benefits *to the public* versus costs (including risks) *to the public,* the focus of technology assessment should be to arrive at a conclusion as to what costs (including risks) the public is prepared to assume in exchange for what benefits. In our democracy, such decisions cannot appropriately be made by an elite body of specialists and generalists (who are specialists in technology assessment). They should be made by the public itself expressing its views through its elected representatives in the Congress who are accountable to their constituents. This requires that the entire assessment process take place in the open with full articulation, in language the public can understand, of the benefits and costs (including risks). In short, I do not agree with Mr. Carpenter that there is any viable distinction between *political* assessment and *technology* assessment. Technology assessment is not an appropriate function for experts; rather, it is a process which should be performed entirely at the *political* level. Those who question whether the public and the Congress have the competence to make the necessary sound assessments express a lack of faith in the ability of the democratic process to cope with modern and future technology. If we act on the basis of such lack of faith, we have a different ball game. In my view, the basic problem is to compel scientists and technologists to present the issues to the public in the language of ordinary public discourse rather than in the esoteric jargon of their disciplines, and if this is done I have no doubt as to the efficacy of the democratic process.

Most public discussion about technology assessment to date has ignored a fundamental point. There is never any lack of articulation of the benefits of a technology. Every technology has powerful vested interests—private and frequently governmental and political—who can be relied upon to press the benefits to the technology assessors. The problem is that the negative factors and the risks are never fully or even adequately articulated. In some cases the risks are totally unappreciated until a later date; in other cases, there may be an appreciation of possible risks that have not yet been demonstrated to be real. The proponents of the technology may always be counted upon to minimize or suppress the risks. Although the proponents are usually well organized and well financed in their articulation of the benefits, those who seek to advance the negative factors tend to be rather disorganized and lacking in resources. Not infrequently—particularly in the case of government-sponsored technologies—it is difficult for the opponents to obtain relevant and adequate information about risks, and even more difficult—because the experts who are privy to the relevant information are usually pro-technology—to obtain experts to assist them in formulation of their contentions. The natural consequence is that the opposition is forced to state its case using information that is incomplete or not wholly accurate, and, therefore, easily discredited. Frequently, the establishment seeks to discredit the opposition ad hominem, and this exacerbates the situation, forcing the opposition to take an extreme position which makes it even easier for the proponents to discredit their contentions on their merits.

The basic problem of building an assessment institution is, therefore, to provide a means whereby the negative factors, particularly the risks, will be vigorously, effectively, and responsibly pressed upon the decision makers in a manner that will permit the Congress and the public to make their own judgments. In a nutshell, the problem is to give equal time, opportunity, and attention to the negative factors.

What is needed for the technology assessment function is an agency that would act as a responsible devil's advocate or technological ombudsman and play the role of adversary in the congressional and public forums. This should be an agency charged solely with the function and responsibility of probing for the negative factors, identifying these factors, and pressing them vigorously upon Congress and the public. The agency should be either totally independent of the government or, like the General Accounting Office, part of the Congress. Between these alternatives, my preference is for the latter, since the agency should have full access to all relevant information available to the government.

In discussing the manner in which such an agency would operate, it is necessary to distinguish between two classes of technology. On the one hand, there is technology that is essentially private and that is developed and introduced primarily as a consequence of private, profit-seeking investment. With respect to such technology, government's role is typically passive until problems arise that require the government to take action in the public interest. On the other hand, there is another class of technology that is developed primarily as a consequence of government investment. In this case, government has a strong affirmative interest in development of the technology and also in its subsequent practical application.

In the first of these cases, the marketplace operates as a continuous technology assessment mechanism. A technology will not be developed or introduced unless its sponsor senses that there will be a profitable return on investment. The price that buyers are willing to pay reflects their assessment of the hazards that may be incident to the technology's products. Both the sponsors of the technology and its customer-users also assess the potential costs to them that may result from liability to others arising out of such hazards. These private assessment mechanisms involve a mix of incentives and deterrents which operate as people pursue their own self-interest. These mechanisms flash a green or a red light that serves to control the rate of development and introduction of technology. It is only when the green light has been flashed as a signal for introduction of a technology that the problem of technology assessment passes into the hands of governmental institutions. Even after the technology has been introduced, government assessment does not occur until problems arise that seem to warrant governmental action.

The initial step in governmental technology assessment occurs when the legislature considers these problems to determine whether social control is required to protect the public against the technology's hazards and, if so, the form such controls should take. The mere existence of obvious problems does not mean that the legislature will act. The legislative process involves considerable inertia and is at best an uncertain and lengthy affair. Typically, the legislative struggle involves two issues: (1) Are there hazards that justify social control? (2)Will the form of social control stifle the technology and deprive the public of its benefits? Where legislation results, it represents the striking of what the legislature believes is an appropriate balance between benefits and risks.

In many cases the social controls are implemented under statutory standards by an administrative agency. The agency's sole function in this respect is to protect the public interest under the statutory standards. These standards usually reflect the legislature's conclusion that the technology is useful and beneficial and should be controlled in such a manner as to preserve its benefits. As the administrative agency functions, it is required to assess the impact of its proposed regulatory actions in terms of benefit and risk. Because its institutional bias is in the direction of protecting the public interest, the regulatory agency generally functions as an adversary of the industry it regulates; i.e., its normal functioning imposes social controls, at the expense of increasing costs and reducing benefits, in order to maximize protection of the public against the industry's hazards.

We have, then, in this case an existing structure for governmental technology assessment. Obviously, it does not work perfectly. Legislative judgments are often inappropriately biased or otherwise unsound. Administrative agencies make mistakes, and, as students of the administrative process have long recognized, they tend to develop unwholesome affinities to the industries they regulate and may become in effect their captives. Such deficiencies are inherent in the political and administrative processes and are subject to corrective action if the public is aroused. On the other hand, a more difficult problem is raised by the fact that the assessment institutions frequently lack sufficient information and knowledge to function with optimum effectiveness. These institutions and the public frequently do not become aware of hazardous conditions associated with a technology at a sufficiently early date, until after considerable harm has occurred and strongly entrenched vested interests have come into being. What is needed is an early warning system to trigger public and political awareness of potential hazards at a much earlier time.

The type of devil's advocate agency I have suggested is ideally suited to overcome these deficiencies. Its functions would include that of identifying possible hazards and ascertaining the extent to which they are real hazards. Hazards and potential hazards, once identified, would be vigorously publicized and pressed upon Congress and the cognizant government agencies. Congressional inertia would be subject to the pressures of public opinion; foot-dragging by the administrative agencies would become more visible and subject to correction. A more substantial burden of proof would be thrust upon the sponsors of the technology.

The second case, that of government-sponsored technology, is quite different. These technologies develop with government investment that is in no way related to the forces of the marketplace; indeed they develop in defiance of the market since government investment is made because the market does *not* provide incentives for development of the technology on the time scale government believes is necessary. Thus, the "deep pocket" of the government supports technology development merely because desirable benefits are foreseen even though there are no market incentives, while none of the restraints and deterrents that are present with respect to privately developed technologies are operative.

It is apparent, moreover, that as the technology is assessed at various points (usually in connection with authorization of the program and appropriation of funds) as it passes from the hands of the specialists-sponsors within the agency through the less specialized offices in the higher echelons of the executive branch to the generalists in Congress, there is a natural tendency to minimize the existence and significance of any potential hazards associated with the technology. Hazards and risks are characteristically rationalized away. The rationalizations take one or more of the following forms: (1) The hazards are not as serious as might appear; at least there has been no demonstration that they will indeed be harmful. (2) Even if there may be some hazard or inconvenience to the public, this may be "tolerable" or "acceptable" in view of the enormous benefits the public will receive from use of the technology. (3) We are conducting research to learn more about the potential hazards and research and development to provide a technological fix to eliminate or reduce the hazards. (4) In any event, there is no need to worry about possible adverse consequences of the technology until its feasibility has been established. (5) Obviously, the government will permit use of the technology only subject to appropriate controls to assure that the public will not be injured, and if such controls are not adequate to protect the public, government will not permit use of the technology. Q.E.D.

One need only consider the history of government development of such technologies as atomic energy, weather modification, the supersonic transport plane, and various military technologies such as biological and chemical agents to appreciate that the existence of substantial hazards has not deterred development of these technologies because of precisely such rationalizations. It is clear, moreover, that such rationalizations have been accepted at the higher levels of technology assessment, i.e., the executive offices, the cognizant congressional committees, and Congress. The impulse to convert science into technology which will be of benefit to society seems to be irresistible at every level. In part, at least, this may be attributable to the fact that information about the adverse consequences reaches the higher and more generalized areas of technology assessment, if at all, in a highly distilled form that does not facilitate discussion and debate.

Although we do not have too much experience, outside of the military and space areas, with the processes through which government-developed technology is introduced into practical application, some generalizations are possible. It seems inherent in the American governmental and political process that government will have an irresistible impulse to see technologies developed by it put to practical use. Can it be doubted that weather modification will be practiced when the technology is developed even though interests of a substantial number of people will be substantially and adversely affected? Again, I do not want to be read as suggesting that government callously will foist hazardous technologies upon the public. There is really no such thing as a clear-cut dichotomy between "safe" and "hazardous." This is an area in which there is no black and white. Whether or not something is appropriately safe or unduly hazardous is an issue that lies in a gray area; its resolution is essentially a matter of judgment on which reasonable men can differ depending upon their outlook and biases. All I suggest is that those who have a vested interest in a technology will inevitably be more relaxed about hazards than those who don't give a damn about the technology but who are primarily concerned with the public safety.

We do have substantial and instructive experience in one area. The government has for many years sponsored and promoted the development of nuclear power technology, and it has supported, subsidized, and promoted the introduction of the technology by private enterprise. This has taken place despite the fact that the public will be exposed to very small increments of man-made radiation which, although never demonstrated to have resulted in manifest injury, are clearly regarded as at least undesirable.[1] The

---

1. There is no evidence that exposure to low levels of radiation has produced manifest somatic injury; nor is there any evidence that there is a threshold of exposure below which no somatic injury will occur. It is, however, generally accepted that *any* radiation exposure produces undesirable genetic mutations. These considerations lead to the general rule enunciated by the Federal Radiation Council that "there should not be any man-made radiation exposure without the expectation of benefit resulting from such exposure." In actual practice, the amounts of industrial radiation to which workers and the public may be exposed are established by the National Committee on Radiation Protection on what is candidly stated to be a "philosophy of risk" or "calculated risk" basis as they assess benefits and risks. Despite the fact that the Chairman of the NCRP has stated that the setting of radiation protection standards is not "basically a scientific problem. . . . It is more a matter of philosophy, of morality, and of sheer wisdom," the people involved in the NCRP's standards-setting function are all specialists in the relevant scientific disciplines.

public is also called upon to assume the "exceedingly remote possibility" of a nuclear power reactor accident which could cause damages to health, life, and property of enormously catastrophic consequences, dwarfing by many orders of magnitude any other conceivable catastrophe that might result from a man-made cause. Protection of the health and safety of the public rests with a regulatory scheme that places reliances on "engineered safeguards"; but, as we all know, man's engineering genius is far from infallible. To further press this point, when the marketplace flashed a red light that would definitely deter private investment in the technology because of the enormous potential public liability (for which adequate insurance coverage was not available) in the event of an accident, government's response was to enact the Price-Anderson Act to remove this "roadblock." That act superimposes upon $82 million of private liability insurance protection (the maximum available) a government indemnity of $500 million and cuts off any further public liability in excess of $582 million.[2] This completely eliminates potential liability as a deterrent, since it is not possible that any firm could sustain one penny's worth of liability out of its own pocket. And, finally, it is candidly admitted that the AEC regulatory program

... exerts all effort which could reasonably be expected to insure that there is no undue hazard to the public health and safety *while at the same time no crippling obstacle is placed in the way of development of [the] industry.* . . . (Emphasis added.)[3]

There is, I believe, substantial reason to believe that the general pattern will be to entrust regulation of new government-sponsored technologies to the agencies which developed them and have an interest in their application. Let me add, however, that I do not think separation of promotion and regulation into two separate agencies would be a panacea. There is also reason to believe that expert bodies, rather than the public itself, will make the decisions as to what risks the public will be required to assume in exchange for what benefits. Experts will decide how much sonic boom the public can stand; how much radiation it can tolerate in exchange for what benefits;

2. A 1956 Brookhaven National Laboratory report estimated, on pessimistic assumptions, that a serious power reactor accident might cause as much as $7 billion property damage in addition to substantial personal injury and loss of life. A more recent study, the details of which have been suppressed, led to the conclusion, as stated by the AEC Chairman, that because of additional experience the chances of such an accident are even more exceedingly remote, but because more recent power reactors are larger and are located closer to population centers, the damages that might result could be even more substantial.

3. Report to the AEC by the Regulatory Review Panel, July 14, 1965.

when it should rain, shine, blow, or snow in the public interest; and what kinds of children the genetic engineers should produce to further policy objectives.

I believe the only effective mechanism for protecting the public against the onslaught of new government-sponsored technologies is the type of devil's advocate mechanism I have proposed. Indeed, such a mechanism is much more necessary in the case of government-sponsored technology because it is the only effective means for building restraints and deterrents into the system. Such an agency would give the public a full opportunity to determine whether it wants the government to develop a new technology that involves potential risks and, if so, the conditions under which development should occur. It would force full consideration of potential hazards upon the government at the developmental stage; and it would compel regulatory agencies to give greater weight to the public health, safety, and security than they do to the benefits of the technology.

Let me recapitulate very briefly. I am distrustful of the experts. Scientists and engineers have a bias in favor of accomplishing what they think can be accomplished. Their assumption that the problem of effective social control will take care of itself at an appropriate time is politically invalid. In a government whose executive and legislative branches are committed to achieving the benefits of science and technology, excessive reliance is placed on the judgments of experts because of the unfounded myth that ordinary mortals are incapable of understanding the issues. What is necessary is that there be injected into the assessment process a clear and vigorous articulation of the negative factors in language comprehensible to the layman. This will compel the proponents of the technology to present their case in similar language, and the decisions will be made in the rough and tumble of the ordinary political process.

I am fully aware of the principal argument that will be made in opposition to this proposal. It will run as follows: If the negative factors are presented to the public, to Congress, and to administrative agencies vigorously and in an unbalanced manner, undue apprehension will develop because the recipients of this information will not be able adequately to evaluate the negative factors and place them in perspective. As a consequence, scientific and technological advance will be unduly retarded.

My answer to this is two-fold. First, the proponents of the technology have greater resources and at least equal access to the eyes and ears of the public, the Congress, and the administrative agencies. Secondly, I can conceive of no reason why the public in a democracy should be forced to accept benefits it does not want, whatever the reason, rational or irrational.

The Role
of the Social Sciences
in the Control
of Technology

KENNETH E. BOULDING

One notices in these days a tendency almost to deify technology, to regard it as an almost sentient agency in society with a will of its own, imposing its own methods and mechanisms on at best a passive and at worst an unwilling mankind. In so far as technology is merely a name for man's ways of doing things and the artifacts which he makes to help him do things, this animistic view of technology may seem absurdly exaggerated. Nevertheless, the view that there are technological processes at work in society with a dynamic of their own which is not very much affected by what goes on in the rest of society is at least a hypothesis worthy of investigation. If, indeed, it should turn out that technological processes have this quasi-autonomous status, the problem of control of technology by the various social mechanisms of control (such as rhetoric, organizations, and government) cannot lightly be dismissed. There is a widespread feeling today that technology is, in fact, an autonomous force largely out of control, and that the problem, therefore, of social control of technological processes is an acute one, especially as the instruments of this control do not yet seem to have been devised.

The problem has become particularly acute since the development of science and science-based technology. All technology arises out of knowledge of some sort. Before the rise of science, the prevailing knowledge outside of literary knowledge might be called folk knowledge, and the technology which was based on it, folk technology. This, one hastens to add, can be perfectly good knowledge. It is attained, indeed, by very much the same kind of processes of image formation, inference from the image, prediction as a result of the inference, and testing of the prediction by waiting for it to be fulfilled or disappointed, which are essentially the processes also of science. We learn to speak our native language, we learn to recognize our own house, we develop an image of the space and the time around us which is quite good enough for the practical purposes for which these images were needed. In finding my way around town, there is no need to postulate anything except a flat earth.

The difference between scientific images and folk images is simply one of complexity and instrumentation. Thus, agriculture was originally developed by folk knowledge and is a good example of folk technology. Agriculturalists know that planting seeds of a certain kind produces crops of a certain kind if appropriate things are done, and this knowledge is true in the sense that it enables predictions to be fulfilled. The scientific agronomist with his molecular biology and theories of hybridization and so on has a more elaborate view of the world and much better instrumentation for observing it, but the truth of his image is arrived at by successive eliminations of error, just as in the case of folk knowledge. The only difference in the case of the scientist is that his predictions and his errors are more refined and his mathematical logical theory enables him to be more certain that the inferences from which he derives his predictions are not fallacious. Thus, scientific knowledge has a smaller propensity to fall into superstition, that is, the perceiving of order when in fact there is none, or the perceiving of a false order.

The impact of science on the social system began to gather some momentum in the eighteenth century, although mainly at first in the realm of ideas; thus, Newtonian physics had a considerable impact on classical economics and democratic political theory. It was not really until the nineteenth century that science-based technology began to appear in economic life and to expand to the point where it now dominates the scene. The so-called Industrial Revolution of the eighteenth century in England, for instance, was in a sense the tag end of a long process of improving folk technology throughout the Middle Ages. Neither the steam engine nor the spinning wheel owed very much to science. It was the steam engine, indeed, that created thermodynamics, rather than thermodynamics the steam engine. From about 1860 on, however, we perceive the development of large industries—the chemical industry, the electrical industry, increasingly the agricultural industry, the nuclear industry and so on—which are science-based in the sense that they could not exist if it were not for an elaborate body of theory in the pure sciences. We cannot imagine the chemical industry without Dalton and Kekulé; we cannot imagine an electrical industry without Faraday, Ohm, and Clerk-Maxwell, or a nuclear industry without Einstein and Bohr. It is hard to estimate what portion of the economic activity, for instance, of a developed country like the United States is composed of science-based industries, but it is certainly more than half.

The role of the social sciences in the study of this problem is crucial for the very simple reason that this is essentially a problem in what might be called the sociosphere, that is, the total social system of the planet, consisting of all the human beings, their significant inputs and outputs, characteristics, groups, and organizations. Both science and technology of any kind are products of the sociosphere. Biological considerations, such as the nature and quantity of the human nervous system are, of course, significant limiting factors in climate, soils, water resources, transportation and so on, which are closely related to certain properties of the atmosphere, the hydrosphere and the lithosphere. These other spheres of scientific interest, however, only provide boundaries, or perhaps certain parameters for the social system. It is to the social sciences that we must turn, therefore, if we are to understand the problem or to find methods for its solution.

I will begin with economics, not only because it is the discipline with which I am the most familiar, but because it is also the social science which perhaps throws the most light on the dynamics of control of technological processes. The problem can be divided into two closely related parts—the problem of the totality and distribution of human knowledge on the one hand, which de Chardin has called the noosphere, and the problem of the totality of human artifacts and their production, consumption, and utilization. This is a totality which economists call capital, which I am tempted to call the artisphere, for just as the biosphere consists of populations of all living things, classified into species, so there is an artisphere which consists of populations of all human artifacts which likewise can be classified into species. The automobile is as much a species as a horse, even though its genetics is a little more complicated. Artifacts enter into complex ecological relationships with biological species in the total ecological system of the world.

Economics enters the picture because both knowledge and artifacts, and indeed some biological species, are commodities, that is, exchangeables, and in so far as economics is the study of how society is organized through exchange and exchangeables, it will have a good deal to say about the determinants of all those species, whether human, biological, or artifactural, which enter into exchange or have a role as exchangeables. Thus, knowledge is clearly a commodity in so far as it can be exchanged for other things. It is indeed a depreciable commodity; it depreciates through people aging and dying, and it constantly has to be replaced in new minds, and the replacement requires both commodity artifacts, such as school buildings, and commodity services, such as those of teachers. Education, indeed, is an industry, now about 7 percent of the Gross National Product, which makes it a little larger than agriculture. Development in any field, whether in biological evolution or in social systems, is very largely a process in the knowledge industry. Knowledge, that is, capital structures of information or improbable arrangements of something which can be mapped onto something else, is the total field within which the evolutionary process operates.

If technology is part of the evolutionary process, then we should expect it to follow the principles of mutation and selection. This indeed it does. Invention is the mutation aspect of technological dynamics; success or failure of invented processes is the process of selection. In social, as in biological, evolution we are beginning to see the possibility at least of a shift in mutation from essentially random alterations in genetic structure into non-random or teleological mutation. The developments in molecular biology suggest that we may be very close to teleological mutation in the biosphere, with man now creating new genetic structures according to patterns which originated in human knowledge. Thus, it seems not impossible that we might recreate the extinct animals and then go on to develop imaginary ones. Similarly, in social mutations in the past many of these may have taken place through rather random processes, through, for instance, the observation of happy accidents, or through the development of men with unusual skill in invention, such as Edison. In social systems, however, mutation has probably never been as random as it may have been in the biosphere. The old adage about necessity being the mother of invention has some truth in it, and obviously invention is much more likely to take place in areas which are recognized as problems, where there are recognized deficiencies, and where there seem to be holes in the system rather than in places which are generally regarded as not in need of change. The development within the last fifty years of massive organized research again represents a diminution in the randomness of invention. Necessity breathes down the neck of research directors in the shape of directives from employers, and in these days most applied research has very specific ends in view. The development end of the research-and-development operation is even more clearly non-random in that it involves applying existing knowledge to practical ends, the ends being rather clearly in view.

The economic system, therefore, plays an important part in both the mutation and the selection process by which technology develops. In this connection, we can distinguish two major components of the economic system—what might be called the *exchange economy* on the one side and the *grants economy* on the other. In the exchange economy, the survival of an organization or a product or a technique depends on its capacity to occupy niches in the system where the value of the product has been greater than its cost. Technique here is almost equivalent to the economist's concept of the production function, which is a functional relation between the inputs and the outputs of processes involving the input and output of exchangeables. If there is a structure of ratios of exchange, all these exchangeables can be expressed in terms of a common numeraire, such as money. Then we can value all the exchangeable inputs in the process at their money value; we can similarly value the outputs, and the difference between the value of outputs and the value of inputs is profit. Profit, and especially the rate of profit, which is the rate of gross growth in the total value of the operation as a result of transformation of inputs to outputs, is a pretty accurate measure of the survival value of the operation. In the simplest model we can suppose a rate of profit above which the operation will survive and below which it will not. In practice, of course, things are more complicated, but there is always a strong tendency for profitable operations not only to survive but to expand and unprofitable operations to contract.

In a pure exchange economy, then, those techniques which are profitable survive, and those which are not profitable do not. The evolution of techniques, therefore, depends on the development of new techniques which could create a situation in the system in which the new techniques are more profitable than certain old techniques. Hence the new techniques expand and displace the old techniques which have been made less profitable. This is very much what the economists mean by competition and it is indeed a special case of evolutionary competition in general. The evolutionary process always implies that certain mutations will have greater survival value than others and hence survive, whereas the introduction of these new species into the system may push other species below the margin of survival. The biological equivalent of profit is the ability to have births exceed deaths of a population. The economic concept of profit is indeed the excess of the "births of value" through the production and sale of outputs over the "deaths of value" through the purchase and utilization of inputs.

Thus, the railroad supplanted the stagecoach, and the automobile and the tractor the horse, in the same kind of process of evolutionary ecological succession by which the mammal supplanted the dinosaurs, or the deer and the sheep in New Zealand supplanted the moa. We thus see the dynamics of development of technology as very much like that of ecological evolutionary succession with the accountant as the arbiter instead of fecundity or predation. An enormous number of techniques are known which are not practiced, just as there are a great many extinct animals, and indeed a great many potential animals, which might fill niches in the existing system but which just do not happen to have been mutated into existence.

In the modern world the *grant*, which I define as a one-way transfer of an exchangeable (an exchange being a two-way transfer), has become of increasing significance. In the United States, for instance, the grants economy is at least from 15 to 20 percent of the total, depending on our definition. It includes most of the government sector of the economy, outside of what might be called government business, which are essentially in the exchange economy. A small part of the grants economy is in the private sector, which consists of grants from foundations, about one and a half billion a year in the United States, and private charitable grants which mostly consist of grants to churches. Even though this is a small proportion of the GNP, probably not more than 1 percent on most optimistic definitions, it has a considerable qualitative importance, as it may affect the mutation rate of inventions. Foundations, especially, are fond of subsidizing research, and frequently justify themselves as private centers of political power, on the grounds that they can afford to be more daring and imaginative in the promotion of invention than government can. Whether this claim is justified is another matter that we cannot go into here.

The grants economy has become of increasing importance not only in the promotion of invention but also in the survival of techniques. Within the grants economy a process does not have to be profitable in the sense in which it does in the exchange economy, simply because any losses can be made up by grants. The whole function of the grants economy indeed is to enable operations and organizations to survive which could not survive in the market. This is especially true of the government grants economy which is supported by taxation, which is a queer kind of compulsory grant, or by the government's capacity for creating money. The war industry and the space enterprise are particularly good examples of operations which survive because of the niches which they have in the grants economy, not because of any niche in the market economy. The size of the grants economy, however, is indirectly related to the market economy in that it does depend on the demand for what economists call public goods, which are peculiarly appropriate for production through the grants economy. These are goods which have costs in the sense that their production absorbs exchangeable resources, but which have the property that my enjoyment of them does not diminish yours. Thus, the automobile is a private good, in the sense that if I have a car you don't have it. If the traffic density is not too great, however, my driving on the road does not diminish your capacity to do so, so that the road is a public good.

Public goods have always been regarded as peculiarly appropriate for a grants economy, especially in the public sector. Hence, the total portion of the economy which is in the grants sector is not independent of the overall structure of demand as between private and public goods. It depends also on the strength of the sense of community. Where there are strong community and integrative relationships among people, the grants economy is likely to be larger than where the sense of community is weak. In any given situation, however, the grants economy is an "economy" in the sense that the total of grants is going to be limited by the circumstances of the society, or at least will have some kind of more or less flexible ceiling, and under these circumstances if A gets a grant B does not. The struggle for survival of techniques and processes and organizations within the grants economy, therefore, is an ecological evolutionary process very much like what goes on within the exchange economy except that the rules are somewhat different, the capacity to get grants being somewhat different from the capacity to make profits.

The real question at issue in this paper, then, is whether we can identify any pathological processes in the evolution of technologies within either the exchange economy or the grants economy. These indeed are not hard to find, and where pathological processes can be detected, there is always a case for social therapy, which is equivalent to the control of pathological process.

Within the exchange economy, a number of pathological processes can be detected. A major one is that described by economists as the externalities problem. Suppose we have a process which either absorbs inputs or produces outputs, either positive or negative, which are free, or underpriced, to the owner or operator of the process itself in the sense that he does not have to pay enough for them if they are positive inputs or negatively valued outputs, and he does not receive enough for them if they are positive outputs or negatively valued inputs. When this happens, profitability in the financial sense ceases to be a measure of social profitability, which is the excess (or more strictly the rate of excess) of the total value of all outputs over the total value of all inputs, whether these are financially valued or not and whether they have any corresponding money outputs and inputs or not.

Externalities of this kind are at the heart of the pollution problem, when an organization such as a firm or a family produces outputs which have a negative value from the point of view of the rest of society but for which the producing organization does not have to pay. Under these circumstances, not only is there no motivation for an evolution of technology towards the elimination of pollution, but also the polluting activity is apt to be too large. If firms or private individuals had to pay the full cost of the pollutants they produced to the rest of society, those processes which produced them would become less profitable and shrink and processes which did not produce them would become more profitable and would grow. A problem which differs from that of pollution only in algebraic sign is that of the production of benefits for which no reward is received. Thus, education is frequently supposed to produce benefits to the rest of society, which does not have to pay the educators for these benefits.

Potentially pathological conditions may develop in connection with the use of exhaustible resources which may have a great effect on the future of the human race. Up to now our economy has been based on the assumption that there is an infinite reservoir of undiscovered resources, that is, as we use up known resources, investment in exploration and in discovery will always reveal more. Hence, in our profit accounting, we virtually only charge off the costs of exploration and discovery and we do not charge off the fact that the total ultimate reservoir of exhaustible resources is decreasing. This means that the market does not have motivation to make provision for that very fundamental transition which the human race is going to have to face in the next few centuries, from an economy which is based on exhaustible resources, such as mines and fossil fuels and pollutable reservoirs, which I have called a linear economy, into a circular or looped economy, as it has recently been called, in which man has to find a comfortable niche in the middle of a circular process of transformation of resources and in which in effect his own effluence is the only source of ultimate affluence. A pure exchange economy can easily lead to the ultimate exhaustion of the reservoir of exhaustible resources without replacing it with the kind of knowledge and techniques which will enable us to do without the exhaustible resources by developing the perfectly looped system.

Other pathological conditions of the exchange economy may be mentioned briefly as they are somewhat less relevant to the problem in hand. Unless a fiscal and financial cybernetic mechanism is imposed on them, exchange economies have a certain tendency to fall into deflation and depression on the one hand or into inflation on the other hand. Deflation is a very severe pathological state which destroys profit altogether, creates unemployment and in its extreme form, as, for instance, in the Great Depression of the 1930s, can easily bring economic development to a halt. We hope we now have mechanisms for controlling this particular disease of the exchange economy. Another possible disease is the development of corruption of the demand system through advertising, propaganda, or even through the infectiousness of fashions. This is related to what Galbraith has called "revised sequence," in which, instead of consumer demand dominating the production of commodities, the producers tend to organize and to dominate consumers' demand. This is indeed relevant to possible pathological states of technological development, as if the promoters of the technology are able to sell it to the potential consumers by manipulating their demands we may have short range successes which turn out to be disastrous in the long run. The propagation of cigarette smoking is a good case in point, in which the producers, in part, were able to manipulate tastes and in which also the infectiousness of fashion created demand which has turned out to have very high external diseconomies in the shape of disease. At least the cigarette industry should be taxed very heavily to support the costs of the diseases which it produces.

The grants economy has a pathology of its own which differs somewhat from the pathologies of the exchange economy. One of its problems is the difficulty of obtaining adequate feedback or a test of success. It is one of the virtues of the exchange economy that feedback is fairly rapid. If the Ford Motor Company produces an Edsel it soon finds out; if the Ford Foundation produces an Edsel, or still worse if the Department of Defense produces an Edsel, for instance, in the shape of the ABM, we may never find out until it is too late. There are, of course, slow processes in feedback to the grants economy. The Rockefeller Foundation, for instance, has realized after a generation or more of supporting health research in the tropics, that it may have created a population explosion and it is now devoting its energies to counteracting that!

By far the most serious pathological condition of the grants economy is in national defense, which is a system so pathological that it threatens the human race with extinction, either by the use of deadly weapons or by the withdrawal of resources which are desperately needed to solve the problem of transition into the "spaceship earth" of the looped economy. National defense is a result of a defect in the world integrative system, the fact that benevolence seldom extends beyond the borders of the national community and is all too easily replaced by malevolence for the foreigner. It also, however, tends to have a technological dynamic of its own, which is supported because of the secrecy and the fear out of which its grants arise. A very good example of this was the terrifying development of chemical and bacteriological warfare preparations in the United States which used to absorb a budget equal to that of all the international agencies put together, which threatened to destroy the equilibrium, however temporary it may be, of nuclear deterrence, and which created a constant and increasing menace through accident for the people of the United States themselves.[1] Fortunately, this activity is now somewhat curtailed. This is perhaps the most pathological of all processes of technological development, pathological because it is producing not goods, but bads, and because it is employed in a threat system which is itself pathological.

Another important source of social pathology which is characteristic of both the market economy and the grants economy is that the conditions of survival depend mainly upon short-run considerations, whereas social desir-

---

1. Richard McCarthy, *The Ultimate Folly: War by Pestilence, Asphyxiation and Defoliation* (New York: Alfred A. Knopf, Inc., 1969).

ability frequently depends on long-run considerations. The conditions of survival have to be short-run; if we cannot survive in the short-run, obviously we cannot survive in the long. On the other hand, short-run survival can easily depend on parameters or conditions of the system which lead to long-run destruction, especially as we move more towards teleological systems. The problem of how to create artificially conditions in the system which will equate short-run with long-run survival is going to be of increasing importance.

It is a peculiar responsibility of the scientific community to work on these problems of the long-run. We see this in innumerable examples—the cigarette example is a scandalous one. The whole problem of deterrence in national defense is another which gives us short-run stability at the cost of inevitable long-run disaster. DDT may easily turn out to have been a disastrous time bomb, the short-run effects of which were extremely desirable in many ways, but the long-run effects of which can only be disastrous. There is a problem here in the sociology of science itself that in science also the payoffs are for the short-run. An assistant professor who starts a research project the results of which are not going to be apparent for twenty-five years is never going to get promoted. There are enormous payoffs for low profits and quick returns in the academic community. One sees the results of this in the deplorable absence of longitudinal studies of all kinds. Indeed, the only thing which has saved the scientific community from the complete tyranny of the short-run is the development of cumulative time series, such as the movements of the planets or the movements of national income statistics.

In the social sciences, this problem is particularly difficult because the main element of the social system, being man himself, has a lifespan equal to that of his investigator. There is indeed a kind of quasi-Heisenberg principle here that systems which require the lifetime of an investigator or more to be investigated will not be investigated, and hence we won't find out very much about them. It may be that the only answer to this problem is the development of a ritual of a data collection which can go on year after year and hence be cumulative in its results, so that scientists of, say, one hundred and fifty years from now can look back on the collections of data for one hundred and fifty years and see things that those of us who are around today cannot perceive, because they only operate over long periods of time. One has very much the same problem in the physical sciences, which is probably why we know so much about the atom and so little about ice ages. There seems to be no answer to this question, except an ethical answer in the development of a sense of priority to this regard, not only in the scientific community, but also among the grants community of the grantors who support science.

The fundamental problem of control of technology can be stated very succinctly. We do have an apparatus in the grants economy, especially in the public grants economy and in the operations of government generally for correcting pathological states of the exchange economy. We do not have any apparatus for correcting the pathological states of the grants economy or of the public sector, apart from the classical notions of checks and balances.

We have now come about as far as economics will take us. Economics can provide a reasonably impressive set of proposals and solutions for problems of pathological states of technology especially in the exchange sector. We must look beyond economics to explain why it seems so difficult to make these political changes and why it is so hard to correct the much more dangerous pathological conditions of the grants economy. Political science here offers some hope of analysis of the processes by which political decisions are made and the way in which political institutions affect these decisions. Political science also has something to contribute to the theory of the threat system, the theory of the international system and to the development of an information collection and processing apparatus which will throw light on the frequently pathological dynamics of these systems.

We may have to go beyond political science, however, in the explanation of why pathological states in the political system are so hard to correct. This forces us back eventually on the theory of the human learning process and it is here that both the social and the biological sciences are so woefully deficient. It is hardly too much to say that the dynamics of human learning, especially in the mass, are the key to all our problems of pathological development, whether this is in the failure of economic development, for instance in the tropics, or the failures of political development in our failure to deal with problems of pollution, poverty, race and war, or even of education. The awful truth is that education and politics are still very much in the condition of folk knowledge and folk technology. Neither of them could be described as science-based industries. It is not surprising, therefore, that we have a sense at the present time that technology may be as much the enemy of man as his friend.

What we have to learn, then, is how to create coalitions which are clearly anti-pathological. In order to do this, we must do a great deal of work in the identification of pathological states and conditions, and we must also do a lot of work in understanding the processes by which coalitions get formed. At the present moment, it is hardly an exaggeration to say that an anti-man coalition is in power almost everywhere, as reflected in the fact that the world spends nearly two hundred billion dollars a year on the war industry, the ultimate product of which is man's destruction, and the fact that our priorities are clearly towards hardware rather than people; otherwise we would not be putting resources into follies like the supersonic transport, or even amiable and heroic follies like going to the moon.

A particularly important aspect of the situation is that the scientific community must learn to take ethics seriously. This is not something that can be relegated to an hour on Sunday morning even for those who go to church. All human behavior is governed by an implicit ethic even if it is not governed by an explicit one. These ethical systems, like almost everything else in mankind, are learned. They have a small genetic base, but their primary content is learned mainly in the course of growing up and learned from inputs of information of all kinds. They are profoundly affected by the rhetoric of society.

Another thing which the scientific community cannot afford to despise is rhetoric, for this it is that convinces people and plays a great role in creating their ethical systems and hence indirectly their behavior. The pathology of rhetoric may be as important to study as the pathology of technology or of the market or of any other system, and up to now we have hardly recognized that this discipline exists. It is time, indeed, for the scientific community to become self-conscious about its own pathological processes, processes, for instance, which lead to a perversion of research into evil uses and a growth of knowledge where ignorance might be bliss. The scientific community indeed has a lofty ethic of its own. Without this, science could never have come into existence. The scientific subculture has been quite remarkably characterized by truthfulness, personal integrity, and a passion for the real world rather than for sensate illusion. Without these high moral virtues, indeed, science would never have developed at all, and it is something of a mystery how a subculture ever developed which had these rather rare virtues. Truthfulness, for instance, is not characteristic at all of political or business subcultures, yet it is absolutely critical in the scientific subculture. A scientist who is found falsifying his results has committed a sin against the Holy Ghost and can never hold up his head again in the scientific community. It is, furthermore, a remarkably self-policing ethic, which, incidentally, opens up another set of systems that we desperately need to examine and propagate. It is the absence of the self-policing quality in the interactions of technology and humanity that precisely creates the problem.